DAGGER LANE

By the same author

Louisa Elliott
Liam's Story

Dagger Lane

Ann Victoria Roberts

Chatto & Windus
LONDON

First published 1994

1 3 5 7 9 10 8 6 4 2

First published in the United Kingdom in 1994 by
Chatto & Windus Ltd
Random House, 20 Vauxhall Bridge Road, London SW1V 2SA

Random House Australia (Pty) Limited
20 Alfred Street, Milsons Point, Sydney,
New South Wales 2061, Australia

Random House New Zealand Limited
18 Poland Road, Glenfield
Auckland 10, New Zealand

Random House South Africa (Pty) Limited
PO Box 337, Bergvlei, South Africa

Random House UK Limited Reg. No. 954009

A CIP catalogue record for this book
is available from the British Library

ISBN 0 7011 40097

Phototypeset by SX Composing Ltd, Rayleigh, Essex
Printed in Great Britain by
Clays Ltd, St Ives plc

For P.R.N.
without whom . . .

Acknowledgement & Author's Note

My thanks to Alison Samuel for her advice, friendship, and unfailing patience.

Like all of the characters and events described in this book, the villages of Denton-on-the-Forest, Brickhill, Sheriff Whenby and Ghylldale are entirely fictitious. Dagger Lane exists only in my imagination, although in that general vicinity just a few miles north of York, there are many such lanes . . .

A.V.R.
York, 1994.

Two evils, monstrous either one apart,
Possessed me, and were long and loath at going:
A cry of Absence, Absence, in the heart,
And in the wood a furious winter blowing . . .

John Crowe Ransom (1888–1974)
'Winter Remembered'

One

A FINE RAIN, almost like mist, obscured the windscreen. Hunched over the wheel, eyes straining to penetrate the darkness, Natasha cursed the wipers, the weather and the headlights with quiet ferocity. On dipped beam it was like driving in a black hole, while full beam reflected nothing more than a glittering haze ahead.

She wished she had insisted on bringing her own car. Although the lights were no better, she was used to handling the little Peugeot, whereas Nick's old Rover, with its powerful V8 engine, seemed to have a will of its own. Braking, changing down a gear for a steep corner, she decided that a dozen miles of narrow, winding country roads were the kind of challenge she could have done without.

But an hour after midnight, in the middle of the week, at least the country roads were quiet. And so was Nick. Ebullient on leaving the party, he had lapsed into silence as they left York's suburbs behind, and seemed to be asleep. Risking a quick, sidelong glance, she noted the pallor of his face, turned away from her, and hoped he was not about to be sick. With an unconscious clenching of hands and jaw she turned her attention back to the road, negotiating another tight bend too fast. Nick groaned a little as his slack body shifted; as he righted himself she heard him mumble something about taking it easy.

'I am taking it easy,' she ground out between gritted teeth, 'it's this bloody car of yours.'

Angry and miserable, she swallowed hard and forced herself to concentrate on driving. Get home, she told herself; get home and then you can let it out.

With relief Natasha recognised the stand of trees which obscured the junction to Denton-on-the-Forest. Not that there was much of a forest left in these parts; isolated patches of woodland, and the same suffix attached to a few other villages in the locality, were all that remained from medieval times. Passing the road-sign, she slowed and indicated for the turn, letting the car freewheel down the slight incline into the village. There were no lights visible, not even from the Half Moon, which was renowned for its late-drinking clientele. But the regulars were no doubt away to their beds on this most inhospitable of nights.

At the foot of the Green, sliding the gear-lever into second, she released the clutch smoothly and turned into Dagger Lane. Close on the left, the headlights picked out neatly trimmed privet and a short expanse of brick wall, marking the boundaries of the last two houses in the village, and from there it was perhaps sixty or seventy yards between unkempt hedgerows to Holly Tree Cottage.

Mindful of the car's suspension, Natasha kept the speed to a crawl over the lane's uneven surface, managing to suppress the urge to make a final sprint for home.

Suddenly, there was a matt black shape in front of the car, visible in the headlights for a split-second before she stood on the brakes.

'My God, what was that?'

'What the – ?'

'It must have been a dog – oh, God, I've run over a bloody *dog* – ' Clutching the wheel, Natasha bowed her head and fought off a sudden desire to burst into tears.

With a muttered oath, Nick flung open the car door, and with some difficulty extricated his long limbs. A moment or two later, having peered all round and underneath, he climbed back in and said: 'What dog? There's no sign of a dog.'

'But there must be! It was *there* – ' She indicated the brilliant haze of drizzle caught in the headlights. 'Right there in front of me!'

'What sort of dog? I didn't see anything – '

'Good grief, does it matter what sort?' She struggled to describe what she had glimpsed in the headlights, the dense black shape, gone before it could be identified. 'Big, black, scrawny – a half-starved labrador, by the look of it. Anyway, you were asleep.'

He shrugged. 'Well, whatever it was, it's gone. And I couldn't see any marks on the car. Still, I'll have another look in the morning.'

Glaring at him, Natasha pushed open her own door and stepped out into the mud and rain. But he was right: there was no sign of a dog, and in such total darkness, not much point in searching further. No whimpers reached her from the hedgerow, no pathetic eyes implored her help. Trembling a little with cold and shock, Natasha resumed her seat and felt for the ignition key.

'I know I hit something – I felt the bang.'

'You stalled the engine,' he said laconically. 'Look – it's still in gear.'

That was the final straw. 'There's no need to sound so bloody superior,' she snapped. 'Just be thankful I've driven you home. If I'd had any sense at all, I'd have left you and come home hours ago!'

Leaning back and closing his eyes, Nick made no response to that.

She wrenched at the gears, started the car and spun the wheels in the mud; seconds later they were pulling into the yard. While Nick climbed out with the house keys, Natasha turned into the barn, parking the silver-grey Rover beside her own small red car. On the cold, damp air there was a noticeable smell of ammonia. Looking round as she locked the car doors, she sniffed and pulled a face, blaming the old tom-cat who, with his small harem, had made the place his home. Leaving the barn doors open, Natasha pulled her coat around her and hurried across to the house.

Nick was in the kitchen, crouched before the open doors of a cast-iron stove which fuelled the central heating system. 'Fire's nearly out – I'd better get it going . . .'

Without deigning to reply, she swept past him and went

straight upstairs to change. Putting her coat on a hanger to dry, she caught sight of herself in the full-length mirror and let out an exclamation of disgust. Without the ears and mask, the remains of her black cat's outfit looked ridiculous, the long velvet tail somehow obscene as it dangled between her legs. Peeling off the body-hugging suit, she slipped into a warm and comfortable dressing-gown, feeling even better once she had scrubbed her face clean of that hideous theatrical make-up.

Short dark hair, pale skin, dark eyes. Her own face peered back at her from the bathroom mirror, tired and drawn but immensely reassuring after the disturbing events of the evening. Towards the end, it had been like some wild *Walpurgisnacht*, a heaving throng of hideous masks and faces, pounding music, writhing bodies, the atmosphere raw with sexuality. At its height, she had been convinced that it would erupt into some kind of violence; and indeed there had been a fight, quickly suppressed, which seemed to have calmed things down.

For a moment she considered the way ordinary people were transformed by masks and make-up and extraordinary clothes. And not just outwardly; somehow personality and behaviour were affected too, as though each disguise reflected a secret fantasy which had to be acted out. Although, given the theme of Hallowe'en, and the amount of alcohol consumed, it was perhaps not surprising that normal restraints were so easily abandoned.

And yet the evening had begun so well. She'd been looking forward to it, had enjoyed putting her outfit together and finding the bits and pieces Nick needed to complete his, and they'd set off together in light-hearted anticipation. In the black velvet cat-suit she'd felt delightfully sensual, almost kittenish with the ears and whiskers and long black tail; and Nick had made an impressive Count Dracula. His features were too irregular to be called handsome, but he had the height and build and the kind of saturnine looks associated with the character, and they'd laughed and joked at the transformation.

She'd felt good just being with him, but, as it turned out, they'd spent so little time together. The party had been in progress when they arrived, and almost at once Natasha was whisked on to the dance-floor by a young student in a fluffy canary suit with speckled orange legs; he was so much bigger than Natasha that the association caused much hilarity, and, encouraged by her good humour, several other students followed suit. She kept catching sight of Nick with a variety of pale-faced girls with blood-red lips and plunging necklines, but he winked and waved as if to intimate that he would join her soon, but seemed in no particular hurry to do so. Eventually, they'd met up by accident in the bar.

Clutching a refreshing glass of fruit-juice and soda, she had looked around for familiar faces and suddenly spotted Nick in the doorway, talking to his friend Giles Crowther. Not until she joined them and Giles turned to greet her, had she realised with shock what he was wearing. The long black cassock and ebony crucifix looked chillingly authentic, as did the leather-bound missal in his hand. Repelled, she'd asked what weird twist of the imagination had prompted him to dress as a priest; and Giles, delighted as much by the question as by her evident disapproval, had explained that he was the exorcist, surely the most essential part of any gathering at Hallowe'en.

Unconvinced, and with a shudder of distaste, she'd turned to Nick for his opinion; but Nick, having had plenty to drink, was ready to find almost anything amusing. He'd even told her not to be such a little puritan, to loosen up a bit and enjoy herself. It was said lightly, with a little hug and a peck on the cheek, but it made her feel both patronised and excluded, like a child at a grown-up party.

Remembering, Natasha shook her head, wishing she hadn't abandoned Nick then. If she'd stayed, it might have been possible to avoid what followed. But at the time she'd been upset and annoyed with Giles, the more so since she was generally fond of him. He'd been one of her tutors ten years ago, when she was studying for her degree, and she had reason to be grateful for his help and kindness then; nevertheless, he could be maddening. The problem was that Giles lectured on the English Romantic Poets, and had an unfortunate tendency to live the part. He was witty, good-looking, and irresponsible, a dangerous combination where women were concerned, and it was that reputation which brought forth so many coarse asides from passing colleagues. Most of them were entertained by the irony of his disguise, but Natasha was not, and in her discomfort could only think how similar was the power wielded by priests and university lecturers, especially over women.

It was a relief to be distracted, and she'd chatted for a while to Nancy Fish, the wife of another of Nick's colleagues; but then she'd been dragged away by the Bursar, almost unrecognisable as a wild-looking wizard. He said a lucky black cat was just what he needed, and insisted on keeping her with him for what seemed like hours. The next time she saw Nick, he was surrounded by a laughing group on the edge of the dance-floor, most of whom appeared to be young and female.

He didn't notice her at all, but Natasha kept her eye on that little group of witches and hobgoblins, watching as they fawned over him, flirted with him, and wrapped themselves inside that red-lined vampire's cloak.

First one and then another persuaded him into the dance, and that he'd been enjoying himself was obvious, playfully and not-so-playfully biting at lips and throats and the seductive curve of exposed white breasts. By the time she managed to ditch her companion, however, Nick had given himself up to a well-endowed creature whose shimmering green outfit left little to the imagination. Within minutes she was virtually eating him alive, while he had hands and eyes for no one else.

It had been shameful and embarrassing to watch.

Sober amongst the laughing, shrieking, intoxicated crowd, Natasha felt that her heart had been pierced by a sliver of ice. Soft, sensuous black velvet was a joke, so inappropriate to her frozen emotions, she wished she had worn stiff white satin instead.

The rest of the evening was like the worst kind of nightmare, in which she was agonisingly torn between wanting to keep track of her husband, and the fear of witnessing his betrayal. After not much more than a year of marriage, it seemed incredible that he could behave like that, especially in front of her.

Then she lost sight of him completely. For a while she was able to keep up the pretence of having a good time, but rage got the better of her. Almost sick with jealousy, she pushed and shoved her way through the crowd in an attempt to find him. He was nowhere to be seen. Seething, she fought her way to the door, and would have headed for the stairs and his second-floor study, had it not been for Giles.

He playfully grabbed her arm as she pushed past him, and tried to persuade her back to the dance-floor.

'I'm looking for Nick!'

'Then you're heading the wrong way. He's in the bar – '

The vulgarity of her reply had amazed him. But even as he laughed, he did not let go of her arm. 'Come on,' he said cajolingly, 'surely you're not jealous? Not of *Nick* – he's the most faithful hound around this place.'

'Then that doesn't say a lot for the rest of you, does it?'

But although they did indeed find Nick in the bar, and the girl with the green wig and vivid theatrical make-up was no longer with him, Natasha was not convinced that he'd been there for more than a few minutes. Imagination tormented her when she thought of the time that he'd been missing, and what he might have been doing. He even looked guilty.

She turned away in disgust. She could not forget that when Nick Rhodes had fallen in love with the young Natasha Crayke, he was still married to someone else. It hadn't seemed to matter then that he had a wife and two young sons at home.

Two

THERE WAS something fascinating about evil.

The thought came to him in one of those extraordinarily clear moments between sleeping and waking, one of those moments in which a truth is perceived or a problem solved, and for good or ill life takes on a new direction.

For a while Nick Rhodes lay with his eyes shut, considering the point, aware that it must have surfaced from some remote pocket of youthful reasoning, since in recent years the idea of good and evil had become abstract and somewhat irrelevant. But if there was power in goodness – and he had believed that once – then there must also be an equal and opposite force in its antithesis, something basic and unprincipled which had always exerted a dark attraction.

Recognising the truth of that, he stirred uncomfortably and opened his eyes to the greyness of dawn. Was that what Haydn Parker had warned him against? 'I don't like Hallowe'en parties,' he had declared with uncharacteristic dourness the other day, 'and I wish I could have squashed the idea of this one before it got off the ground. Why don't you just stay at home?'

But at the time it had seemed the young assistant chaplain was simply being a kill-joy. Nick had responded lightly, saying it was all in fun, and a way of breaking the ice for the new intake; and, since it was a college thing, his presence was expected. The chaplain, of course, was not obliged to attend. As Giles sprang to mind in his guise as an exorcist, Nick realised that it was just as well. Haydn would have been no more amused by that outfit than Natasha, which was an odd thought when their views were so diametrically opposed.

The Hallowe'en party was the first of its kind in college for many years, and should have been, as Nick claimed, no more than innocent fun. Mainly, and for most people, he supposed that was true. He also presumed that it would go down in college annals as a great success; on a personal level, however, he would have preferred instant amnesia. Envisaging some heavy-handed witticisms from colleagues and students alike, he wondered briefly whether to claim to have been more drunk than he actually was, and to feign complete ignorance of his behaviour. But Giles, no doubt, would find it all wickedly amusing. Which it might have been, except for Natasha. The thrust and parry of college arguments were one thing, but disagreements at home were quite another, and that cutting exchange last night had laid bare some not very pretty bones.

Dejected, and more than a little hungover, Nick swung his legs out of bed and padded across to the low window. Beyond the curtains it was a dank, miserable morning. The first day of November, he thought joylessly, and yet it seemed not so long ago that he had looked forward to winter, enjoying the rugby and never minding the weather. Ferocious games, however, were now a thing of the past. He would be forty next birthday, and these days preferred less dangerous ways of keeping fit: regular games of squash with Giles, and a brisk run down the lane most mornings.

Catching sight of himself in the mirror, he grimaced at eyes which showed too clearly the signs of last night's debauch, and a couple of deep facial scars which were always more noticeable when he was tired. The knee which troubled him occasionally was stiff this morning, and he flexed it tentatively, wondering whether to give in to his hangover and retire to bed for another hour.

After a shivering bout of indecision, he pulled on a tracksuit and went downstairs.

Like everything else in the glazed porch, his training shoes were damp. A fresh fall of wet leaves littered the garden path and open yard beyond, while low cloud, rolling down like a drenching mist, obscured the tops of trees along the lane. It was bound to be treacherous and for a moment Nick paused to consider the options. Sometimes he took a quick sprint into the village and around the roughly circular route of its narrow roads, but he was not in the mood this morning for coughing exhausts and the black looks of frustrated drivers.

He chose the lane, setting off at a slow jog between dense, untrimmed hedgerows. Spiked arms of hawthorn, with bunched red berries like old blood, reached out through the mist; ancient oaks dripped overhead, while the long, grey leaves of willow and ash lay in slippery layers underfoot. For perhaps a mile the going was firm enough, but where the track dipped into the hollow just before the wood it became more earth than stone, with grass and weeds threatening to obliterate it completely. Like the hedgerows, the ditches here were sadly neglected, the wood itself in an isolated pocket of land whose ownership had become unclear. It was not in dispute; it seemed rather that the two major landowners who each farmed hundreds of acres to either side did not care to be bothered with it, nor did they put themselves out to maintain the lane. That was looked after, in desultory fashion, by two or three local farmers who rented fields nearby.

Dagger Lane was a relic of other times, part of a once-busy thoroughfare which had linked several small townships between Helmsley and the city of York. With land enclosures in the eighteenth century and the coming of the turnpikes, the old way had largely been abandoned, but between Denton-on-the-Forest and the village of Brickhill to the south, the lane had survived as a means of access to the new fields and between the two communities.

Now, however, it was seldom used. The edge of Denton was touched by one lateral road, while yet another linked Brickhill more directly with the main road into York. By car, the distance between the two villages was about six miles, and these days people preferred to drive; not many had time to waste on a challenging walk across country. Groups of ramblers were sometimes to be seen in summer, less often in winter, and while local dog-owners frequented the first part of Dagger Lane, Nick rarely saw anyone beyond the wood known as World's End, where the track became firm once more.

It climbed quite steeply away from the hollow, towards a low ridge from which could be seen the lonely spire of Brickhill church on its own little promontory, and, on a clear day, the unmistakable outline of York Minster, on the horizon.

Nick was inordinately fond of the ridge, not just because of the view, but because it marked the first rise of land north of the city. Much of that flat, fertile plain had been uncultivated commons until comparatively recent times, whereas the land on which he stood had been arable since its clearance from the forest of Galtres in the fourteenth century. That thought pleased him, like the idea of continuation and survival, of untold generations moulding the landscape into what he saw today. He liked the lane, too, which was certainly much older than its recorded history, and was probably in use well before the Romans came. Since it travelled in a fairly straight line, it was claimed locally that the Legions had built it, but Nick thought not. Dagger Lane, he was sure, was one of the routes used by ancient peoples in their journeys between the hill settlements and the navigable rivers of the plain.

That sense of history, of actually living in an area which had caught his interest as a student and held it ever since, was one of the reasons why he had wanted to settle here. It was not that he had tired of living in York, but that Holly Tree Cottage had been for sale, and, having viewed it purely from curiosity, he had been fired by the idea of restoration. Of course the name was misleading, since it was in fact a seventeenth-century farmhouse, then in a poor state of repair but reasonably sound. The previous owner, an elderly bachelor, had been the last of his line, and it seemed that little in the house had been changed since the late 1930s, and before that, at a rough guess, Nick would have said the turn of the century.

The land had been sold off years before old Mr Whitehead's death, but what he had done with the money, Nick could not imagine: he had not spent it on the house, that much was certain. The job of restoring a Jacobean farmhouse, listed as being of architectural interest, had proved far bigger and more expensive than even Nick had first anticipated. That factor alone had contributed to the problems of the past year, especially with Natasha struggling to finish her second novel, and being distracted by noise and dust and importunate workmen.

But the work was over, and although there were disadvantages to living so far out of town, he thought peace and quiet and a strong sense of achievement outweighed them. And the existence of Dagger Lane had persuaded him to start running again. Hangover or no, he was fitter now than he had been for a long time.

It was cold on the ridge, and not the day to force the extra mile to Brickhill. Having paused to catch his breath, Nick turned back, concentrating on the ground beneath his feet as he descended the slope and re-entered the sheltering tunnel of trees. He was almost clear when a sudden shout startled him. Slithering to an abrupt halt, he glanced round for the source of that guttural voice; a movement just within the wood's margin, followed by a glimpse of shiny blue feed-bag tied across thin shoulders, revealed the presence of old Toby Bickerstaff.

'Mornin', Doctor.'

'Morning, Toby. You startled me – didn't expect to see you out this early, not on a day like this.' As the ramshackle figure negotiated the ditch and came up beside him, Nick nodded towards the gun. 'Wouldn't have thought you'd bag much, either.'

Toby looked shifty and cleared his throat in a great rumbling cough that might have caused a doctor of medicine some anxiety. Nick, with a doctorate in history, simply shook his head as the old man broke the gun and fished in a sagging pocket for his battered tin of home-rolled cigarettes. He coughed again and spat into the ditch before lighting up.

'Won't catch owt now.'

They walked on together, Nick breathing deeply, the aroma of tobacco reminding him temptingly of breakfast and coffee and the fact that even after two years without a cigarette, he could still miss the first one of the day.

'Summat queer last night,' Toby grumbled. 'About dusk – just as it were comin' on that fine drizzle. Real queer,' he sniffed, 'seen nowt like that . . .'

He was not given to long sentences, and had a frustrating habit of breaking off midway, as though afraid of revealing too much. Nick knew better than to prompt him, however. A year of living as Toby's nearest neighbour on Dagger Lane had taught him that questions were things the old man avoided like the plague. Just one ill-judged enquiry could silence him for days. Not that they saw much of each other, but Nick passed Toby's decrepit old caravan when he was out running, and occasionally met him returning from one of his poaching expeditions. He was a real old codger, forced into solitude and eccentricity by unfathomable quirks of character and circumstance. In the summer he still did a bit of gardening for people in the village, mostly older inhabitants who were used to his peculiarities. The incomers, the majority of whom lived in a small development off the Green, either distrusted or were afraid of him. And he was not a pleasant sight, especially in his cups, shambling down the street or across that precious stretch of grass before the church.

Nick, however, was fascinated by him. Although he would have resented being called sentimental, he was, like most historians, subject to bouts of nostalgia, in which the passing of old things, old ways, old customs, could inflict something akin to physical pain. In Toby he saw a relic of the itinerant village labourer, the man who shifted beasts for local farmers, helped with haymaking and at harvest, carted dung for the roses when byres were mucked-out, and did a bit of poaching on the side. In his life, Toby had done all those things and still did some, although his jobs were fewer these days. Mostly he lived on his pension.

And yet there was a paradox somewhere. The Bickerstaffs, what remained of them, were a respectable local family whose forebears lay in several local churchyards, and Toby was no village idiot. Misanthropic he might be, but he was not stupid. There was a shrewd glint in his eye whenever he could bring himself to look at people directly, and he could take pleasure in a job well done. Although he had no brothers living, there were a couple of male cousins still resident in the village; the wife of one of them, a retired farm worker, came one day a week to help Natasha with the housework. Mrs Bickerstaff should have been able to satisfy all Nick's curiosity about the old man, but unfortunately even his most casual enquiries had been met with thin-lipped disapproval and curt replies. It was clear that Mrs B's main regret in life was that they shared the same surname.

With the worst of the mud behind them, Toby nodded over his shoulder, at the place where he had emerged from the trees. Again there was that air of shiftiness about him, a spark of calculation as he met Nick's eye, as though he weighed all the pros and cons and was having difficulty reaching a decision.

Eventually, he said: 'Fancied a bit o' pigeon, I did. Bagged a couple, easy like . . . had a longish wait for a couple more. Fetched 'em, tied 'em, just about to set off 'ome when I sees it. Back there – edge o' them trees.'

There came another long pause, in which Nick obligingly turned to regard the spot.

'Weren't a *dog*,' he said accusingly, as though the point had been disputed. 'Didn't move like a dog . . . didn't move like owt I've seen . . . bloody queer . . .' He shook his head slowly, ruminatively, then said: 'Bloody big it were . . . and *black* . . . Aye, I'm telling thee – blacker than fire-black!'

'Not a dog?' Nick said, thinking of the labrador that had startled Natasha on the way home. 'You're certain?'

'Aye. Never seen nowt like it afore. Spent that long lookin' at bloody thing, never thought to *shoot* it! Then,' he paused for breath, 'then it saw me, the bugger. Stopped it did, just stopped – an' there weren't no noise nor nowt. Then it backed off – sort o' *shrank* into them bushes back there.'

'Shrank?'

'Aye, like it were growin' *smaller*. Heard it then – it were makin' a sort o' garglin' noise, like it were gettin' ready to give a good spit!' He cackled with laughter at his own witticism and almost choked on it. Wiping rheumy eyes, he added with surprise: 'An' then it were gone. No noise, no crashin' about – just gone. What d'ye make o' that, then?'

It was the longest, most coherent speech Nick could ever recall the old boy making. He was astonished and it showed, and his astonishment pleased the old man.

'Aye, got ye there! Though that'd fox thee!'

Ruminating on this strange phenomenon, Nick said: 'Couldn't have been a deer, could it?'

'Nay – I knows deer. This weren't a *deer*.' He was obviously irritated by his companion's lack of perspicacity. He shook his head vehemently. 'I knows deer and I knows dogs – I knows most beasts, come to that – and this weren't any of 'em. Dunno what the bloody 'ell it were, but I don't want to see bloody thing again, I'll tell thee that for nowt!'

In the face of such utter conviction, Nick forbore to question him further. He was even reluctant to mention the black dog which had crossed their path last night, for fear the old man would interpret the comment as disbelief. Instead, he asked whether the creature had left any tracks.

Toby shrugged his thin shoulders and a cascade of droplets flew from the blue feed-bag. 'Might've. I weren't hangin' about to look – an' rain's washed it since. Nowt there now.'

Clutching at straws, Nick said: 'Maybe something's escaped from a zoo or whatever. I could phone the police and ask.'

A loud sniff illustrated Toby's opinion of the police. 'Aye, well, I dare say . . .'

They parted company by a rickety gate in the hedge. Behind it, Toby's green caravan with its foggy Perspex windows and sagging roof seemed to be oozing into the ground. Rust streaked the bulging walls and moisture dripped from every minor projection, making it one with the trees and the saturated landscape. Nick often saw a thin little spiral of smoke leaking from the tin chimney, and wondered how Toby survived. Still, he reflected, gypsies did, and often into old age. But they had families to care for them when they were old and ill, and who gave a damn about old Toby?

He was, however, intrigued by this animal which seemed to defy classification, and thought it strange that they should also have encountered something large and black on the lane last night. He walked the intervening stretch towards home, carefully scanning the hedgerows to either side. Entering the yard a few minutes later, he went straight into the barn to look at his car; the old Rover's bodywork showed no fresh dents, only a thick rime of mud along the sills. No marks there, and nothing in the lane, so either the animal had escaped unharmed, or Natasha had been distracted by shadows in the hedge. It had, after all, been a filthy night.

In the back of his mind, however, there lurked a third possibility, linked to a vaguely remembered account in some publication or other. But was it to do with this area? For the moment he could not remember.

There was a smell of toast as he entered the kitchen, and the kettle was still hot, but no other sign of Natasha. Not so much as the creak of a floorboard; all was silent in the house. Because he had harboured good intentions, and with his return had been looking forward to relating Toby's tale, Nick was wounded by that deliberate snub. A moment later, he was furious.

Stripping off his tracksuit, he threw it into the barrel of the washing machine and took the stairs two at a time. Breathing hard, he paused on the landing, then slammed into the bathroom, turning the shower full on. Within twenty minutes he was washed, shaved, dressed and ready to leave the house. He stopped only to drink a cup of black coffee before grabbing his briefcase and heading for the door. He banged it behind him as he left.

Three

STANDING BACK from the spare room window, Natasha watched him leave, wishing, now that it was too late, that she had gone down and at least met him halfway on the road to apology. He was a powerful man and anger made him more so. Long strides seemed to bite at the path, while beneath his hand the heavy, cast-iron gate shuddered on its hinges. Watching him cross the yard, head down, tweed jacket flapping, just for an instant Natasha was transported back to the early days of their acquaintance, when apprehension, rather than love, was the emotion he had inspired. In the years since, she had often found that aspect amusing; at the moment, however, it was all too real.

There came a subdued growl from the engine of the Rover, and a nasty crunch of tyres and gravel as Nick turned it in the yard. The house cat, slinking through the gate, stopped to watch, head low, until the car was gone. With a sinking feeling Natasha reached for her cigarettes and went downstairs.

The cat was mewing pathetically by the porch door, its ginger and white fur fluffed up, tail quivering as she let it in.

'Yes, Colette, I know exactly how you feel . . .'

She picked up the timid little thing, soothing her with whispers before setting her down again and serving a portion of tinned fish in a bowl by the pantry door. Natasha had rescued her from a sickly litter of kittens in the barn, but unlike her namesake this Colette was not entirely happy in the company of men.

With regard to the rest of the litter, it had been kinder to take them to the local vet, and to have the mother and her female companion speyed. The old tom, unfortunately, was too wily to be caught, and Natasha wished most heartily that he would stop leaving his calling-cards in the barn. The smell of tom-cat last night had been quite nauseating.

With a cup of coffee in her hand, Natasha left the kitchen and headed automatically for her office on the ground floor. It was at the far end of the house, across the wide, stone-flagged hall and newly carpeted sitting-room. Pleasant and spacious, it boasted windows front and back, a wall of bookshelves and the warmest radiators in the house. On her desk lay the evidence of recent hard work: a sheaf of editorial notes with comments in red and blue scribbled all over them, several sheets of paper with just a few typed lines, discarded pots of correction fluid, and a wire tray full of unanswered correspondence.

She was not in the mood for answering letters. Not at the moment, anyway. The editorial notes caught her attention and she glanced down several pages at various critical points and suggestions, all now dealt with. Successfully, she hoped. After the intensity of the last three months, during which she had been working the kind of hours that tore the Factories Act into shreds, Natasha prayed that the new book and its latest revisions would be accepted and praised like its predecessor. At this point she was no longer sure whether it had been a good idea even to begin it; and with its ending it was impossible to say whether she had produced an excellent piece of work, or one that should never have seen the light of day.

Her copy of the manuscript lay in three spring-clip folders on the floor, the plain sobriety of the covers echoing the title, *Black Earth*, and the darkness of this morning's mood. Although she would have preferred not to think of it, last night's row, and its cause, were still at the forefront of her mind. Nick had denied everything, of course, which was ridiculous, since she had watched him with that girl in green and could read his desires and intentions like a child's first book. Pinned down by that, he had then been defensive and apologetic, claiming that he was drunk and the girl had led him on – until he suddenly realised the folly of the situation and had steered her back to her friends. After that, according to him, he had escaped to the bar for a drink with Giles.

As a story it was just about plausible, although not a scenario she would have used. Last night, incensed by his appeal that she should take Giles as his witness, Natasha had refused to believe a word of it, and had demanded to know the girl's name, whether she was one of his students, or simply resident in college. He said he had no idea, that the incident Natasha was so bent on exaggerating was in fact so trivial that names had not come into it.

But the girl would know him, Natasha thought. Oh, yes she would know Dr Nicholas Rhodes very well indeed. In spite of his stern looks and tough reputation, he was attractive, and there were many young and beautiful girls on campus who would regard him as something of a challenge. Some of them, as she knew very well, would utilise almost any means to invade the personal lives of tutors and lecturers. Nick referred to the most persistent as 'camp-followers', and reckoned he could spot the dangerous ones at a hundred paces; they were one of the pitfalls of the job, he said, to be avoided at all costs.

Not all his colleagues were so punctilious, however, and he himself had not avoided Natasha nine years ago; for the first time she wondered how many more there had been since, and whether affairs with students had been a regular feature of his life. But that was impossible to answer, since there had been a long gap in their relationship, seven years in which she and Nick had gone their separate ways, to meet up again only a couple of years ago. And that meeting had been engineered by Giles.

Fifteen months ago, when he had stood as best man at their wedding, Natasha had hugged him and thanked him for that; remembering last night, she wanted to smack him, not least for his disguise, which had brought back the kind of memories she had been trying to exorcise with *Black Earth*.

This second novel of hers was essentially about the pains of adolescence, and it very much reflected her own experience of growing up in an isolated Fenland community. There was a priest in the novel too, a central figure just as blind and egotistical, just as hooked on the abuse of power as the one who had influenced her own life. If the other male figures in the book were more sympathetic, they were also less directly drawn from life, and, in their own ways, equally flawed.

There were differences, of course, between fiction and reality, but for the past three years Natasha had been slowly working out those aspects of the plot which corresponded to her own life, and to the moral questions which continued to plague her. It had been a difficult and painful book to write; the emotions it inspired had hardly been the best with which to begin married life, and this last year had been further complicated by the purchase of the house and all the chaos attendant upon its restoration.

Both were largely finished now, and a few weeks ago, armed with a copy of the manuscript, Natasha had made the journey to Portsmouth to visit her sister. Her prime intention had been to explain the novel, and why she had felt compelled to write it. Given the subject-matter, she had not expected an easy ride, but she had thought that once her motives were explained, Helen would understand.

But Helen had not understood. Helen had been outraged, accusing her sister of anti-Catholic bigotry, of defiling Father O'Gorman's character, and – what was infinitely worse – of presenting their mother as a vacillating, weak-minded woman who was almost criminally irresponsible where her children were concerned.

'Child,' Natasha had corrected, tight-lipped.

'Oh, yes, the child – *you*, I suppose – the one we're all supposed to sympathise with!'

It was hopeless trying to explain that the book was a work of fiction, that the characters were not meant to be literal representations of real people, and that the adolescent viewpoint was merely a device: Helen was having none of that. She recognised her sister in that awkward and unhappy adolescent, and loathed having to confront her pain. She also hated the thought of 'all that garbage' being read by people back home, dreaded what they would think; and they were sure to think plenty, because Natasha was vain enough to use her unmarried name instead of a pseudonym.

Then, before that fusillade could be absorbed, she had launched another broadside. The husband in the novel, who was so patently a whitewashed version of their own father, emerged as some kind of hero, when in reality he'd been no more than a pathetic shell of a man, who cared so little for his family that he drank himself to death.

At that, it was Natasha's turn to be outraged. What did Helen know of him? She had been eight years old when their father died, and Mother's little darling; whatever opinions she held had been shaped by their mother's bitterest memories. He was a hero as far as Natasha was concerned; a warm, compassionate, sensitive man who drank too much for a variety of reasons. Because of the war, because as a country doctor he worked too hard, and probably because he was unhappy at home. Nevertheless, he was loved by everyone who knew him, by every single one of those sick and elderly patients he visited so regularly. Helen wouldn't remember that, of course; she could only remember a man in his decline, a man almost old enough to be their grandfather, who had been ill for months before he died.

'Tell the truth and shame the devil,' was what their mother used to say; but the truth was never as simple as that, it was particular and slanted, and depended upon your point of view. Natasha could see that, very clearly; the pity was that her sister could not, and they had parted with badly injured feelings on both sides. But although Nick said that it was only to be expected, and that if she had been intending to consult Helen at all, it should have been beforehand rather than afterwards, Natasha still felt that her sister was being deliberately obtuse.

The fact that those three major characters were all dead, and had been for some years, seemed to make things worse, not better; Helen had even accused her of libelling those who could not answer back, and had sworn that if Natasha published *Black Earth* as it stood, she would never speak to her again.

Mindful of that, she had toned things down at editorial stage; but it was measurably the same story, with the same conclusions. It wasn't that she wanted to hurt Helen – although she did feel that her sister surrounded herself with too much emotional padding – it was a matter of having to write the story, and in a certain way. Natasha found it frustrating that Helen had so little conception of what that meant.

But she was not the only one who regarded the writer's life as a comfortable, dilettante existence. She'd had various friends in the past few years who seemed to think that such work could be picked up and put down like a piece of embroidery, and resented the fact that she was not always available. Even Nick failed to understand that, however seemingly autobiographical, the stories picked the writer, and the characters had minds of their own, often stubbornly refusing to be whipped into line. And Natasha's writing had a tendency to take over her life, making flesh-and-blood people with everyday problems seem more than a little remote.

At that thought, she began to wonder whether she had neglected Nick for a little too long. Certainly in the last few weeks, with the editorial notes uppermost in her mind and that terrible row with Helen presenting its own problems, she had thought of nothing but the manuscript. With a deadline to meet she had often worked until two in the morning, sleeping in the spare bedroom so as not to disturb Nick. He had said that he understood, that it was all right, they would make up for the deprivation later; but in the light of last night's behaviour she began to wonder whether he had been deprived at all.

Had she been too blind, or merely too trusting? Nick worked peculiar hours, sometimes at home, sometimes in college. There were occasional night-classes and frequent games of squash with Giles, all of which might easily cover other activities. And Giles was never the most virtuous of companions, even when he was seeing someone on a regular basis, as he was at present. With his connivance, Nick could have been conducting any number of affairs in the past few months, and Natasha would have been the last to know. But that, she thought despairingly, was probably always the case.

Lighting a cigarette, she gazed moodily out across the yard. As it cleared, the mist was turning into definite rain from a leaden sky, intensifying her sense of despondency. Autumn, with its clear days and glorious colour, should have been having a final fling before the onset of winter, but this year the season had never really come into its own. After a beautiful summer, of which she had seen very little, the fine weather had broken in mid-September; October had been a wet and disappointing month, and now November was sliding into the misery of winter without so much as a pause for breath.

Natasha dragged her gaze back to the chaos of her office. Something needed to be done if she was not to spend the day sunk in gloom, and perhaps she should begin by tidying up. Perhaps if she made an effort in that simple direction her mood would lift a little, and at least Mrs Bickerstaff would be pleasantly surprised when she came in on Monday morning.

Vera Bickerstaff was Natasha's weekly help, and although the office was not part of her usual province, it was frequently obvious that she longed to get in there with her dusters and detergents. Hourly cups of coffee, however, were all that Natasha allowed when she was working. She felt she needed a comforting cluster of ashtrays, books and papers around her, and the freedom to be slovenly without the remotest twinge of guilt. It was enough to know that Mrs B's efforts kept the rest of the house immaculate, and that her expertise with an iron had finally silenced Nick's complaints about his crumpled shirts. He was as meticulous in his appearance as he was about his research, and if the state of his desk sometimes belied the fact, he liked the house to be tidy too. For such peace of mind, Natasha was prepared to put up with Mrs Bickerstaff's silent reproofs, the well-meant advice, and even her snobbery, which was founded on several years of service at Sheriff Whenby Hall.

The snobbery irritated Nick almost beyond endurance, to the extent that he generally made a point of being out early on Monday mornings, before Mrs B arrived. Even during the holidays he would find an excuse to be absent, either that or shut himself in his study with firm warnings not to be disturbed. The situation did have its funny side, however, since Vera Bickerstaff thought him difficult and moody, and in various small ways managed to express her sympathy with Natasha for having to put up with such a man.

Well, she was right, Natasha thought; Nick could be like that, and was being so at the moment. She emptied ashtrays, tore up deleted pages of manuscript and polished her desk with a sense of grievance. She had just kicked the vacuum cleaner into life when the telephone rang.

The caller was her editor, Judy Lawrence. Recognising that bright, cheerful voice, Natasha grinned with relief. The revisions were fine, Judy was very pleased with the result, and just had a few minor queries to deal with. She also wondered whether they could fix up a date to go through the manuscript together, to give it a final check and polish before it went off to the printers. The schedule was getting a bit tight for publication, so the meeting would have to be soon. She suggested a date ten days hence and, after a glance at her calendar, Natasha agreed.

Replacing the phone a few minutes later, she stared through the window at the rain, not really seeing it but thinking about the novel and her prospective trip to London; then her focus changed and she noticed the film of grime upon the glass. With a sigh she decided to leave it to Mrs Bickerstaff.

Nick negotiated dense early-evening traffic along the city's outer ringroad, and was thankful to turn off and head north towards home. The wind was increasing, and all along the road were fresh leaves, dangerously wet on the bends, with twigs and loose debris skittering ahead like small animals fleeing before the storm. The night was rapidly closing in, and it was almost dark by the time he reached Denton and made the turn for Dagger Lane.

Lights were on in the kitchen, he could see the glow through the trees as he approached the house, and at once found himself wondering what his reception would be. Whatever Natasha's mood, he was going to have to say something about last night, although his whole being fought shy of another post-mortem. After that row in the early hours, followed by a full day in which the party had been mentioned, discussed, laughed over and complained about by almost every person he had met, Nick simply wanted to forget the whole thing.

As he walked in, the signals he received were conflicting.

Natasha had taken some trouble with her appearance, and for once was wearing a skirt, softly patterned in autumn colours, with a flattering silk shirt. The outfit made a pleasant change to the genderless clothes she favoured for working, the jeans and leggings and sweat-shirts that on her slender frame often put him in mind of one of J.M. Barrie's Lost Boys. She often had that same quality of abstraction, he thought, of searching for something and meanwhile needing someone to look after her. It was an image that sometimes disturbed him, since in such moments he was unsure whether she had found what she was looking for in him.

With a murmured compliment, he approached to kiss her cheek, but his lips had barely grazed her face before she was turning away, making the preparations for dinner her excuse. A certain compression about the mouth, which reduced the sensual curves to a surprisingly narrow line, confirmed the fact that he was still in disgrace.

As he sank down into a fireside chair to unlace his shoes, Natasha said: 'Dinner won't be ready for an hour or so. Are you hungry now? Do you want a sandwich?'

Often, he came home feeling ravenous, but not this evening. He shook his head. 'No, I was late having lunch. Just a cup of tea will be fine.' As she switched the kettle on to boil, he followed her with his eyes, willing her to turn and meet his gaze. When she did not, that wooden refusal to play by the rules annoyed him. Abruptly, he stood up. 'Look, forget the tea, will you? I'll get myself a drink instead.'

He crossed the stone-flagged hall and found, to his surprise, that the log fire was lit in the sitting-room, crackling away to itself as the wind sucked bright orange flames up the chimney. Unable to recall the last time Natasha had lit that fire herself, Nick wondered whether the gesture was intended as a peace offering, an attempt at providing a cosy, romantic setting for apologies and reconciliations. But perhaps not. Perhaps she had other intentions, ones he had yet to divine. Nevertheless, the room looked welcoming, and in the half-light the massive but disreputable sofa had never seemed so inviting. He eyed it longingly as he poured himself a large scotch, but told himself that he still had work to do.

Although the work would have waited, some devil of perversity drove him upstairs to his study.

A little after seven, Natasha called him down for dinner. Assailed by the delicious aroma of lamb with garlic and marjoram, Nick suddenly realised that he was hungry. He took his place at the table and poured two glasses of wine, raising his eyebrows as he noticed the label; it was good enough to have heralded some sort of celebration, although he was not quite sure whether she had opened it by accident or intent. Either way, it was a good omen, and, as he sipped at the wine he began to feel that everything would be settled amicably.

The dinner was excellent and he tucked in with gusto, raising his glass to his wife in a small but eloquent toast. Her answering smile was still a shade tight, he thought, her dark eyes wary, and he found himself talking of inconsequential things, anything to cover the void left by the party and last night's argument. Several things had occurred during the day that ordinarily Nick would have enjoyed relating, despite the fact that they were essentially stories against himself, but he was afraid she wouldn't laugh. He was even more afraid that it would open up the topic of the party for further discussion, and he balked at that. Guilt weighed rather too heavily, and he had not yet apologised.

He balanced the moment, not wanting to spoil their meal, yet determined to say his piece before it was finished. For some reason he was extraordinarily aware of her this evening, the faint citrus tang of her perfume which cut through the heavier scents of food and wine, the shape of her small breasts jutting against the silk of the blouse, the changing softness of her mouth as she ate and drank or paused to answer him.

Eventually, when the table was cleared and he was making the coffee, he said ruefully: 'I'm sorry about last night. Can't think what got into me – the booze, probably. Anyway, darling, I'm sorry. Not just about the party, but everything else – it wasn't meant, any of it.'

Just at that moment, a sudden gust of wind rattled the window-panes behind him, and he had the impression that she turned in response to the sound, rather than to him. That impression was reinforced when she moved past him to close the curtains.

'Yes, I was sorry too,' she agreed distractedly. 'I haven't been so embarrassed in years.'

His frown deepened. 'Well, if it's any consolation, I've had more than my fair share of embarrassment today.'

As she met his glance, Nick saw a flicker of reproach before she shivered and looked away. Bemused by the shiver, he said: 'Surely you're not cold? It's like Kew Gardens in here.'

But she was drawing the other set of curtains behind the table, shutting out the night and the wind and the rain. 'It's a cold night,' she said flatly, and so it was, with the wind now more north than west, and the rain ferocious.

Ignoring a growing sense of unease he said evenly: 'In that case, let's take our coffee into the sitting-room. That fire's eating up logs to no avail at the moment.'

But in spite of the thick carpet and the cheerful fire, the room was not warm. The wind was drawing most of the heat up the chimney, and the logs were hissing as spatters of soot and rain came down. Natasha, who had been to find a sweater, shivered again as she extended her hands to the blaze.

'So,' she said challengingly as he turned to face her, 'they put you through it in college, did they?' Again, there was that tightness in her smile. 'Well, it serves you right.'

'I know, I know,' he replied lightly, prepared to take the teasing at face value, even though he knew she meant it. In a similar tone, he said: 'But we both said some pretty dreadful things last night, Natasha – and I've apologised already. Don't you think that's enough?'

At the sudden diffusion of colour over her cheekbones, he sighed and reached for her hand, as aware of her tension as he was of his own eagerness to cross the void and make amends. She had been working too hard and he felt that of late they had grown a little apart; it was time to claim her back again, to reaffirm what had always been between them, and he wanted to do so now, before words and circumstances could widen the gap.

'We should talk, Nick.'

This time his sigh was exasperated, not indulgent. 'Oh, darling, surely we've said enough on the subject? Let's forget it, for God's sake. I don't even want to think about it any more.'

'That's the trouble, you never do.'

'Never do what?' he asked, laughing. 'Think? I think all the time!'

'Not about me,' she said sharply, evading his touch, 'not about *us*. We need to *talk*, don't you realise that? About you and me, and – '

The light went out. They were not plunged into darkness, because the fire was still providing its flickering illumination, but even as he thought it no more than an expired bulb, Nick turned and saw that the hall light was also out. The fire flared at a sudden gust of wind, and Natasha clutched his hand. With some surprise, he realised that she was alarmed.

'It's all right, don't worry,' he said, gently disengaging himself. 'It's probably just a fuse.'

Picking up a large box of matches from the side table, he went into the kitchen and lit one of the ornamental candles which stood on the mantelpiece. The fuse box in the pantry seemed in order, but when he flicked the switch, nothing happened. Cursing, he went upstairs to peer out of his study window: the village was in darkness too. A power cut, obviously, and probably because of the storm. He pulled the telephone directory towards him, and dialled the emergency number. A female voice informed him that yes, there were problems being experienced in the area of Denton-on-the-Forest, and power would be returned as soon as possible. No, the female voice responded to his next questions, she did not know the cause, nor how long the repairs would take.

'All bloody night, I expect,' he muttered ungraciously as he put down the phone. 'Ah, well . . .'

In the sitting-room, Natasha had managed to light the Victorian oil lamp which usually stood on one of the deep window ledges. Within a small radius, the light was strong enough to read by, but the shadows were closer, softer, the far corners of the room more distant. He was suddenly aware of the surrounding darkness, and of a heightened intimacy between them.

But if his senses were pleasurably heightened, Natasha's were poised for alarm. The noise of the storm, this sudden darkness, served only to sharpen the edginess that had plagued her all day.

It seemed ridiculous to be afraid of the dark, but when it was sudden and unexpected, and when that darkness was suffused with howls and groans, rattling tattoos upon the glass, and periodic knockings from above, logic departed and childish fear crept in. Although she wanted to talk to Nick, had been determined that certain things must be discussed this evening, it was now difficult to concentrate. All her attention seemed to be focused elsewhere.

'Did they say what was wrong?'

'No, but there's probably a line down somewhere, in which case this could go on for hours.'

'Like the storm.'

'Yes, like the storm.' He looked at her with a smile in his eyes, a smile that just lifted the corners of his mouth. 'We could always go to bed,' he suggested lightly, 'bury our heads under the covers, and forget the power cut and the weather.'

The idea was tempting, even though she could not imagine going to sleep. He kissed her forehead and the tip of her nose, then tilted her chin so that he could reach her mouth. Natasha saw the teasing light in his eyes, and the deep scar between his brows which often made him appear to be frowning when he was not. His lips parted as he bent towards her, his kiss expressing, as ever, that extraordinary blend of firmness and sensuality which had stirred her so deeply in the beginning. Inexperienced then, she had made several comparisons since, and all were disappointing. No other man had ever touched her in the way Nick did, and familiarity had barely dulled the edge of it.

Nevertheless, she was beginning to resent that power he had over her, the way he assumed that all problems could be solved in bed. She thought of all the times he had persuaded her away from work in just such a fashion, the times when she had tried to talk about the past and he had silenced her with a kiss. She was halfway to being persuaded now, but then a violent gust rattled the windows, and she was suddenly thinking of him with those girls last night, particularly that creature in green. Warmth fled before an arctic chill. As she shivered and turned her mouth away, Nick drew back, his disappointment obvious.

'You keep shivering,' he said, looking at her intently, 'and it doesn't appear to be with pleasure. What's wrong – is it the storm?'

'I expect so,' she replied, rubbing her arms and forcing an apologetic smile. 'I'm cold. I think the central heating must have gone off with the power cut.'

'Yes, it will have done – the circ. pump won't be working.' He studied her for a moment, and then poured the last of the wine into their glasses. 'Come on, drink up and let's go to bed. I didn't get much sleep last night, and I don't expect you did, either. We may as well catch up tonight.'

Separating the logs in the grate, Nick placed the fireguard in position, then went into the kitchen to fuel the stove; as he said, if the rest of the house was cold in the morning, at least the kitchen should be warm.

A minute or two later, he rejoined her to carry the oil lamp upstairs. Moving through the darkened house in that small halo of light was a strangely unnerving experience. For some reason she did not think of similar occasions in childhood but of the biblical metaphor, and felt, for the first time, the impact of that image. She did not find it comforting; right now, the darkness seemed so much greater than the light – vast and somehow menacing.

In their bedroom, under the sloping rafters of the roof, the noise was even more insistent, the bangs and crashes so much louder as tiles moved and lifted, and thudded back into place. It sounded like something trying to get in. Undressing hurriedly, she slipped into bed and burrowed under the quilt, not just because she was cold, but to muffle the sound. She told herself that it was only the wind, that the house was strong and had been virtually rebuilt a year ago; nevertheless, when Nick reached for her she was glad to turn to him.

Although there was warmth and reassurance in his arms, and eager persuasion in the way he kissed and caressed her, the sounds above their heads were as distracting to Natasha as the squeaks of an unfamiliar bed. She found it impossible to relax. She felt awkward with him, all uncomfortable angles; it was like being in bed with a stranger, a man with whom she shared nothing, not even desire. The feeling produced a sense of claustrophobia, an urge to break free, and yet she sensed that he was trying to secure her with love and sexual pleasure and the physical unity that had always bound them so closely in the past. If he did she would melt, forgive and forget, as she had always done before. She wanted to submerge herself, to drown that inner resistance; she wanted to relax and submit, but her tension was too great, too attuned to the noise of the storm.

That lashing and beating, however, seemed only to drive him on. She could feel how anxious he was to enter her, every muscle hard beneath the smooth warmth of his skin. The gentle stroking became a kneading, the teasing of lips and tongue a series of nips and bites that began to hurt. Even as she protested, he drove his fingers into her, so sharply that she cried out. With a murmured apology he was gentler, kissing her mouth and throat and breasts; but what should have been a pleasure was not, it was a dry, insistent invasion of her body that Natasha wanted only to be rid of. If only it would go away, she thought, and was not sure whether she meant the storm or him or both.

He rubbed his face against her cheek. She became aware that his urgency was gone. 'I'm sorry,' she said as he uttered a wordless complaint.

'Mmm. Me too.'

Staring into the darkness, clutching the quilt under her chin, Natasha winced as another gust shook the house. Nick seemed not to notice. As he moved away from her and sat up, he said tersely: 'You're not still worrying about last night, are you?'

She shook her head. 'No, of course not.' But in part of course she was. Anxiety had dogged her all day; she had tried so hard to create an atmosphere in which they could talk about it amicably, but somehow the storm and the blackout had conspired to prevent that. With every sense aroused and alert, she could have cried out with frustration. 'It was the wind and the rain,' she told him crossly. 'All that bloody noise – it's so distracting. Anyway, you seemed to be enjoying it, I don't know why you didn't just carry on. You could have done, I'm sure.'

She heard his indrawn breath, felt him turn to look at her

through the darkness. 'I'm not a bloody rapist,' he whispered harshly. 'Forcing a woman who exhibits no discernible interest is not the sort of thing that turns me on. Quite the reverse, in fact – as you have just discovered.'

That declaration rang warning bells in Natasha's mind, bells that were associated with Bernice, Nick's first wife. He had lived with her for almost ten years, and endured a five-year separation rather than go through the messy business of suit and counter-suit to obtain the divorce he wanted and she refused to give. Bernice, however, was not often discussed except with regard to his sons. Once, revealingly, Nick had described her as a woman with a high IQ and a low boredom threshold, who got more kicks out of making trouble than she did out of making love.

But he rarely talked about his first marriage or his early life; and indeed, for a man who spent his life examining the past in minute detail, Natasha thought he was strangely reluctant to examine his own. That reluctance left a vast expanse of unknowing, occasionally glimpsed through unexpected chinks in their relationship, and it worried her. While things were going well she had no need to question him, but when things went ill she had too little knowledge on which to judge his reactions. What chilled her now was the thought that he might be holding her up for judgement alongside all the other women in his life.

Under a particularly violent blast, the windows rattled in their frames. Turning to Nick, she wrapped her arms about his waist and persuaded him to hold her. 'Look,' she said sorrowfully, 'I'm tired and so are you. Let's try again in the morning.'

But it was worse in the morning. It was blessedly quiet and still outside, but in the grey and chilly gloom that passed for daylight, Nick could not only feel that dry lack of enthusiasm, he could see the expression on her face.

Four

NICK WENT downstairs to make some tea. The newspapers had arrived, and the post. There were a couple of letters for Natasha, one for him, and a postcard of a sun-kissed beach in Cyprus, from Nick's youngest brother who was with the Parachute Regiment. It was the usual, uninformative missive: '*Thanks for your letter, this is a great posting after the other place* (until recently he had been in Northern Ireland) *and we're all making the most of it. Won't be home for Christmas, but I'll be in touch. All the best to both of you – Paul.*'

He wasn't much of a letter writer, but Nick was pleased that he kept in touch. Other than a Christmas card, his youngest sister never bothered, and she was only in London. He heard from the other two once or twice a year, but they were in Australia, with families of their own to worry about. He looked again at the golden beach and experienced a sudden desire to be there; anywhere, he thought, other than this.

The ginger and white cat was rubbing around his legs, demanding to be fed; for the sake of peace he did that job first, then set about fuelling the stove and putting some warmth back into the house.

The activity took some of the edge off his frustration, but not enough. He thought about going out for a run, although it was not his usual practice on Saturdays. During the week it was essential to him, clearing his mind, generating energy and enthusiasm for the day ahead; but at the weekend, with research and writing to attend to, he generally preferred a quiet morning in his study. Today, however, he felt very much in need of some hard exercise.

Moodily, he stood looking out of the window, wondering what to do. The wind had dropped away completely, leaving a still, misty morning which almost belied last night's violence. Almost, but not quite, since the evidence was all around in stripped branches and piles of dead leaves. Surveying the yard and garden, Nick knew he should make some attempt to clear up. It was a necessary job before winter, but although he told himself that the storm had done him a favour by stripping most of the dead leaves at once, he could not raise any enthusiasm for it.

Nevertheless, having made a spartan decision in favour of the garden, he pulled on an old parka over his sweater and jeans, and tramped across the yard to the barn. Outside, it was even colder than he had imagined, the season's first hint of frost evident in a silvery rime beneath walls and hedges. It was certainly too cold to hang about, so he set to work with a will, raking up leaves and barrowing them around the house to a point where they could be safely burned.

To Nick, the house seemed back-to-front, since the yard and what had once been the old kitchen garden faced roughly south and caught all the sun; and that entrance was the one they always used. But the house had been designed to overlook the village, so its northern face was rather more imposing, with a pedimented front door and a small terrace. Nowadays that entrance could not be used, since the old gateway into the lane had long since been devoured by the hawthorn hedge. Nick paused for a moment beneath the arch in the high protective wall at the north-eastern corner of the house and surveyed the front garden. Neglected for years, it was less a garden than a wilderness of weeds and overgrown shrubberies, with dog-rose and wild honeysuckle running riot through the hedges. In the summer, it had possessed all the charm of an ancient meadow, grasses and wild flowers bending before the breeze and providing a haven for bees and butterflies. Now the shrubs were bare, the grass flattened, only the weeds standing as defiant as pikemen before a battle.

He was defeated just surveying them. For the first time, considering the half-acre on which Holly Tree Cottage stood, Nick wondered whether he had taken on rather more than he was able to handle. Thankfully, the yard was surrounded by clamp-brick walls, but even they were beginning to crumble in places.

With the feeling that he was about to become seriously depressed, he dumped the barrowload of leaves and returned to the kitchen garden. By eleven o'clock he had all but finished the immediate task, and a struggling sun was doing its best to transmit some warmth. He was just thinking of taking a break when Natasha came out to join him, carrying two cups of coffee as a peace offering.

They spent another hour or more outside, Natasha lifting the skeletal remains of bedding plants from the borders, while Nick trimmed roses and a straggling clematis by the wall. He was surveying the spreading holly bush when he noticed someone coming down the lane. It was the woman they referred to as Mrs McCoy, with her Irish wolfhound. McCoy was in fact the dog's name, and as usual he was dragging her along, eager to be off the leash. His owner released him, and with no surprise whatever Nick watched the scruffy, spindly thing lope towards him, eating up the intervening forty or fifty yards with no apparent effort.

McCoy had a disconcerting tendency to jump up. Remembering the last occasion when that long, gaping snout had been within a couple of inches of his own face, Nick pointed at the ground and ordered the dog down. In sheer astonishment it stopped in its tracks and, as he continued to glare, lowered its frayed rope of a tail and slunk off to investigate a smell on the far side of the lane. With a nonchalant cocking of the leg it glanced back at him in reproach and continued on its way. Nick glanced back to see the woman hurrying to catch up. The dog, he thought, bullied her unashamedly.

As always, he felt sorry for her. She was about his own age, maybe a little older, fair and thin and faded-looking; very nice, but in a polite, over-apologetic sort of way, which spoke volumes to Nick about her husband and teenage sons. They were never in evidence on these dog-walking expeditions, and he had only ever seen them tinkering with cars and bikes outside their house on the new development.

As she came up, he said to her: 'I don't know if you're already aware of it, or even going that far, but there are sheep in that field on the ridge.' He smiled. 'If McCoy should decide to round them up, the farmer might not like it . . .'

'Oh, I didn't know, that's kind of you,' she gushed, 'and you're right, McCoy can be naughty sometimes. I'll put him on the lead when we get to the wood. Although on second thoughts,' she added anxiously, 'it's muddy down there, so maybe we won't go that far.'

'Well, it's up to you – I just thought I'd better let you know about the sheep. They've only just been moved into that field, and it's a bit close to the track.'

'Yes, yes it is. Thank you so much.'

Nick watched her on her way, imagining her husband slumped in an armchair, enjoying the Saturday sport on TV. That thought made him check his watch, and it occurred to him that if they hurried, they might have lunch at the pub and be back in time for him to watch the rugby international at three.

Denton-on-the-Forest was protected from general view by trees and the lie of the land; and its location, off a very minor road, meant that it was easily overlooked by the casual tourist. Nevertheless, it was known by connoisseurs of pretty north Yorkshire villages, and – thanks to its beautifully-preserved Saxon church tower – had also appeared in a couple of guidebooks.

Facing the junction of Dagger Lane lay the Green, a sloping acre of grassland that had once formed part of the medieval enclosure within which the villagers protected their animals. The beck that had watered them ran in a deep ditch alongside, disappearing under the road to flow more gently through the meadows to the south.

Above the Green, a row of cottages and houses formed an attractive crescent defined by the post office and shop, the church with its squat Saxon tower, and the village inn, the Half Moon. All the dwellings were well cared for, most of them belonging to professional, ex-city people who had moved out of town for the peace and tranquillity of country life. The genuine villagers had been pushed out to less salubrious cottages huddled behind the church or scattered along the main road, while their offspring married and moved into town because local jobs were scarce and the accommodation beyond their income.

There was a great sadness in that, Natasha felt, but it was typical of rural life these days; and she and Nick were just as guilty, just as much foreigners in local eyes. Even so, neither of them had any particular wish to mix with the elevated strata of village life, other than on a polite, everyday level, nor could they be said to have integrated with the real villagers. The locals seemed to regard Dr and Mrs Rhodes – or was it Dr Rhodes and Ms Crayke? – with the same ironic tolerance they afforded to everyone else who was not a natural-born Dentonite with at least three generations behind them.

To a great extent, the Half Moon reflected that divide. It was an old-fashioned pub owned by one of the big northern breweries, but the landlord had been a tenant for many years and was locally accepted. Although he had succumbed to pressure and provided bar lunches every day of the week, he refused to expand into evening meals because he said the smell of food ruined the enjoyment of his beer; and besides, if he made too much money on catering, the brewery would terminate his lease and install a manager, complete with chef, new dining-room and new décor.

The locals always looked glum when he said that, and Natasha sympathised. She had become fond of the old place with its oak beams and nicotine-coloured ceilings, and felt that any serious alteration would spoil the atmosphere completely. A single bar ran through the centre of the pub to serve two main rooms – the stone-flagged 'public' in which darts and dominoes were played most nights of the week, and an L-shaped area known as 'the best room', which boasted carpets and a fire. It was a place of tiny windows and innumerable nooks and crannies, where stuffed animal heads peered out of the shadows and strange artefacts hung from blackened beams. In winter, the log fire's dancing flames lent an illusion of life to long-dead hares and foxes and squirrels, causing more than one stranger to halt in alarm and look again.

Natasha made straight for the fire, warming her hands while Nick ordered the drinks. She was aware of feeling slightly better for the fresh air and exercise, and would have felt better still had it not been for a deep-seated sense of frustration. Although it was partly sexual, she had a wider awareness that things were in danger of going badly wrong, while being unable to set them right on her own. Glancing at Nick's broad back and the pleasing shape of his thighs and haunches as he leaned against the bar, she wished that she had been able to respond to him physically. Fatigue was one thing, but she had never before felt so thoroughly turned off by the thought of sex. Well, not with Nick, anyway. She loved him, and right now she even wanted him; and for his sake she wished that they could have a physical making-up, if only to make conversation possible afterwards.

That momentary desperation seemed to communicate itself. He turned to meet her gaze and there was a marked hesitation before his mouth twitched into a small, rueful smile. It was a look that made her burn with guilt.

He indicated the menu. 'The soup's leek and potato – do you want some?'

'Please. And a cheese sandwich.'

Close to, the heat from the fire was fierce. Natasha moved away and took a seat by the window. Already the meagre best of the day was over and a dense white mist was collecting around the trees and over the beck. She was just thinking that they had abandoned the garden at the right time, when she caught a glimpse of something streaking out of Dagger Lane and into the road. It was a second or two before she recognised McCoy, and almost at once he came into the open, skidding and scrambling as he took the corner into the new development.

McCoy was such a canine bully that his obvious terror on this occasion brought forth a low chuckle of amusement, although even as she wondered what had scared him it occurred to her that his owner was nowhere to be seen. No doubt she would appear in a moment, gasping after him with a trailing leash.

Nick brought their drinks across to the table, wanting to know what was so amusing. His own smile quickly faded as she described McCoy's streak for home. With a furrowed brow he bent to look out of the window.

'How very odd.' He took a long pull of his beer and seemed lost in thought. 'I do hope it's not – '

'What?'

'There's no sign of her, is there? And would you believe I told her about the sheep and never thought to warn her about – '

Natasha opened her mouth to ask what he meant, but he was already heading for the door. 'I'll explain later,' he called over his shoulder, 'you'd better stay here.'

Utterly bemused, she watched him leave, following him with her eyes as he ran past the window and across the road. She hesitated for a while, wondering what to do, but as she made up her mind, the landlord arrived with the soup and sandwiches.

'Sorry, Tony, it'll have to wait – got to go.'

She dashed outside but Nick had long since disappeared. Mist was billowing like smoke down Dagger Lane, rolling across the road and settling by the beck. It was eerie enough to slow that headlong dash, to make her pause at the junction and think twice before plunging into it. Then she saw three figures silhouetted and coming towards her, one obviously Nick, another so much smaller that it had to be old Toby Bickerstaff, and a woman between them. As they came closer she saw that the woman had been crying, and was still dabbing her eyes; at the sight of Natasha she straightened and disengaged herself from Nick's protective arm.

'. . . all right now, honestly . . . thank you so much . . .'

There was mud on her hands and most of the way down her right side, but while Natasha was anxious to know what had happened and why Nick had gone shooting off like that, it hardly seemed the time to ask. Instead, she confined herself to essentials. But it seemed as though the woman really was all right, with no bones broken and her shock abating. Now that she was safe, she was inclined to be dismissive and apologetic, more concerned about what people would think if it took three people to escort her along the village street. With some reluctance she allowed Nick and Natasha to walk beside her, while Toby, taking the hint, hung several paces behind. At the end of the Green, however, she thanked them firmly and insisted on going home alone.

Nick sighed and glanced at Toby, already heading across the road towards the Half Moon. 'Come on,' he said to Natasha, 'let's have that lunch.'

But with the soup on reheat and their sandwiches waiting, she demanded to know what was going on. With a sidelong glance, Nick apologised for not telling her the first part of the story earlier; he had, he said, forgotten about it in the light of other concerns.

She listened, feeling the rise of goose-flesh along her arms and thighs. Suppressing a shiver, she forced herself to analyse Toby's tale of an unidentified animal seen at dusk, and came to the conclusion that the old man had probably had one drink too many, mistaking a stray black labrador for something mysterious and slightly sinister.

'It was probably the dog I saw in the lane the other night – '

'No, I don't think so. You were certain it was a dog – Toby and Mrs McCoy are equally certain that it wasn't.'

He went on to relate the woman's version of events down the lane. Apparently she had walked the dog almost as far as World's End Wood, where the fog was thick in the hollow and rapidly spreading. As usual, McCoy was snuffling about in the undergrowth some distance away, so she hurried to catch up and was about to call him when she saw his head come up and his hackles rise. He looked, she'd said, as though he was about to go into the attack; then he let out a long, low growl, suddenly yelped as though he'd been bitten, and did a sharp about-turn before taking to his heels.

'. . . and when she turned back to see what had scared him, she saw this dark shape emerging from the fog and moving towards her along the edge of the track. It had a big, broad head, held low, she said – and it was slinking along like a cat.

'Then she took to her heels as well,' Nick added, draining the last of his pint, 'for which you can hardly blame her. But then she slipped in the mud, which made her panic more. By the time she reached the gate into Toby's field, I gather she was practically jibbering with fright.'

Disturbed in spite of herself, Natasha tried not to show it. 'Hmm. I suppose she must have been scared if she shouted for him . . .'

'Oh, she was scared, all right. Do you want another drink?'

'Please.' She lit a cigarette and thought about the woman they called Mrs McCoy, trying to be more impressed by her fear than by this tale of shadows moving in the mist. There was no doubt that she'd been badly shaken, but on her own admittance, the fall had made her worse. And it had been very foggy down the lane, almost uncannily so. That was frightening in itself.

'So what did she think she'd seen?'

Nick sat down and took a mouthful of the landlord's best bitter. 'Would you believe a *black panther*?'

'Not really?'

The light caught his eyes as he laughed. 'Yes, I know it's unlikely, but there is that zoo place, remember.'

'Oh, for goodness' sake, Nick – that's a children's zoo. Black panthers are pretty rare, aren't they? I wouldn't have thought they had the money for exotic creatures like that!'

'Look, don't get so uptight about it,' he responded lightly. 'I know it all sounds crazy, but you wanted to know what happened, and I'm telling you as it was told to me.'

'But you must have believed what old Toby said the other day, otherwise you wouldn't have gone dashing off just now!' She was annoyed that he could credit other people's fantastic stories while doubting her veracity. It was a dog, she had seen it, and had even been convinced that she'd run it down. Nick hadn't believed her then; but now he was trying to convince her that there was something vaguely mysterious about it. It was too much.

He drank deeply before setting the pint glass down. 'Yes,' he said quietly, 'I did believe him. And now I think it's time we were going.'

Despite her scepticism, she found it an unnerving walk home. In the fog, every branch and clump of grass assumed a looming aspect; even the silence seemed ominous. Twice the muffled growl of a car going through the village set every sense leaping, since the sound seemed to come from all directions at once. Her desire to cling to Nick's arm was almost overwhelming, but a renewed sense of offence kept them at least a foot apart.

As soon as he walked into the house, Nick switched on the television to find that the rugby match was already under way. Without another word he stretched out on the sofa to watch, while Natasha headed for the kitchen and the phone. The walk home had illustrated what she suspected: that given the right conditions, most people can imagine anything, even black panthers prowling along country lanes. But just to prove herself right, she rang the local zoo and police stations at Easingwold, Helmsley and Strensall. Nobody had heard of a missing panther, or indeed anything that resembled one. Not even a large black labrador. Two alsatians, a golden retriever and a West Highland white terrier had been reported as lost, Natasha discovered, together with several domestic cats; but each policeman dutifully took her number and promised to call back if they should hear anything pertinent to her enquiry.

'I've checked with the police,' she said, going into the sitting-room, 'and there are no wild animals missing.'

'What you mean,' he said heavily, 'is that so far nobody's *reported* anything missing . . .' He continued to watch the screen, groaning as more points were awarded to the other side. But as Natasha turned abruptly for the door, he added: 'By the way, I'm meeting Toby first thing in the morning – we're going down the lane to look for tracks.'

Overnight, freezing fog had etched everything with white. Bathed in the diffused light of a rising sun, the landscape that Sunday morning was hazy and romantic, a winter wonderland after weeks of gloom. Walking briskly down the lane, Nick felt stimulated by the cold, enjoying the change of weather as much as the sense of adventure attendant upon this little outing.

Toby edged his way out of the caravan, a bulky figure in layers of old sweaters, his cap pulled firmly down over his forehead. The hands that gripped the shotgun were encased in fingerless mittens, but although he indulged in a good cough before they set off, he did not complain about the cold. He seemed, in fact, to be pleased by it.

For an elderly man with respiratory problems he could move quickly and quietly when it suited, and age had not dimmed the sharpness of his sight. While Nick kept his eyes peeled for any untoward movement in the hedgerows, Toby scanned the ground, pointing out McCoy's paw-prints here and there as they gradually made their way down towards the wood. He gave a running commentary too, on the spoor of fox and deer, a scatter of pigeon feathers where some unlucky bird had met its end, and the inevitable cluster of rabbit-droppings in the centre of the track. Not far from the wood, he found the spot where the wolfhound had taken fright, tracing the prints up to that point and away from it.

'See,' he muttered, pointing a gnarled finger at the ground. 'Soft enough yesterday to make 'em – hard enough s'mornin' to keep 'em!'

The prints were clear enough for Nick to trace a meandering route up to a grassy patch which had been gouged by a violent turn; and leading back in a wide arc over the stony centre of the path was a widely-spaced series of frosted pebbles where long claws had bitten deep as the dog sprinted away.

Beyond the patch of churned and frozen earth the track seemed undisturbed. Nick looked up, leaving the hunt to Toby. The edge of the wood was closer on the right; to the left it was perhaps twenty paces to a great pile of uprooted elm stumps, beyond which the trees stretched some distance into the surrounding fields. Hugging both sides of the lane, World's End was a dark, dense, untended piece of woodland, roughly oval in shape. It was ditched around its entire circumference, and, where these ditches mattered to the farmers, they were scoured on a fairly regular basis; but either side of the lane they were made up with mud and leaves and dying vegetation. Evidence of past care lay in the remains of a wooden bridge on the right, leading into a less overgrown gap in the trees which vaguely resembled a path.

Today, frost alleviated the darkness; the trees were ghostly, the undergrowth of brambles and bracken looking like a forgotten mass of Christmas decorations. Natasha would have exclaimed over it, but Nick was reluctant to breach its defences. While Toby risked the bridge and began poking about on the far side, Nick waited for him by the elm stumps. It occurred to him that in dense mist, those upended roots might easily be mistaken for something weird and unnatural. As the possibility took hold, his glance was distracted by the brilliant colour of two spent shotgun cartridges beneath the biggest stump; and, less than a yard away, in a patch clear of leaves, the imprints of two large paws.

Like the ones further back, the pattern was deep and clear, clear enough to distinguish a roughly circular pad with five smaller 'toes' and matching indentations where long claws had sunk into impacted mud. The imprints were certainly large enough to have been made by a wolfhound, and at first Nick thought that McCoy had passed this way. But surely the pattern was different?

He called Toby.

The old man advanced cautiously and peered hard at the evidence. Eventually he straightened and pursed his lips. 'Looks like a bloody great dog,' he said dubiously, delving deep for his tin of cigarettes. 'I tell thee what, though – it's not that there Irish thing. *He's* only got *four* claws.'

Five

'ALL RIGHT, fair enough – dogs don't usually have five claws. Nor do cats, but I once knew somebody,' Natasha said, 'who had a cat with five toes on each of its front paws, so it's not impossible. The poor thing's probably just a stray – a mongrel chucked out of a car when last year's Christmas present started eating them out of house and home.'

Toby said nothing, just shuffled his feet and stared at the denuded garden. Nick handed him a mug of coffee and muttered something about it needing to be a bloody big mongrel with paws that size. He could have shaken Natasha for not allowing the old man at least the pretence of a mystery, even though privately he acknowledged the truth of her argument. What really annoyed him, however, was that defensive attitude, her steadfast refusal to consider the more esoteric side of possibility. If he hadn't read her books, Nick felt that he might be forgiven for thinking his wife had no imagination; but he had read them, and knew otherwise. That Natasha appeared to him to keep her gift under lock and key somewhere in her office, was a fanciful thought but a frustrating one.

After lunch he retired to his study in the hope of pursuing more rewarding tasks. His intention was to write up some notes for an essay, one he had been invited to submit to the *Agricultural History Review*; sadly, however, the decline of the small landowner in eighteenth-century North Yorkshire failed to hold his attention.

He found himself gazing absently from the window, watching the mist closing in again, obscuring what remained of the afternoon. He switched on his desk-lamp and with an effort forced his mind back to the task in hand. Another paragraph and his thoughts wandered again, drawn inexorably back to the twin mysteries of Natasha's peculiar behaviour and Toby's gargling dog.

Restlessness forced him out of his seat. He prowled the confines of the room, studying the contents of his bookshelves. Here and there a title caught his attention, and he glanced briefly through the book before setting it back in place. Then, at the end of a shelf, amongst an unsorted pile brought back from college the other day, his eye lit upon a most unlikely paperback. One of his students – and it had to be a girl, although he could not think who – had left this copy of Anaïs Nin's *Delta of Venus* in his room after a seminar. Out of sheer curiosity he had read a couple of chapters and found the contents imaginative but stimulating. It was, however, the kind of stimulus he did not need. Not at the moment, anyway.

He paused in the act of pushing it into a drawer, weighing the book in his hand. Although he had not mentioned the incident to Natasha, he thought he might do so when she was in a better mood. Perhaps she would read the book for herself and remember what it was they were missing.

But even momentary fantasies were disturbing, and he was supposed to be looking for something else. Memory was proving elusive, but Nick was almost sure that he had read something about a dog or hound, something really rather strange, which was pertinent to this area; he was certain it was in a book, and he was almost certain that it was in his own collection. Resuming his search, he scanned through the contents of two or three more, before finding a more likely contender.

Dated 1899, Beauchamp's *History of the Howardian Hills* was a book to dip into occasionally, a glorious mish-mash of local folklore and spectacularly wrong antiquarian interpretations, put together by a country clergyman with an MA. It was the kind of book he loved. Such writers spoke to him of comfortable livings, satisfactorily mild Christianity and limitless opportunity for the pursuits of the mind, illustrating a way of life which was not only gone for ever, but totally foreign to his own experience. Although he was not sure why, Nick had an amused and affectionate regard for them, rather as he had for the dated murder-mysteries of Dorothy Sayers and Margery Allingham.

He opened the book at the chapter headed: 'Some Curious Myths and Legends', smiling a little as his eye scanned local tales the Reverend Beauchamp had seen fit to include. There were the usual ghost stories, one to do with Slingsby Castle, regarding the John de Mowbray who was beheaded after backing the wrong side at the Battle of Boroughbridge, another about Sheriff Whenby – but the Hall, Nick noted with interest, not the Castle – and yet another about a ghostly monk at Kirkham Priory. There were tales about witches who turned into hares – not cats in this area! – and hares which suddenly became women; and following this theme of mysterious animals was the piece that he had been looking for.

According to the Reverend Beauchamp, locally it was claimed that a black hound haunted these parts, and although he had not been able to find anyone who would admit to having seen it, Beauchamp believed it to be based upon an old account regarding Brickhill church. According to this old account – and he did not give the source, Nick noted with annoyance – a black hound had suddenly appeared amongst the congregation during a service in 1635. Coming from the chancel, the hound had wandered down the nave, watched by an astonished congregation. The churchwardens had been unable to catch it, and had apparently been confounded by its sudden disappearance and the smell that was left behind . . .

Wondering what kind of smell, he read on, and discovered that this event was supposed to have taken place in the same week that the altar-table was returned to the east end of the church, and that various factions had claimed it to be a visitation of the hound of the AntiChrist, come to approve the idolatry.

And that, Nick thought as he read the piece through again, was probably the nub of it: anti-Catholic feeling running high during a period not noted for its religious tolerance, and the chance appearance of a black dog in church which had given the local zealots maximum mileage for their propaganda. Beauchamp phrased it differently, but his opinion seemed much the same. Nick *had* read it before, and, had it not been for Toby and Mrs McCoy, and those extraordinary prints found by the wood, he would have dismissed it again in the same fashion. As a piece of nonsense.

Now, he was not so sure.

Just as he was wondering where he might find the original account, Nick heard a car coming along the lane. He opened the window and looked out, but in the foggy dusk could see nothing but lights. Nevertheless, something told him that their visitor was Giles.

With the book still in his hand, Nick hurried down to greet their visitor, and with a grin ushered his friend into the warm kitchen.

Giles indulged in a dramatic shiver. 'God, but it's cold out there! Yes, Natasha I'd love a coffee, and something warmer to go with it, darling, if I may?' He extended his hands to the heat of the stove. 'Christ, this bloody weather – suicidal, isn't it? And Fay's escorting a party of Japanese round York this afternoon. Not that the poor buggers will have seen much – when I left, it was thick as a bag in town. I was so pissed off with it, I thought I'd have a drive to the coast.'

'And what was it like over there?'

'Bloody gorgeous – clear skies, calm seas, lots of doggies frolicking on the beach.' He laughed and hugged Natasha. 'Anyway, how are you? Recovered from the Hallowe'en party yet?'

'But of course,' she replied, her tone a match for the temperature outside. 'Unlike the rest of you, I was sober.'

Giles made quite a play of realising that he had said the wrong thing, but as ever he was more amused than genuinely contrite. Before long, however, he had Natasha laughing, and for a fleeting moment Nick was envious of that ability. Giles, it seemed, could get away with anything where women were concerned; but there again, he wasn't married.

Nick poured a couple of tots of whisky, and led the way into the sitting-room. A minute or two later, Natasha brought in the coffee, but did not stay. She said she had the dinner to prepare, and, almost as an aside, asked Giles if he would like to eat with them. He thanked her enthusiastically, and then, when she was out of earshot, made his usual observation to Nick, that he was a lucky sod to have persuaded Natasha to marry him, and that girls like her just didn't grow on trees.

Grimly amused, Nick turned away, coaxing the fire into a blaze with a few small, dry chunks of wood. As they took light, he sat back on his haunches, admiring the ornate, cast-iron fire-back which protected the bricks behind the dog-grate. He had discovered it in the barn, partially buried beneath layers of compacted straw and earth. In fact he had stubbed his toe while clearing out years of accumulated rubbish, and in his anger was digging the thing free before he realised what it was. The effort had certainly been worthwhile. The fire-back was broken only in that one corner, while the pattern, reminiscent of an Elizabethan knot-garden, was amazingly well preserved.

'What's this you've been reading?' Giles asked, brandishing the copy of Beauchamp's *History*. 'It looks rather splendid.'

'Yes, the cover's wonderful, isn't it? Contents are a bit bloody frustrating, though. He tells some intriguing little stories, but doesn't give his sources.'

'Hmm.' Turning the pages, Giles said: 'And for which intriguing little story were you wanting the source?'

With a grin, Nick took the book and found the right page; when he had read aloud both the account and Beauchamp's conclusion, he said: 'And in spite of the fact that most of his other conclusions are way off the mark, in this case I agree with him. And I'd be quite happy to leave it there, except that . . .'

With a small sigh of exasperation, he picked up his glass, studying the amber-coloured liquid as it sparkled in the firelight.

'Except what?' his companion demanded. 'Come on, don't leave me in suspense.'

Knowing Giles's predilection for ghost stories and tales of the occult, Nick was a little reluctant to divulge the rest; not because he thought he would be disbelieved, but because he thought his friend would make too much of it. His own interest in such things was scholarly rather than prurient, based upon the social history of the countryside, where folk tales and myths had their sphere of influence, probably less than politics and religion, but an important sphere, nevertheless. He needed to talk about it, he needed someone else's angle, an intelligent one if only Giles could be persuaded to set aside some of his more fanciful ideas. With scrupulous care, Nick related Toby's story, and that of the woman they called Mrs McCoy.

Giles was impressed. 'And you say you saw it too, the night of the party?'

'No, I didn't see it. Natasha saw something she swears was a dog. I must confess I thought she was imagining things – it really was a filthy night, if you remember, and the hedges are so overgrown – '

'But she thought she'd run into something?'

'Yes, but she hadn't, the sudden jerk she felt was just the engine stalling.'

'So, in effect, what you're saying is that she saw something that wasn't really there? A ghost, or whatever, that simply looked like a dog?'

'But ghosts don't leave footprints. Do they?'

'No, they damn well don't,' Natasha interjected as she came into the room. 'For the simple reason that they don't exist. Ghosts are no more than hallucinations – figments of the imagination.'

Giles laughed. 'So you imagined this dog?'

'No, I didn't – it was there, right in front of the car. Obviously, in the dark, it must have seemed closer than it really was – I braked hard, stalled the car, and the dog shot off into the darkness. It's as simple as that.'

'And this same dog terrified the Irish wolfhound?'

She took a seat at one end of the sofa and turned to look at Giles. 'The wolfhound's just a bully, and like all bullies, he's probably terrified of his own shadow.'

Nick passed her Beauchamp's *History*, open at the page which reported the incident at Brickhill in 1635. 'Well, answer me this –

if ghosts are no more than hallucinations, how come the church-wardens and an entire congregation saw a black dog disappearing through the wall?'

Her lips tightened as she read the account. Reaching for her cigarettes as she handed the book back, Natasha said: 'I shouldn't imagine that report was based on what you'd call evidence. It sounds to me like something you'd read in the tabloid press today.'

'Quite so,' Nick responded calmly, 'that was my reaction too, when I first read it. But don't you think it seems a little odd that several people at one time in 1635 should claim to have seen this mysterious animal and then you, and Toby, and Mrs McCoy see something answering a similar description in the last few days?'

'No, I don't. I don't think the two things are at all connected. It's pure coincidence, and I think you're trying to stretch a point way beyond the bounds of credibility.'

'I'm not trying to stretch *anything*,' he retorted, 'I'm merely intrigued by a snippet of folklore – *a black hound is said by many to haunt these parts* – as reported in 1899, and the fact that none of you who've seen this black animal over the last few days can agree what it is!'

'I saw a *dog*,' she snapped at him, 'and you probably found its prints today down by World's End. I don't think there's anything very mysterious in that!'

As she flounced out of the room, Nick gritted his teeth and silently vowed never to raise the subject again. With a grin and a shrug, Giles reached for the whisky bottle.

'Have another drink,' he urged consolingly, 'and take heart in the fact that black hounds have been known to provide great inspiration. Take *Dracula*, for instance – classic horror, never been bettered, in my opinion – and ask yourself where Bram Stoker got some of his ideas from. In the book, if you remember, the hound leaps off the foundering ship and disappears up Whitby church steps. Well, I can reveal to you that our old friend Bram took his holidays in Whitby – which is where I've been today – and there really was a Russian ship that grounded on Collier's Hope about the time he stayed there. And of course, local people would have told him about the Barguest.'

'Barguest?'

'The great black hound that haunts the yards and alleyways of Whitby.'

'A hound of ill-omen?'

'Oh, most decidedly!' Giles replied with relish.

There were times, Natasha thought irritably, when men were just like children: sensible on their own, but unutterably silly when encouraged by their friends. This thing about the dog might have died a natural death, but with Giles's participation it would no doubt gain embellishments and be repeated at other people's dinner tables.

Too ridiculous for words, she decided, taking the lid off the casserole and giving the chicken *cacciatore* a vicious prod with a fork. Natasha wished now that she had not asked him to stay to dinner; but then Nick probably would have done so, especially after a few drinks. And that was another thing: Nick drank sparingly as a rule, but when he and Giles got together, it seemed neither of them knew when to stop. Giles must be well over the limit already, and unless she volunteered to drive him home – which she had no intention of doing – he would have to stay the night. The situation was not unusual, but did not please her; the sight of a half-empty whisky bottle, and the smell of the empty glasses, brought back too many painful memories.

Generally speaking, Natasha drank very little, but in a gesture of defiance she opened a bottle of supermarket Lambrusco, cheap and cheerful, and sweet enough to suit her taste. After two or three glasses, it was doubtful whether anyone would ask her to drive anywhere.

It was a pity, she reflected, that Giles was on his own. It would have been good to see Fay this afternoon, she was bright and amusing, and had become a good friend in the last couple of years. It was rather a pity that they had seen so little of each other recently, but with work on the book practically over, perhaps that could be rectified.

Giles said the same thing over dinner. 'Why don't you give Fay a call,' he suggested, 'and fix up a date for the theatre? I've got the new season's programmes at home – I seem to remember there were a couple of plays that might be worth seeing.'

Natasha said that she would. Giles and Nick finished off the bottle of dry white wine she had opened for the casserole's benefit, saying that otherwise it would go to waste. They ate and drank appreciatively, praising the meal. Natasha enjoyed cooking, and found it a satisfying change from writing. Since she loathed domestic chores, that discovery had been surprising, but had come about after spending a long, hot summer working in a burger bar on the seafront at Great Yarmouth. Like a course of aversion therapy, it had cured her of a fondness for junk-food, and in reaction she'd bought the first of her collection of cookery books, which now ranged from vintage Mrs Beeton to the latest from Claudia Roden.

The conversation progressed to food and restaurants at home and abroad, until they were making enthusiastic plans to revisit some of their more accessible favourites. Now Natasha's book was finished, it seemed anything and everything was possible.

Afterwards, they settled down in the sitting-room to watch the last episode of one of Ruth Rendell's murder mysteries. It kept them quiet for almost an hour, although once it was over, characters, plot, clues and solution all came under scrutiny. As ever, Nick was primarily concerned with Inspector Wexford's interpretation of the facts, while Giles and Natasha were more interested in the style and presentation of the novels. They accused Nick of being too pedantic in his criticisms, and of being soulless and narrow-minded in his views. Ordinarily, Nick would have ignored such jibes, or even refuted them lightly; but after scotch and wine and more scotch, he was not inclined to take that kind of insult, particularly from his wife.

'Don't give me that,' he retorted, 'not after the way you've been behaving recently. It strikes me you could do with a few lessons in broadening the mind as well as the imagination!'

With that, he drained his coffee to the dregs and said that he was going to bed.

Giles stared after him in open-mouthed amazement. 'For heaven's sake – what's got into Nick?'

'God knows,' Natasha said tersely. She reached out to fill the void with music, and, as the lively strains of a piece by Jean-Michel Jarre dispelled the tension, managed to force a smile. 'A combination of things, I expect. I'm not the flavour of the month just now, as you've probably gathered.'

'Whyever not?' But as soon as the question was out, Giles shook his head. 'No, sorry, don't answer that – it's none of my business.'

With a weary, negative gesture, Natasha relaxed against the sofa cushions. 'It's all right, it doesn't matter. If you must know, we had a row after that blasted Hallowe'en party, and I'm afraid we haven't really made it up since.'

'Oh, I see,' he murmured, pulling a face. 'Are you still furious with him?'

'In some respects, yes. It annoys the hell out of me that he can spend so much time discussing something as trivial as a stray dog, and yet he won't talk to me about what was going on that night.'

For a moment Giles said nothing, then he turned to her, his eyes troubled. 'Listen, I don't know whether you noticed, but there was all bloody sorts going on that night – cocaine, cannabis and God knows what being passed around. Nick wasn't partaking, I don't mean that – it was just the atmosphere that night, it was so . . .' Unable to find the right word, he shook his head, then said drily: 'Well, let's put it like this, I doubt if there'll be another do like it in Hesketh College – the cleaners had too much to complain about afterwards!'

'What are you saying?' she asked stiffly. 'That Nick wasn't responsible for his behaviour, and therefore I shouldn't mind?'

'No, I'm saying he probably got a bit carried away – I think most people did, it was that kind of party. But don't you think you're over-reacting? After all, love, necking on the dance-floor's not that much of a crime!'

'Oh, come on, Giles, you saw him with that girl – you know there was more to it than that!'

'No,' he said earnestly, 'I don't. And in my opinion you're making too much of it.'

She wanted to believe him and, after three days, even found

herself doubting those instincts which had said so clearly that there was a case to answer. But she could not dismiss them completely, nor forget that the two men were friends.

They'd known each other a long time, since schooldays, in fact, although the friendship dated more from the time when Giles arrived in York to take up his post in the English Department. After three years lecturing in History, Nick was already well established and married, and seemed to have provided a point of stability in Giles's frequently unstable existence.

Nick did not, however, encourage his friend to talk about the old days, which Natasha found odd, and of the recurring topics, she was never quite sure which grated more: the echo of ingenuous hero-worship which crept into Giles's voice whenever school and sport were mentioned, or his jokey, disparaging references to their old home town. He either called it the Grayshaw Gulag, as though it were some place of internal exile on the Siberian tundra, or else described it as a bloody awful monument to the Industrial Revolution, full of mills and Methodists. He reckoned he only ever returned there to remind himself how fortunate he was to have escaped.

In fact he returned quite often to visit his parents, and, as Nick had often pointed out to Natasha, Giles's background was hardly one of deprivation. His father had been manager of the same woollen mill where Nick's father had worked as a weaver; and whereas Giles's parents still lived in a substantial Edwardian villa on the edge of open moorland, Nick's family home had been rather more humble, a tall and narrow terraced house in the heart of town.

Although she was curious about the place where Nick had spent his childhood, he would say only that the mills were gone now, ploughed under, like the Methodist chapels, to make way for supermarkets and housing estates and car parks. Grayshaw, he had once informed her with heavy irony, even boasted a McDonald's hamburger joint and bowling alley on the site of the old weaving sheds where his father had spent his working life, and while he claimed to feel no sentiment for the passing of the woollen trade, the transformation of Grayshaw saddened him. It illustrated the death of manufacturing industry in general, and revealed an enormous hole in the national economy.

She could understand that, but still wondered why he was so irritated by Giles's references, and also why Giles insisted on being disparaging about a place that seemed, in spite of all the evidence, to mean so much to him.

But that was Giles. He mocked everything, himself most of all, and Natasha often wondered whether that jocular, irreverent attitude of his was no more than a mask to cover some deep-seated regrets. That he admired Nick was obvious; and sometimes Natasha thought that he envied him too, professionally as well as personally. She found that sad, since Giles was a first-class tutor, far more approachable than Nick, who had always tended to be somewhat distant and formal in his relationship with students.

Nevertheless, she reminded herself cynically, there were bound to be exceptions . . .

But Giles would have none of it. He maintained that there had been nothing serious going on with that girl, and if Natasha persisted in thinking otherwise, she was really punishing no one but herself.

There was a certain amount of truth in that. She knew, deep down, that she wanted nothing more than to be able to forgive and forget the incident, but she could not do that without airing the grievance, and at the moment he seemed so prickly and annoyed by the failure of their sexual relationship, everything was in stalemate.

Sensing her unhappiness, Giles squeezed her hand and tried to provoke a smile. 'Come on, don't let me down on this. Who was it got the two of you together again after all those years? If I can't settle down myself, I need a bit of success with other people to justify my existence!'

He gave her the benefit of his lop-sided grin, but his blue eyes were very shrewd. 'You're not going to let it all go, just for a moment of foolishness, now are you?'

She shook her head, touched by the unexpectedness of his concern. 'No, of course not,' she murmured, suddenly feeling guilty and kissing his cheek because of all the times she had doubted him.

'Good,' he said seriously, 'because I care about you both.'

'Yes, I know you do,' she smiled, returning the pressure of his hand. His sympathy prompted a surge of warmth and affection, and she found herself remembering his kindness when she had been in despair as a student, and wishing he could advise her now. But time had moved on and she had grown up, and sexual problems could hardly be discussed with one of her husband's closest friends.

Instead, she returned to the subject of the dog, venting some of her pent-up frustration in that direction. 'But you see,' she explained, 'I can't abide all this superstitious nonsense, Giles – it's so childish. Talk about it long enough and it's almost as though you're wishing something into existence. It makes me think of Helen, when she was little, telling me there was an old woman sitting on the end of her bed. There wasn't, of course there wasn't, but not only did she frighten me to death, in the end I'm sure she'd managed to convince herself as well! And guess who got into trouble for causing such a fuss? Me, of course, who happened to be four years older, and should have known better!'

And then, she thought, when they were both some years older, and Natasha really did feel as though she knew better, she was in trouble again for mocking Helen's saintly and mystical phase – what an act that was! – and for decrying all those masses said for their dead father's soul. *Daddy didn't believe in all that*, she had protested again and again; and it was true. As far as Alex Crayke was concerned, death was the end of it; after that you were food for the worms, and anyone who believed otherwise was deluding themselves. The most upsetting thing, however, was that in his lifetime their mother, Celia, had apparently gone along with his beliefs; or at least never challenged them in Natasha's hearing. But as soon as he was gone, *everything* changed . . .

She kept those reflections to herself, however, forcing a laugh to match Giles's amusement even while she assured him that the story about Helen was true.

'It bothers you, though, doesn't it?' he said teasingly. 'I think you're just a bit scared that there might be some truth in this story of Nick's.'

'Oh, don't be ridiculous, Giles! I don't believe in such things!'

'*The lady doth protest too much, methinks . . .*'

'And *don't* start quoting Shakespeare at me,' she admonished, 'or I'll turf you out of here, over the limit or not!'

With a throaty chuckle, he slipped a friendly arm around her shoulders and hugged her close. 'You wouldn't do that to poor old Giles.'

'Wouldn't I? Just try me!' She shook her head and laughed, but before the smile left her lips she was seized by a most extra-ordinary awareness. Everything seemed heightened: the music, the smell of the birch-logs burning in the grate, the warmth of Giles's thigh touching hers, and the pressure of his body against her arm. His face was only inches away, and he was smiling at her in his usual teasing fashion, but as the music reached a crescendo something sparked and flared between them. She had a wild, un-welcome urge to press her mouth to his and to feel his hand upon her breast; a moment of burning heat which seemed to suck the air from her lungs and leave time suspended; a split-second in which his smile faded and eyes widened –

In the heart of the fire something crackled and spat; the cat leapt up in alarm as a log collapsed in a shower of sparks.

She heard his indrawn breath. She felt her heart begin to beat again, frantically, as though making up for that moment of failure. Very slowly, Giles eased himself away, making the excuse of reaching for his cigarettes. He passed one to her and she took it gratefully, avoiding his eyes and trying not to notice that his hands were not quite steady.

From some detached corner of her mind came the reminder that Giles was a very responsive person who often hugged her and kissed her cheek; it was simply the way he was, there was nothing sexual about it. Never, in all the time she had known him, had he given any indication of lusting after her; and, prior to this moment, Natasha would have sworn on oath that she did not fancy Giles Crowther, had never done so, and cared about him only as a friend.

So why this? And why now?

The cat, which had shifted to a position of safety away from the hearth, suddenly came to attention, ears pricked towards the window. Natasha watched her rise and, in a sudden, stiff-legged rush, leap up to the window ledge to peer anxiously through the glass. Wondering at that, she then heard Nick's footsteps above, a pause, and then the muffled sound of him hurrying down the carpeted stairs. She stood up, smoothed her hair, and opened the door into the hall.

He was standing in the porch in his towelling robe, shining a torch into the garden. 'Hell of a fight out there – didn't you hear it?'

'No – no, the music's still playing.'

Although nothing could be seen, from the direction of the lane came a series of anguished yowls, interspersed by a deeper and more sustained growling.

'Where's Colette?'

'She's here,' Natasha said, alarmed in spite of herself. 'It'll be that bloody tom, I expect, defending his patch . . .'

'We ought to get something done about him,' Nick said, his tone so disgruntled and accusatory that Natasha immediately felt guilty.

'Such as? I defy you or anybody else to get near him – he's wild and he's evil, you know that.'

'Who is?' Giles demanded from the doorway.

Amidst the talk and conjecture, the sounds outside became intermittent and finally ceased completely. Satisfied that the fight was over, but by no means certain as to the protagonists, they went back into the warmth. Natasha suspected that both men were thinking of the mysterious creature seen by Toby and Mrs McCoy; as though in deference to her sensibilities, however, neither of them mentioned it. Instead, they talked about the appalling noises cats were capable of making, telling each other that it was probably just another marauding tom, or maybe even a stray dog, mistakenly seeking shelter in the barn.

Natasha left them to their pretence and evasion and went to bed.

Six

NEXT DAY, there was no sign of the outdoor cats. Natasha put down some food in the afternoon, as usual, but it remained untouched until Colette went out that evening. She returned a little while later, licking her lips and looking eminently satisfied. Natasha was both cross and concerned, but there was nothing to be done. It was dark and foggy, and those cats had ways of their own.

The females returned the following morning, wet and bedraggled but otherwise unharmed; of the vicious old tom there was no sign at all.

Nick said that he would look out for him, but the weather was such that he confined his running to the village, and it was not until the end of the week that he decided to risk the lane. It was on his return that he noticed the remains of something underneath the hedge not far from the house. At first he thought it was a dead rabbit, but on investigation found that it was a cat, and, from what was left of it, that it was the body of the old tom. The carcass had been picked by scavengers – rooks and crows probably – so it was hard to tell whether the cat had been savaged or had simply died of natural causes. Either way, it was a mess, and Nick was more disturbed than he cared to admit.

For a moment, thinking of Natasha, he was uncertain what to do. He did not want her to see this, yet he was not happy about leaving the remains to be cleared up by nature's refuse-collectors. On a sudden impulse he sprinted to the house and returned with the garden spade. It was not a pleasant task, but he carried the remains back with him and buried them hurriedly in a soft piece of earth near the compost heap.

At first he thought he would say nothing, and the fact that Natasha was still asleep when he went in made that easy; but she mentioned the cat again that evening, and he felt she would go on doing so until he told her the truth. Even so, what he gave her was an edited version, leaving out the more unpleasant details. He stressed the fact that the animal was not young, and that cats living wild could not expect to attain great age; but Natasha had not forgotten the fight, and kept asking whether there were any injuries.

'No,' he lied, 'none that I could see. It could have been natural causes . . .'

'Or a broken neck,' she said tautly. 'Dogs shake things, don't they? Shake them until they're dead.'

'Well, yes, I dare say they do . . .' He felt that he was getting into deep water, and hesitated. A moment later, he said: 'But I've yet to see one get the better of a cat, and that old tom was a seasoned campaigner . . .'

It was obvious, however, that Natasha was not convinced.

They seemed destined to rub each other the wrong way. Natasha was feeling awkward and irritable, uneasy with no work in hand yet unable to find a satisfying alternative. Although she was unhappy on her own, she was even more unsettled with Nick in the house, and the weekend did not ease things.

Nick's sons had been to stay for a few days during the October half-term, and would be staying again at Christmas; in the meantime Nick and Natasha were due to pay one of their regular visits to take the boys out for tea. She was not looking forward to it. She told herself that her feelings were nothing to do with the boys, and that it was churlish to resent the outing; but the present void between herself and Nick turned the simplest things into an effort.

They made her feel guilty, that was the trouble. They didn't have to work at it, either, although Adam tried his best and generally succeeded, and even Adrian played on her sympathy at times and had a knack of turning it against her. The thing was, she understood their difficulties; she remembered her own misery and confusion at a similar age, losing her father, changing schools, having to cope with a whole new set of circumstances at a time when puberty was rearing its unwelcome head. But, after all the changes of a year ago, the twins were now settling down, and the discipline of boarding-school seemed to be suiting them.

At the time of Natasha's brief affair with Nick, the twins had been three years old; they were six when he decided the marriage was unworkable and that it would be better for him to leave. As far as Natasha understood, there was at the time no other woman involved, although Bernice refused to believe that, just as she'd also refused to give him a divorce. She made her religion the excuse, although Natasha suspected spite was at the root of it, since during the period of their separation she had apparently been as awkward as it was possible for her to be. During the five years of their separation, she had allowed Nick access to the children as it suited her, which generally meant those times during the school holidays when she could find no one else to look after them.

Although that period had been difficult for him, with the finalisation of the divorce he had looked forward to rather more fair and sensible arrangements: alternate weekends, and perhaps half the holidays. But, having been awarded custody of the children, Bernice then discovered that Nick was planning to marry again, and that was when she had played her trump card. Her children should not suffer for lack of a permanent father, she said; her children deserved the best. And the best, according to Bernice, was a costly education at one of the country's foremost Catholic boarding-schools.

To further her career in computers, Bernice needed to travel, so having the boys at home would have presented a dilemma; but when Nick suggested that she should give up custody, and that the twins should live with him and Natasha and attend school in York, Bernice refused outright. There was no way that her children were going to be brought up by a pair of non-Catholics living in what she termed an adulterous relationship; it was bad enough for them that their parents were divorced.

Well, the latter statement Natasha could agree with, but the rest struck her as deliberately intolerant, less a matter of sincere belief than a convenient axe with which to hack at Nick.

But if her motives and behaviour had seemed iniquitous to begin with, the results were less so. The boys, away from their mother's undermining influence, were better behaved and had begun to treat Nick with respect; and now that they were into their second year at school, with the initial problems of boarding sorted out, they seemed to be doing well. Adam, technically the elder of the two, had discovered a certain prowess on the sports field, and since it was the kind of school where sports were very much encouraged, he had also discovered popularity. Natasha was afraid that it had gone to his head, and wished that Nick would praise him less and give just a little more attention to Adrian, who was gentler and more reserved. Adrian tried to keep up with his brother, but, given a choice, would rather watch than take part, and much preferred his books to all that hectic activity on the sports field.

Of the two, Natasha found Adrian more likeable. His academic interests coincided with her own, and, had he been less influenced by his brother, who still seemed determined to make life difficult for Natasha, she felt they might have become friends. As things were, however, she felt that prospect was remote.

They arrived at the school on Saturday afternoon in time for the junior house rugby match, met up with Adrian and stood with the other supporters and a handful of parents to watch. Although she felt she ought to be used to it by now, Natasha was never quite sure which horrified her most: the boyish violence of the game or the violently partisan yells of the young supporters. Nick and Adrian were almost as bad, but in spite of all Nick's attempts to explain the rules, she still found herself shouting encouragement just a fraction behind the rest.

Eventually Adrian took pity on her, and attempted to explain in simple terms and from the viewpoint of one who had only recently learned the game himself, exactly what was happening. For the first time she began to understand; and also began to feel that she was making a bit of headway.

Nevertheless, she was pleased when the game was over and won, when they could retire to the car and thaw themselves out while Adam dashed off with the other players to shower and change. He was full of himself when he joined them, ignoring Natasha except for a cursory greeting, while he regaled his father with the news that he had been chosen to play for the under-14s against one of the York schools the following week.

Natasha was pleased for him and joined in the congratulations, but it was difficult to change the subject, especially since Adrian was such a devoted fan. Even over tea he kept the dialogue going, and just occasionally gave Natasha the benefit of his secret smile, a smile so like Nick's that it never failed to touch her heart. The trouble was, she was never quite sure in Adrian's case whether she was being included in the joke or deliberately kept out of it; in some respects he was just as clever and subtle as his father.

Other than in certain gestures and facial expressions, however, the twins did not resemble Nick. Adam was slightly taller and heavier than his brother, and it was possible that one or both would eventually have their father's height and build; but their mother was also tall, and both boys had inherited her pale skin and curly red hair.

It was that reminder of Bernice's striking looks that made her wish the boys could have been more like Nick; then she might have felt less aware of their mother and a little less guilty about her relationship with their father.

Unaware, the twins chattered on about school and various friends, at the same time putting away a huge plateful of sandwiches and two enormous banana splits. They looked and sounded as though neither of them had a care in the world.

'Why does one worry about them?' Nick wondered aloud half an hour later, as they returned the boys to school.

Natasha smiled sympathetically, watching them as they rejoined their friends, two identical red heads bobbing amongst the more sober shades of brown.

It was a dark and misty drive back to York, with no time to return home either to eat or change before meeting Giles and Fay for the theatre. Natasha found that her sense of relief at having discharged one obligation that day was then exacerbated by the thought of facing Giles again. She would have conveniently forgotten his suggestion about the theatre, but Nick had reminded her; not only reminded her, but specifically asked her to ring Fay and make a firm date. And Fay, like Nick, had seized upon the suggestion at once.

She'd thought, privately, that Giles might have wanted to postpone the arrangement indefinitely. After that episode on Sunday evening Natasha felt desperately uneasy. At the very least she must have embarrassed Giles, for he was too experienced to mistake that look of hers for anything other than what it was; and at worst he was even now wondering how to avoid her. But no, she thought, the very worst scenario was recognition and response. Giles enjoyed the thrill of the chase, and if he should decide to pursue her . . .

Banishing such thoughts, Natasha steeled herself for the meeting. They were early, and took a seat in the bar. For a moment she almost gave in to nerves and ordered an alcoholic drink, but then, remembering the effect of the wine last Sunday, changed her mind and settled for Perrier instead. Nevertheless, with one cigarette finished she promptly lit another, earning herself a reproachful glance from Nick.

She knew at once, as soon as their eyes met, that Giles had not forgotten; but after that he seemed as keen as Natasha to avoid the smallest acknowledgement. Feeling like a Judas, she returned Fay's embrace, asking and answering the same kind of questions with similar enthusiasm. While the men enjoyed a drink and talked shop, the two women smoked and tried to catch up with what had been happening in their lives during the past few days and weeks. Fay was an official tour guide, whose range included the city and most of Yorkshire. She was self-employed and much in demand, particularly by parties of foreign businessmen who seemed to find their guide, with her blonde hair and glamorous looks, just as fascinating as the tours. She had a fund of amusing stories, and was still talking about her most recent job when the call came for the first act. 'We'll have to get together soon,' she said to Natasha. 'I've got a quieter week coming up – how about lunch on Wednesday?'

Natasha pulled a face. 'Can't, I'm afraid. I'm in London next week – final stint on the editing. How about the week after?'

But as they joined the crowd entering the auditorium, they were still unsure about it. Herded by Nick, Natasha suddenly found herself pressed up against Giles and, as he half-turned to give her a smile that managed to be apologetic as well as conspiratorial, she felt a sudden rush of desire washing over her like a hot, guilty wave. At once her glance darted away; she tried to hang back, but Nick was pushing her forward. Hemmed in on both sides, there was nowhere to move but on towards their reserved seats in the circle. Battling with the urge to touch Giles, to simply follow him along the row of seats, she tried again to manoeuvre herself out of line and earned an irritated reprimand from Nick. There was nothing for it but to take her seat next to him, yet she was sweating so much her hands were slippery with it, and so torn between dread and desire she thought she would be sick.

Unwittingly, Fay came to the rescue. She was sitting towards the middle of the row, beyond Giles, and after a whispered word in his ear she changed places.

'I don't know about you,' she confessed to Natasha a moment later, 'but I hate sitting next to strange men in the dark. I'm always convinced they're trying to fondle my knee, or worse . . .'

With a weak little laugh Natasha nodded, thankful that the lights were down and the curtain rising. She took the first of several deep breaths, and, as the rush of panic subsided, discreetly wiped the palms of her hands on her scarf.

Over York the sky was clear, but along the narrow road which led to Denton they suddenly ran into patches of low-lying mist. It was a common phenomenon here, but that made it no less eerie. Natasha found herself pressing an imaginary brake-pedal as Nick drove through that army of wraiths, her heart leaping in alarm as they swept on through the village and along Dagger Lane.

The yard and barn were wreathed in it; it clung damply to her face and clothes as she stepped out of the car, yet the house stood clear. As Nick unlocked the door she turned to look back at that marked division and was glad to get inside.

They ate a makeshift supper of cheese and ham and wholemeal rolls, with some red Australian wine. Deliberately, Natasha drank a couple of glasses, hoping that it would calm her nerves and help when they went to bed. Watching her, Nick asked, not unkindly, what on earth was the matter, since she had been so edgy all evening.

'I don't know,' she said with a lie and a smile, 'maybe it's the book. I've got to go to London on Wednesday, and when that's over, that really is it. No chance to change my mind.'

'Do you want to?'

'Professionally, no. But,' she added with a sigh, realising that this at least was true, 'I have a personal sense of dread about it. Am I doing the right thing? I keep thinking of Helen, you see.'

With an exclamation of disgust, Nick said: 'If anyone had called my work a load of old garbage, I wouldn't be worrying too much about their feelings.' He gave an exasperated sigh and took her hand. 'But she's your sister, I know, and you're unhappy about the breach between you.'

'Yes, I am. I just wish she could understand, and be less concerned about what other people might think. After all, it is a farming family I've written about, not the local doctor and his wife. I don't know,' she said gloomily, 'maybe I should have set it in the Outer Hebrides – or better still, Australia.'

He laughed gently and drew her into his arms, kissing her forehead as he said: 'Why did you write it? Because you felt you had to, and because the story was relevant to its particular setting. You've explained that to me so many times, and I'm sure you said the same to Helen. Apart from her, who else is likely to be hurt by it? Nobody – they're all dead now. So what is she worried about – a bit of gossip and local speculation? So what? She doesn't even live in that area any more – she hasn't for the past six years.'

'Maybe I should publish it under a different name, as she suggested.'

She felt him stiffen with indignation. 'You're joking! You can't do that – this is an important follow-up to your first book. It's *your* name the publishers want to see on that cover – they're banking on that, Natasha, and I mean that literally.'

'So you think I should just go ahead?'

'I most certainly do. All right, I can understand you worrying about Helen, but be honest, love, would she worry about you in the same situation? I don't think so. This is your life we're talking about, not hers. And it's your career at stake, *your* reputation as a writer. You might just as well ask me whether I'd be prepared to suppress an important piece of research – or publish one of my books under a different name – just because the results might offend someone I cared about. I wouldn't do it.'

'Wouldn't you?'

'No, I wouldn't. I wouldn't even consider it. What we're talking about is professional integrity versus personal feelings – and if you're a professional, you go ahead. Publish and be damned to everyone else. And after all,' he added reasonably, '*Black Earth* is a work of fiction, it's not meant to be anyone's biography, or a piece of historical fact. If I can understand these things, why can't she?'

Natasha glanced up, a small dart of apprehension in her breast. Did he understand? She was never quite sure. Their original affair had been the subject of her first novel, but if *The English Lesson* had been a runaway success, it would have taken someone seriously in the know – someone like Giles, for instance – to work out who was who and what had really happened. In that novel, the sexes were reversed, so that the student concerned was a young man, and his lover an older woman. But if Nick had found the ending difficult to comprehend, Natasha had since explained that it was written in an attempt to purge herself of what had occurred between them that year, and written at a time when the chance of meeting him again had seemed more than just remote.

If she had written it now, of course, it would have been a very different book.

Assailed by regrets, yet aware that he was trying to remove them, Natasha reached up and kissed his cheek.

For a moment his eyes held hers, his gaze as green and troubled as a winter sea. 'I love you,' he said softly.

'Yes, I know you do.' In that moment she believed him, but her own emotions were rather more complex, still tainted by the hangover of uncertainty and her memory of Giles.

Fortified by wine and sympathy, when they went to bed she was sufficiently relaxed to let Nick make love to her, but found herself faking sighs and responses in the darkness while her mind and body remained unmoved. It was the first time that she had ever tried to fool him, and, since it had never been necessary before, Natasha was more concerned by her own coldness than proud of the performance. She felt a great sense of relief as he rolled away from her, and turned guiltily to hug him in compensation. Beneath her arm, however, his body felt unexpectedly tense.

After a moment, he said quietly: 'I know you meant well, but I'd rather you didn't do that again.'

'Do what?' The defensive question was out before she had time to think; but she knew very well what he meant, and he did not trouble to explain.

Seven

NICK FELT the distance between them growing rather than receding, and was not sorry when his wife went to see her publishers in London. He drove her to the station on Wednesday morning and saw her on to the eight o'clock train. She was tense and anxious, but seemed more cheerful than she had been for some time. The challenge of work, he decided wryly as they parted, wishing he could have sensed a measure of regret.

With the challenge of his own day to look forward to, he pulled out of the car park and into the density of York's early-morning traffic. The air was sharp, the sky pale and fragile with the promise of a lovely winter's day. As he followed the curve of the city walls towards the river and Skeldergate Bridge, he saw the sun coming up, dazzling off the water and the white hulls of boats moored along King's Staith. After all the mist and fog it was a sight to lift the spirits; he was even glad of the traffic hold-up which gave him a moment to enjoy it.

Above the rooftops, the white spire of St Mary Castlegate caught his eye, and the great quatrefoil keep of Clifford's Tower, jutting into the blue. Ahead of him and standing a little apart were the later buildings of the castle bailey, rising defensively to the south-east. The old unifying wall was gone, which often led to misconceptions about its size and importance, but there had been a castle here since the days of William of Normandy. After the Conquest, and for several hundred years, successive garrisons had kept control of a turbulent area, acting as the eyes and ears of the monarch and sometimes as his mailed fist.

The castle had endured a chequered history as royal fortress, arsenal, centre of administration and place of detention. It had witnessed riots and pillages and burnings, had tried felons and recusants, and condemned men and women to transportation and to the gallows. It should, Nick reflected, have looked as bleak as its long and terrible past, but with the sun shining on that mass of white limestone, it stood out like a theatrical set-piece, an innocent attraction for tourists.

It was all very different, he thought, from the industrial landscape of his youth. Although he never cared to talk about it, his childhood had been at the forefront of his mind too often in the past year. Natasha's book, which was so concerned with unhappy adolescence, had given rise to memories which nagged at him, people and places he had not thought of in years, incidents he would have preferred to forget. His memories of Grayshaw, particularly, prompted feelings which were much more akin to grief than nostalgia, and too close to guilt to bear comfortable scrutiny.

In many respects he envied Natasha her ability to turn painful memories to valuable account, but he did not pretend to understand it. When she talked of the bleak winter landscape of the Fens, of those enormous skies pressing down on the low, flat land, and those easterly winds sweeping in across the North Sea, he felt for her and shivered. And then would come a second chill, as he recalled other winters in another place. Not the flat lands for him, but steep Pennine valleys, tall chimneys rising above tall mills, and a skyline fading into a perpetual haze.

When Nick looked back, he did not want to write about his past, or even talk about it; he would have liked to change it, and to change himself most of all. But he, more than anyone, knew that the past was immutable. That child he remembered, looking out of his attic bedroom window, would always see the industrial Aire valley; and that boy, who had always felt such a stranger there, could not be reconciled now. It was far too late for that.

He could see now that life had been difficult for his mother, with five children to feed and clothe on very little money, but at the time he had silently railed against the fate which had set him down in such uncongenial circumstances. Whether his mother had felt guilty, looking at her eldest son, Nick had no way of knowing; but once he discovered that he was not his stepfather's child, guilt had certainly become part of Nick's emotions. His mother had said he should be grateful, but he was not, he resented it, just as he resented his siblings for being neat little pieces in the jigsaw of family life. He had been a piece from another puzzle, awkward in size and temperament, too clever for his own good as he was constantly told in those days, and with too much pride by half. The implication being, of course, that one day he would trip himself up and be brought down to their level.

In truth, towards the end of his schooldays, and certainly at university, there had been a measure of contempt in his attitude, but it had been defensive, a means of protecting himself against a majority which had comprised, if not all his family, then most of their friends and acquaintances. He was different, he did not fit in, and by rejecting the norm of leave-school-at-sixteen-and-get-a-job, had proclaimed that difference had laid himself open to all the petty jealousies which had been festering for years. The irony was that now, almost twenty-five years later, those same people were actively encouraging their children to do what he had fought so hard to do.

In heavy traffic, it was less than ten minutes from the hold-up on Skeldergate Bridge to the tiny village of Heslington, a couple of miles or so to the east. Although he was now so familiar with the university buildings he rarely noticed them, originally Nick had found the campus extraordinary. On the one hand was Heslington Hall, a graceful Elizabethan mansion which now housed the university's centre of administration, while on the other lay a sprawl of colleges and lecture halls erected in the early 1960s; linking the two was a magnificent lake.

His study was a couple of floors up in Hesketh College, with an excellent outlook; for a moment he stood enjoying the view of the lake and the attendant wildlife, and the unusually deserted walks. He thought how pleasant it was to come in this early; time to steal a march on the day.

With an hour and a half at his disposal, he should have utilised it to clear his desk, but he was not in the mood for admin. problems. Shifting a pile of directives from Heslington Hall, he made a space for his books and started to read, every now and then pausing to make notes. By Christmas he was hoping to have the bulk of his research over, and, with his next sabbatical coming up after Easter, to begin writing the new book. *Aspects of the Rural Economy: North and East Yorkshire 1535-1850* might not earn much in the way of hard cash, but it would have a broad field of interest and would certainly add to his reputation for sound scholarship. And that, he reflected, was what really mattered.

He worked steadily until just before ten, when he had a tutorial with three first-year students. At eleven he had an appointment with one of his postgraduates in the main library, and was returning to his room afterwards when he spotted yet another of his pupils waiting in the corridor. Since the young woman was one he would really have preferred not to meet, Nick made an abrupt diversion into the departmental office. Feigning absent-mindedness, he stood for a moment racking his brains for a plausible query; one of the secretaries sighed and carried on with her work, while the other smiled up at him indulgently.

'While you're thinking, Dr Rhodes, perhaps you'd like to cast your eye over these?' She handed him a sheaf of memos to add to the pile so recently shifted from his desk. 'And do you think I could have those reports for admin. before the end of the week?'

With a groan, he nodded. 'Sorry, Flora, I'd forgotten. I'll get them to you soon.'

A soft, deliberately seductive voice spoke at his shoulder. 'Excuse me, Dr Rhodes, but could I speak to you for a moment?'

Suppressing his true reactions, Nick switched on a polite, half-smile. 'Is it important, Jane? I'm rather busy just now.'

She coloured visibly and studied the papers in his hand. 'Well, yes, it is, sort of . . .' She took a deep breath. 'It's about that essay on the effects of the Corn Laws.'

He gave her a sidelong glance, noting the long chestnut hair and downcast eyes, the full, slightly petulant mouth. Corn Laws, he thought in disbelief; surely she wasn't still struggling with those? With the feeling that he was being pushed into a corner, Nick glanced at his watch and suggested that she might like to come to his study at four; he could possibly spare ten minutes then.

As she nodded and moved away, Nick noticed that the secretary's glance followed her; a moment later it switched back to him, and in Flora's eyes was more than a hint of knowing amusement.

'Never give you a minute, Dr Rhodes, do they?'

He remembered then that Flora had been at the Hallowe'en party; they had danced together. He muttered something fairly innocuous and turned to go; but then Graham Fish arrived and managed to deepen his embarrassment.

'Was that, er – ?' The department's senior lecturer cleared his throat and frowned in the direction the girl had taken.

'Jane Bardy.'

The frown deepened. 'Ah, yes, Miss Bardy – she of the eternal problem. You know, I've been meaning to have a word . . .' Steering Nick along the corridor Dr Fish said: 'She's one of yours this year, isn't she? How's she doing?'

Nick pursed his lips and decided to be noncommittal. 'She could do with a bit more self-discipline, although I suppose she's all right on the whole.'

'But not brilliant? Well,' he admitted, opening the door to his study, 'I can't say I'm surprised. She was one of mine last year, you know – devil of a job getting work out of her – needs jollying along all the time.' He shook his head. 'I'm not entirely convinced she's the right material . . .'

They spent several minutes discussing Jane Bardy and two more students whose work was consistently falling short of the required levels; then, as Nick was promising to keep a closer eye on all three and preparing to leave, Dr Fish waved him back to his chair.

'I'm glad I've seen you today – on two counts, actually.' He leaned across the desk, shuffling papers in a wire tray. 'Since our conversation the other day, I came across something which might be of interest . . . Ah, yes, here it is. I found this in a diary kept by one of Cardinal Richelieu's functionaries, and thought you might like to see it. You see,' he explained, handing over a sheet of paper filled with cramped, spidery writing, 'when you told me about that strange little incident in your village, and that attendant report in – ?'

'Beauchamp.'

'Ah, yes *Beauchamp*, that was it – I thought it seemed familiar, that I'd come across a similar reference, quite recently. Of course it turned out not to be in this country at all, but . . .'

As Nick started reading, Dr Fish added apologetically: 'It's a pretty free translation, of course, but it does give you the gist of the thing.'

It did indeed. Although it took Nick a moment or two to decipher the idiosyncratic style, after that his eye went down the page fairly quickly, while his eyebrows rose in astonishment. 'But this is extraordinary – it tallies so well with what I was told first of all.'

'Yes, I thought so too. Of course, this thing's an *aside*, really, from a notebook of memoranda mostly concerning business affairs. But the experience clearly bothered our man . . .'

'Enough for him to write it down,' Nick murmured, reading the piece again. 'And he encountered this animal – this *black beast* as he calls it – on a road near –' He peered at the page. 'What is it? Villy-Bocage?'

'Yes, in Normandy.'

'Ah, hedgerow country, not unlike England.' He nodded and read on. 'It says here that the thing appeared directly in front of him, and then shrank back into the ditch. Is that his word, *shrank*?' Dr Fish nodded. Nick went on: 'And he heard a sound he believed came from the beast, like water draining from a sluice – a gurgling noise, in fact.' Pausing to digest the coincidence, Nick found himself smiling. 'Well, how about that!'

'Curious, isn't it?'

'It certainly is!'

'There was something else, too – I didn't bother to write it down, but you might be interested anyway. Some weeks later, there was apparently a witchcraft scare in the area – several women accused of consorting with the devil and indulging in certain . . . well, shall we say deviant practices. I don't know whether there's a link between the two incidents, but it struck me as, well, *strange . . .*'

Nick thought so too. They discussed various possibilities, wondering whether people other than Richelieu's man had seen this black beast, and if so, whether fear and rumour had then created an atmosphere conducive to accusations of witchcraft. The discussion became quite serious, encompassing other witchcraft scares of the sixteenth and seventeenth centuries, and one or two specific cases; after almost half an hour, Nick suddenly realised the time. It was lunchtime, and if he did not eat soon, he would be lecturing on an empty stomach.

That mention of food reminded Dr Fish of his other reason for wanting to see his colleague. 'Are you and your wife free for dinner next Wednesday evening? You see I've got Charlie Cramp coming up for a viva and he's staying with us; so we thought we'd invite mutual friends. How's that sound?'

'It sounds excellent. Natasha will be pleased,' he added, which was a long way short of the truth, but it enabled him to remind Graham Fish of her name. After all these years, he still remembered Bernice.

'Ah, yes, Natasha – lovely girl. Very talented. Wasn't she your pupil, Nick, once upon a time?'

It was said innocently enough, but Nick had a guilty moment, wondering whether his superior was trying to remind him of the official attitude towards relationships between tutors and students. Jane Bardy had been the initial cause of this meeting, and it seemed an unhappy coincidence that Graham Fish and his wife had also been present at the Hallowe'en party. Close enough to witness that idiotic behaviour? Shrewd enough to guess the present situation?

Nick forced a smile. 'She was for a while – about ten years ago.'

'Really? Is it as long ago as that? It seems like yesterday,' the other man confessed. 'Anyway, convey my best wishes, and tell her we very much look forward to meeting her on Wednesday. Shall we say seven-thirty for eight? That all right?'

'Fine. I'm looking forward to it.' Nick smiled and thanked him again for the information, tucking the paper into his pocket. As he went to find some lunch, he thought of his four o'clock appointment. It was time for him to have a word with Jane, but *not* about the effects of the Corn Laws.

The final editing of *Black Earth* might have been finished that evening if the two women had been willing to continue, but after two full days it seemed wiser to take a break. Just after six, Judy Lawrence patted Natasha's hand and pushed the manuscript to one side.

'Let's finish it in the morning. You look tired, and what we both need now is a decent meal and an early night.'

Natasha was relieved. All those hours of intense concentration had left her feeling drained and light-headed, and with her ability to be detached and self-critical completely gone. She smiled and nodded gratefully. 'But I'll phone Nick, if I may? He's expecting me back this evening . . .'

While Judy went off to the cloakroom, Natasha dialled the number. Nick answered almost immediately, the warmth of his voice lighting an unexpected response. As he asked how things had gone, and what time she would be back, Natasha was overwhelmed by an unexpected surge of longing and affection. That sudden need brought a tightness to her throat, making it difficult to reply.

'Natasha? How are you going to get home from the station tomorrow? I'm lecturing at two.'

'Oh – don't worry – I'll get a taxi.'

He asked then whether she wanted to come into college and wait for him; after the lecture he could finish early and they could travel home together. But she was too tired to make plans; she wanted to be able to take things as they came and not be pressed by more decisions. Swallowing hard, she tried to explain that. A moment later she found herself apologising.

'Whatever for?' he asked lightly. 'You can't help the delay. Anyway, I think a meal and bed right now is probably just what's needed.'

'No. I didn't mean that. I meant I'm sorry for being so – so *awful* just lately. I don't know why,' she added, stammering a little, 'I don't know what's got into me – '

'You're tired,' Nick said softly into her ear, 'and you've been under a lot of strain – I've been telling you that for the last couple of months.'

'But I've been horrible to you, haven't I?'

With a dry chuckle, he agreed that she had. 'But I think it's best forgotten now. Come home and let's make things up – *properly* . . .'

The warmth of his forgiveness, the illusion of intimacy the telephone conveyed, intensified her longings as much as her regrets. With a catch in her voice, she whispered: 'I do love you, Nick,' and felt her heart beat faster as he said that he loved her too.

It was a little after half-past two in the afternoon when Natasha arrived home, but she had that sense of emotional and physical fragility which often comes in the middle of a sleepless night.

She paid the taxi, dumped her overnight bag in the kitchen and made herself a cup of strong black coffee; and then, with an effort, she went upstairs to run a bath. A little while later, surrounded by bubbles and scented steam, she began to feel better, light and warm and vaguely comforted. It was an extraordinary relief to realise that all decisions regarding the novel were over and done with, although that sensation of being drained to the very dregs was far from pleasant. For a moment she could have wept for the emptiness, for the passing of something which had occupied almost every waking thought for so long. She felt divorced from it now, as though part of her life had been cut away and cauterised, and whatever happened to it from this point on was someone else's responsibility.

But that was not strictly true. Whatever happened, it would always be hers, because she had written it, and her name would always be on the cover; to pretend otherwise was foolish. It was just that she did not want to think of what she had done. Having spent the best part of three years examining her early life, constructing it and taking it apart, and then reconstructing what was left, she would have preferred never to think of it again. And without her sister Helen, that might have been possible.

Strange, she reflected, that her thoughts and emotions now were so different from those experienced previously. After editing the manuscript of *The English Lesson* she had been tired, yes, but there had been satisfaction and elation, a sense of something going forward. It was her first novel, and a good one; and not only had she proved something to herself in writing it, she had proved to Nick that she could succeed in the area where he had been so doubtful.

Although they were not in touch at that time, Natasha had felt sure that he would read it eventually, and realise that the story was based upon their former relationship. What he might think of it was of secondary importance; and indeed the primary aim had been intensely personal, nothing to do with thoughts of publication or future success. She had wanted to write the episode out of her system, and had used the vehicle of fiction to express her feelings on love and betrayal and the abuse of power. Nick had inspired a whole range of conflicting emotions, and through writing she had found a medium for them. They were not cured, but they were easier for being utilised; and if the ending of the book was different, a complete reversal of what had actually happened between them – well, did it matter? The ending contained its own truth, even if she was the only one to see it.

In *Black Earth*, the people to whom she wanted to yell and scream her point of view were dead; and while she might have come to terms at last with the loss of her father and the traumatic events which followed his death, in the process she had broken the fragile thread of her relationship with Helen. Except in the commercial world, Natasha was aware that the life of this book was finished, over; it was an end, not a beginning.

She grieved for it, and for her sister. Although they had never been close, she still felt like a betrayer. And in spite of all Nick's assurances, his arguments about professionalism versus Helen's petty-bourgeois outlook, Natasha still felt that she had done something wrong. But what could she do? Change her mind, stop it going to the printer? Return the advance?

Couldn't do that, she thought with a sudden chill; the money was already spent, and on this house.

The bath was no longer warm. She considered adding more hot water, but that first sybaritic pleasure was gone. She stepped out and dried herself, and in dressing-gown and slippers reached across to open the window.

Steam billowed for a second or two, then cleared. She was just about to wipe away the condensation when she was startled by the presence of a stranger in the yard. A woman in the oddest clothes. Her cap and collar and long white apron stood out against the shadowy interior of the barn. What on earth was going on? Natasha was about to shout when she realised that the woman had seen her. She hesitated, expecting some enquiry, an acknowledgement at least.

But the woman kept on staring.

Fear gripped; and as it did so, Natasha slammed the window shut.

For several seconds she stood there, rigid, her mind blank. Then, as fear came skittering back she thrust it aside, dashed down the stairs and out into the yard. The woman was gone. The barn contained no more than Natasha's car and a collection of junk and gardening implements. She even switched on the lights to make sure. She ran back across the yard and looked up and down the lane. Nothing, not a sign of a living soul.

Swearing volubly through teeth that were already chattering with cold, she dashed around the house to the front. There was no one below the terrace or in the shadow of the archway, but anyone could have hidden in the shrubbery. With that in mind she hurried inside, and took up a position from where she could see the whole of the front garden. Twenty minutes and two cigarettes later, only the shadows had moved. The light was going rapidly, and whoever was playing tricks would soon be able to escape under cover of darkness.

With the subsiding of her adrenalin levels, Natasha was suddenly weak and trembling. And angry with herself for being so frightened. She had been startled, of course, that was quite natural; but the woman was real enough, in fact quite substantial under that theatrical disguise. She lit another cigarette and went through into the office. Winding a sheet of paper into her type-writer, she made a record of the incident, together with a description of the woman. Young, not very tall, pale, squarish face, hair hidden beneath white cap. Dark dress – blue or brown? – which seemed ankle-length, and of course the apron and shawl collar which had stood out so clearly against the interior of the barn.

The clothes, she decided, could have been those of a late seventeenth-century lady, or a mid-eighteenth-century servant. They were most likely a late twentieth-century approximation, worn by someone with a very odd sense of humour. Natasha refused to believe that the woman was any less solid than herself, or that the disappearing act was attributable to anything other than speed of movement and a knowledge of the garden. And yet she shivered every time she thought of that woman looking up at her, and could find no reasonable answers to the questions of *who* and *why*.

She kept expecting Nick to arrive any minute, and by the time he did arrive had almost convinced herself that he was the instigator of an elaborate charade, contrived with the aid of one of his students. For what reason though? To scare her? To make her think that the place was haunted? Maybe he thought that if she saw a 'ghost' here she might be more amenable to the idea of a spectral hound haunting the lane? It would certainly be easier to arrange!

But perhaps the whole thing was a charade, from the mysterious animal reported by old Toby Bickerstaff to the recent failure of their relationship. Last night, in London, Natasha had felt that she was the one behaving unreasonably, but from her present viewpoint the guilty party seemed to be Nick. In her mind's eye she kept seeing that girl at the party, the lascivious movements of her body as she devoured him with her mouth. Perhaps she was even more important to him than Natasha had imagined; perhaps they'd planned the whole thing together . . .

After all, she reasoned, this house was important to him. In spite of her own contributions she still thought of it as his. Given a choice, she would much rather have stayed in town.

Determined not to give him the satisfaction of knowing that she had been even faintly alarmed, Natasha decided not to mention the incident. Her pretence at a welcome, however, was a little forced, and he noticed immediately that something was wrong.

Murmuring sympathetically, he took her in his arms and nuzzled her cheek. 'Never mind, love, it's all over . . . you're home now, you can relax and forget it . . .'

But she was unresponsive, moving away as soon as he relaxed his hold on her. Nonplussed by the look she gave him, which was so at variance with what she had said over the phone the night before, he wondered what had happened since. But she did not seem inclined to tell him. Changing tack, he suggested they go out to dinner, hoping that in different surroundings she would be more relaxed and able to talk.

He thought at first that she was going to refuse, but after a moment's deliberation she agreed. The restaurant he had been thinking about on the way home now seemed too bright to suit the current mood; after several minutes spent flicking through the telephone directory he remembered another place, a quiet country hotel where the prices were high but the atmosphere, like the service, was very discreet.

Natasha made no comment and her mood continued silent and abstracted. He talked college gossip as they drove to the hotel, and mentioned the dinner Dr Fish was giving for Charlie Cramp. That there was not an immediate groan of protest rather surprised him; she simply said yes, Wednesday, that would be fine.

To all his questions about her trip to London he received little more than monosyllabic replies, and she did no more than pick at what was an excellent meal. That too was unusual, since she enjoyed good food and generally had the kind of appetite which belied her slender frame. That hearty appreciation was one of the things he loved about her, and that she seemed to be spurning his efforts along with the food unsettled him even further.

As the waiter cast an anxious glance in the direction of Natasha's plate and asked whether they had enjoyed their meal, Nick smiled dryly and assured him that nothing was wrong. He ordered coffee and then reached across the table to light Natasha's cigarette. Her normally soft, expressive eyes were veiled, her features almost chiselled in their stillness, and although he was used to her frequent abstractions he knew that this was a deliberate shutting out.

With the smoke curling between them, he said: 'Are you going to tell me what's wrong, Natasha, or are we playing guessing-games? If so, you'll have to give me some clues, because I don't know what went wrong in London. So far you've told me nothing.'

Eventually she looked at him. It was a look calculated to inspire guilt in the most innocent and he felt a spasm of dread; but when she spoke he was thrown by the seeming irrelevance.

'I wasn't frightened, you know,' she said defiantly. 'I might have been, but in fact I was just *bloody* annoyed by the whole thing. What on earth possessed you?'

Frowning, he opened his mouth to speak, and then shook his head. After a moment, he said: 'What are you talking about?'

With a short, mirthless laugh, she looked away. 'Oh, of course you would say that, wouldn't you? All part of the charade, I suppose.' Her glance returned to him, as penetrating as before. 'It was well done though, I'll grant you that.'

'*What* was?'

'By the time I got outside, she'd gone – cleared off, hidden under the compost heap, scooted down the lane, I don't know. Anyway, wherever she disappeared to, she did it pretty damn fast, Nick – you should be proud of her.'

Sheer guilt made him think of Jane Bardy and her dogged pursuit of him. He'd explained to her yesterday afternoon that there was no point in it, that she should forget about the Hallowe'en party and just get on with her life. Recalling the look of hurt in the girl's eyes, he bit his inner lip and ran a mental check of all the things she might have done in reaction to that. Would she have come to the house? That she could have done prompted a rise of alarm.

He took a deep breath and spread his hands in a gesture of defeated innocence. 'Look, love, I don't know who you're talking about, or even what it is we're discussing. I get the feeling I'm being accused of something, but I don't know what it is. Can't you simply start at the beginning and tell me what happened?'

Her beautiful brown eyes narrowed and a sudden flush of colour heightened her cheekbones. 'The woman – or the girl – who appeared in the yard this afternoon. I take it she was one of your students?'

'Not as far as I know. What did she do? Describe her.'

'She didn't *do* anything. She was in the yard – well, no, actually she was standing in the doorway of the barn when I saw her, looking up at me. I was in the bathroom at the time, and I have to say she gave me quite a shock.'

'And?'

'And nothing. By the time I got outside she'd disappeared. As she was meant to, I suppose!'

'Well, where did she go? Did she take anything? What did she look like?'

'You mean you really don't know?'

'Natasha, as God's my witness, I sent no one to our house this afternoon.' He watched her face, the rapid flicker of her pupils as she studied him in return, and was far from sure he was believed. 'She was probably a gypsy, on the look-out for something useful in the barn – you know what they're like. Maybe she wanted to sell you some pegs, or tell your fortune or something. You probably scared her – '

'A gypsy – in eighteenth-century costume?'

'*What?*'

'She was wearing period costume. You know the sort of thing – it looked like a copy from one of those illustrations of rural life: *Farmer's wife, North Yorkshire, circa 1710*. It was really well done,' she said admiringly, lighting another cigarette. 'If she hadn't looked as solid as you or me, I might have been convinced.'

He felt the hairs rise at the back of his neck and along his arms. 'Come on,' he said abruptly, pushing back his chair, 'let's get out of here.'

When they reached home, he read Natasha's note of the incident and was thankful for her journalistic training. The spoken and written descriptions tallied, and it was clear that the woman Natasha had seen was slender and below average height, while Jane Bardy was five feet ten at least and generously built. But his sense of relief was short-lived. If not Jane Bardy – and clearly she was not – who was this woman? And what was she doing in the barn?

If all possibilities of a practical joke were ruled out – and he thought they had to be, since he could not think of a motive or even a satisfactory explanation for that disappearing act – Nick had to consider the other options. The type of costume fitted easily within the age of the house, and it might have been possible to believe that the woman was a ghost, but it was equally possible that she was no more than a figment of Natasha's imagination.

For all his fascination with folk tales and superstitions, Nick's mind was trained to be factual. He believed that there was no smoke without some kind of spark, and that whatever fantastic stories evolved over the years, they usually had some basis in real events. It was those events, however small, that he liked to discover. Most were mundane and disappointing, but he never ceased to hope that one day he would find something extraordinary. Hence his interest in Beauchamp's story and Toby's mysterious beast.

In this case, however, no matter how much he would have liked to believe that the house and its environs were haunted by a former inhabitant, he was inclined to different conclusions. He knew how hard Natasha had been working, and under what levels of anxiety; and while he found her accusations hard to take, Nick realised that she was overwrought and had probably imagined the whole thing.

That hypothesis seemed even more probable when he considered her insistence that the woman was real, and that there had been recognition in that stare. He did not see how the ghost of a woman who had been dead for at least two centuries could possibly recognise someone in the present day. Unless, of course, the ghost was not a ghost but mere hallucination. In which case the question of significance was turned on its head, and the real meaning was hidden in the mind of the beholder.

Eight

'YOU'RE SURE you don't mind?'

'Of course not, why should I?'

'Well, I hate the thought of leaving you alone.'

'Don't be silly,' she said sharply, 'I spend most of my time here alone, why should this afternoon be any different?'

'You know why – I'm concerned because of what happened yesterday.'

She continued to reach for things in cupboards and fridge, and did not look at him. 'You don't think anything happened yesterday, Nick – you think I imagined it.'

Drawing a deep breath, he tried to keep the frustration out of his voice. If this went much further they would end up having a blazing row, and he did not want that. Eventually, he said: 'I don't know what to think, and that's a fact. You saw something outside, I don't doubt that, and if someone *is* playing damn-fool tricks out there, I don't want to leave you on your own.'

'Look, you've promised Adam you'll go to this rugby match, and come Monday you'll have to go into college. You can't baby-sit here on the off-chance that something else might happen.'

'And what are you going to do?'

'Good grief, Nick, does it matter?' she demanded. 'I might go for a walk or write some letters. I might even do both, who knows?'

He kissed her briefly, and went.

The edginess Natasha had been fighting all morning transformed itself, as soon as the car pulled out of the yard, into an almost overwhelming desire to go straight to her office and start work. The fact that the book was finished hurt her, like a gaping wound, but she still longed for the familiarity of desk, chair, typewriter, the things with which she felt secure. As soon as she fed paper into the machine, something would come to mind, and in the words she could lose herself, forget life's mysteries and torments, create a whole new world with controllable situations and people she understood.

It was a powerful temptation. She could feel herself weakening as the need took hold. Only a hard little kernel of self-preservation kept her from giving in.

'Don't be an idiot,' she muttered harshly to herself as she reached for her wellingtons and waterproof jacket; and once outside, with cold air astringent against her face, good sense rapidly reasserted itself. She was very much aware that the last thing she needed right now was to start work on something new. Much more mental effort and she really would crack up; enough had been expended already, and especially in the last few days.

As Nick had become so fond of saying, what she really needed was fresh air and exercise, lots of good brisk walks to calm the mind and circulate the blood. And perhaps he was right; he certainly took his own advice and thrived on it.

With the rugby match in mind, Natasha glanced up and wondered whether the rain would hold off for the afternoon. Part of her hoped, maliciously, that the heavens would open and ruin the match for players and spectators alike. She felt it would serve them right, pay Nick back for deserting her when she was feeling so anxious and insecure, although to be fair he had asked her to go with him. But school rugby matches were only tolerable occasionally, and she was not in the mood today for another of Adam's star performances. Anyway, she thought more kindly, it would do the boys good to have their father to themselves for a while.

Across the Vale, the clouds were low, meeting woods and fields in a solid wall of grey, but it seemed to her that the horizon was too clear for rain. She walked on, her booted feet crunching acorns and crab-apples, and kicking up the drifts of leaves. It was cold and still and quiet, the smoke from Toby's chimney rising in an almost vertical spiral before fanning out where some unseen current of air disturbed it. It was like a miniature version of a whirlwind, and made her think of Dorothy in *The Wizard of Oz*, being carried away and deposited on the yellow brick road.

Well, she had been brought here by Nick's enthusiasm, but while Dagger Lane was neither yellow nor brick, it was certainly developing a few extraordinary features. If one could believe in such things, of course, which she did not. No, it was a locality which she could have described as being of undramatic charm, of gently rolling hills and pretty villages, only the ruined remains of castles and priories bearing witness to a rather more dramatic past.

Nick, of course, saw it from a different viewpoint. The castles and priories did not interest him particularly, he was more preoccupied with the land itself. He saw it as a workface at the mercy of wind and weather, against which untold generations had pitted strength and wit to wrench a living, both for themselves and their successors. For him, that was where the true drama lay, and he could read its language in every seemingly insignificant mark.

A thousand years of habitation, and for those long-dead generations he felt the kind of regard he might have had for his own forebears. Local churchyards with their ancient memorial stones could move him deeply, and yet he was always keen to point out that the majority had no memorial other than the changing face of the landscape. History was about people, he said, and when he spoke the facts were never dry. His lectures were leavened by curious details, anecdotes that injected life into kings and commoners alike; that was what made him so good to listen to, and what had attracted her to him in the first place.

And yet, strangely, there was a paradox somewhere. Although he possessed that well of compassion, and was the kind of man who felt things deeply, in his personal relationships he could sometimes be reticent to the point of coldness. He rarely mentioned his own parents, and yet as a father he was loving and concerned; in fact his sons' needs frequently came before her own, so she could not fault him there. But as a husband he was often difficult to understand. In the past she had ascribed his distant moods to scholarly absorption, but recently, and with good reason, she had drawn different conclusions.

Last night, though, he had denied it. Quite categorically, even though she had been careful not to accuse him of being unfaithful. She had not needed to, since he was one step ahead of her reasoning when she accused him of setting up that unpleasant incident in the afternoon. 'I know what you're thinking,' he had said in the car, 'but you're absolutely wrong. There is no one else in my life, I don't want anyone else, and if truth be told I haven't any bloody time to be messing around with nonsense like that. I almost wish I had,' he'd added bitterly, 'since it would provide a modicum of light relief from the way life is at the moment.'

'Do you mean that?' she had asked, her voice faint with apprehension.

'No, no of course I don't. But I would like things to return to normal, Natasha – I'd be lying if I said otherwise.'

He had been deeply wounded, she knew. Remembering, she felt ashamed. After a night's sleep the events of yesterday afternoon still bothered her, but her conclusions seemed ludicrous. Of course he hadn't set it up, why would he? Even if Nick was having an affair – and she now thought it unlikely – if he wanted a divorce he had only to say so. Surely he knew that she would leave; he wouldn't have to *drive* her out.

But such harsh and logical thoughts were painful. Hating herself for all her doubts and insecurities, she began to think again about that woman in the yard. But that was even more alarming, because if she hadn't been a trick, and she was not a ghost, then she must have been imagined . . .

'But she seemed so *real*,' Natasha said aloud, echoing the claim she had made to Nick at least a dozen times last night. Suddenly, as if in answer, she heard a clatter of wings and the honking laughter of a flight of geese. Startled, she turned to see them gathering in formation as they left the stubble field of Forty Acre; she had not noticed them feeding because of the hedge.

The lane curved sharply to the right, and beyond the derelict barns, where part of the hedgerow had gone, she could see across World's End Wood to the ridge. Sheep were bleating in a corner of the field, and somewhere a tractor was working. The wood was a shaded mass, grey-brown, almost violet in places, with just a touch of russet here and there, where the oaks were clinging to their dense swags of foliage. Along the nearside margins, between the oaks, stood ghostly groups of silver birch, their tall, spindly trunks highlighting the darkness within. To the right, where the old wooden bridge crossed the ditch, she had collected Michaelmas daisies just a few weeks ago, but there was no temptation to enter the wood today. Beneath a leaden sky it looked an alien place, the narrow lane descending the slope to disappear like a tunnel through the trees.

She found herself thinking of Mrs McCoy and that strange episode in the fog. She had not seen the woman since, and wondered whether she had ventured back down Dagger Lane, or had taken to walking her dog elsewhere. For a moment, Natasha thought of what had scared the dog, and considered turning back; but that seemed cowardly in the face of all she had said on the subject. Telling herself not to be so foolish, she deliberately walked on as far as the elm stumps, and paused there to light a cigarette.

Amongst the leaves at her feet were several spent cartridges; as she hoisted herself up on to a well-worn perch, Natasha realised that this was where Toby did much of his shooting. It was also, she recalled with a start, the place where the tracks had been found.

She looked down uneasily, but the muddy patches revealed only human footprints, and most of those appeared to be her own. Gazing around at the trees, she became increasingly conscious of the stillness here, a deepening quiet that was difficult to define. Nothing stirred, nothing rustled, but on the air was the scent of autumn, a smell of earth and moss and rotting leaves, a hint of rising woodsmoke and the slow spread of winter across the open countryside. It was an expected smell, but unusually intense, mixed with that of old and abandoned buildings, smells she associated with castles and abbeys, the odour of dripping walls, of ruination, and the emptiness of centuries.

Before her eyes everything seemed fogged and blurred; it was as though those mingled odours were drifting like smoke through the trees. She inhaled them deeply, aware that she was poised and waiting, and that the stillness was centred on her. Something trembled within, like the fluttering weakness induced by hunger or too much effort, and she realised that the presence was drawing its strength from her, leaving behind it palpitations and a sense of imminent collapse.

She saw the woman then, the woman from the barn, but faint this time, like a poor piece of film flickering through a haze of smoke. But she could see what was happening: the woman's skirts were up and her legs were splayed, and they were busy with her, two of them, their faces dark and featureless while hers was pale, her mouth open on a long, soundless cry of release.

Natasha saw what was happening and felt it too, as though unseen hands were touching her, trying to hold and push and invade, wanting only a moment's acquiescence to achieve their ends.

The sudden roar of the tractor dispelled it. That palpable silence was lifted and shattered against the trees and the gutter and the wind-ravaged grasses. Like a sudden halt on the point of orgasm, it left her shaking and whimpering, the roar of blood in her ears louder than that of the machine. Covering first her ears then her eyes, she dropped her hands to find the thing paused in front of her, a growling, shuddering monster, with bright blue paint and a driver mouthing furiously from the cab.

He was gesticulating too, but it made not a scrap of difference. With the engine still running, he jumped down, a young man, not tall but well-built, his black, curly hair worn long and tied back. The blue jeans and Puffa jacket seemed oddly incongruous; she felt they should have been knee-breeches and a leather jerkin.

His face was suffused with rage. 'All right, where is it? Where's that fucking dog?'

She stared at him blankly, registering his fury but more afraid of the vehicle, still shuddering with menace a couple of feet away. The huge wheels were almost as high as herself; she had a vision of them blindly crushing her into the mud.

'Look – use your eyes, woman – see what that fucking dog of yours has done!'

Only then, as he jerked his right arm, did Natasha notice the trailer and the two dead sheep. They looked like bundles of bloodstained rags, the fleece matted and limp, heads lolling as though no longer attached.

'Two bloody good ewes – *two*, killed for the fun of it!' He paused for breath. 'I'll get that bastard, you see if I don't.' As he swung himself up into the cab, he was once more above her. 'It should be you, do you know that? You, you stupid bitch!'

With a roar, the tractor lurched and surged forward, the trailer with its sickening cargo jerking along behind.

For at least a minute, she was too stunned to frame a coherent thought. Then it came to her that she had been mistaken for one of the village dog-owners, probably because few women walked alone without an animal in tow. And of the owners, Mrs McCoy was the likeliest, since the wolfhound was notoriously ill-trained and had always been viewed with the gravest suspicion.

She had a sudden urge to run after him, to shout: 'Look, I've never even owned a dog. It wasn't me, I'm not responsible.' But the tractor was well out of sight.

As she slid down from her perch, Natasha also realised something else. If she was a victim of mistaken identity, then so might McCoy be. He was a great lolloping bully of a dog, but was he a killer? That thing with five claws, which had left its tracks right here for Nick to find, seemed a far more likely suspect.

Stiffly, she flexed her knees and ankles and examined the ground again. No paw-prints, only a half-smoked cigarette, fallen from nerveless fingers into the mud. The reason for that came upon her like delayed shock. Shivering violently, she stared at the trees with something akin to panic. The sudden flutter of an alighting pigeon galvanised her limbs into movement; she ran until she was out of breath, and only when she reached old Toby's field did she shorten her pace to a walk.

Nine

STARTLED INTO wakefulness she jerked away from the figure bending over her, then realised with relief that it was only Nick. Heart pounding, she subsided against the pillows and tried to separate dream from reality. The landing light was on, but it was dark in the bedroom; she had no idea of the time, and wondered how long she had slept.

'It's just after five,' Nick said in answer to her question. 'Sorry I startled you, but the house was in darkness and I wondered where you were.'

'Your hair's wet,' she murmured as he bent to kiss her.

'Yes, it's raining now, quite heavily. It kept dry for the match, though. It was a good game – they played well, and the opposition didn't have it all their own way.'

Forcing her powers of deduction to the fore, she said: 'Oh, did they lose?'

'Only by three points, and Adam did manage to score a try. Anyway, I'll make a pot of tea and bore you to death with the details in a minute.'

'I'm coming down – '

'No, stay where you are – '

'No, I'm not ill, Nick, just a bit tired. I'll wash my face and come down.'

Under the glare of the bathroom light, her reflection in the mirror was not one to inspire confidence. To her own eyes, Natasha looked ghastly, with bruised eyes and bloodless lips.

Drying her face hastily, she dabbed on some moisturiser and a bit of green eyeshadow; a subtle shade of lipstick, barely there, added an impression of warmth. Taking a long look at herself, she breathed deeply for a moment and told herself that she would mention the dead sheep to Nick, but not the earlier experience. She did not think she had the words to express the seductive horror of it; and even if she had, there was something so gross, so repellent in what she had felt and seen, her mind flinched away in shame.

Guilt followed that sense of shame. She had been so convinced that Nick was playing tricks on her, but he could not have done so this afternoon, nobody could. What she had seen in the wood was not reality, it was an echo, a mirage, some sort of illusion. But powerful, very powerful.

She shivered suddenly, and gripped the edge of the washbasin. Maybe she was hallucinating after all.

'That land's part of the Norton-Clive estate,' Nick said, 'but I'm almost certain Jack Morrison rents a few fields down there for his sheep. He's a miserable old devil – have you ever met him? Farms all that land above the road, yet to talk to him you'd think he was on his beam-ends.'

Natasha shook her head. 'I don't think so. Where does he live?'

'Up at Forest Hill Farm – the track to it is the extension of Dagger Lane, but it's obliterated beyond there, of course.' He sighed at the folly of farmers. 'Anyway, I'll phone the old bugger and find out first of all whether they were his sheep. Then I shall suggest – tactfully – that his men should get their facts right before yelling obscenities at the first person they meet.' He pushed back his chair, then said: 'What did he look like, by the way? Can you remember?'

'I don't think I'll ever forget,' she replied tersely, and as she proceeded to describe the driver of the tractor, Nick nodded, his frown deepening.

'Sounds like one of his sons, I've seen him a few times up and down the lane. Anyway,' he sighed, 'I'll phone the old man now.'

He returned a few minutes later, not entirely satisfied. 'Yes, well, he offered an apology of sorts – very grudgingly, I might add. Two of his *best yows*, he said, *and if it weren't for folks like us movin' into t'village, they'd still be alive . . .'* Nick said with a grin. 'You know the sort of thing.'

'I can imagine. You told him we don't own a dog?'

'I did. I also told him that it might be a stray, but he wasn't interested. He says if he sees that bloody Irish thing off the lead again, he'll shoot it.'

'He can't do that, surely?'

'He can if he sees it worrying his sheep.'

'But not if he only thinks it is.' She considered for a moment, then said heavily: 'I suppose we ought to go up to the village – Mrs McCoy deserves a warning, at the very least.'

But it was dark and raining outside. Nick suggested leaving it until the morning, and Natasha was glad to agree.

The next morning, Nick went up to the village to speak to Mrs McCoy, and afterwards was glad that he had gone alone, since the woman was upset to the point of incoherence, and her husband defensive in the extreme. Their denials and protestations had all the ring of guilt, and for the first time since he had heard about the sheep, Nick began to think that the culprit might indeed be the Irish wolfhound. Whether the dog had been let out carelessly, or had broken out of the garden with its low, flimsy fence, Nick had no way of knowing. Still, he had warned them. He could do no more.

Although his report to Natasha was sparing, he did express those doubts. She was unconvinced, preferring to believe that the killer was a stray. For the first time, thinking about the dog she had glimpsed in the headlights that night, and comparing it with Mrs McCoy's description, she wondered whether it might have been a Rottweiler, rather than a labrador or an exotic beast of prey. Rottweilers were largely black, with big, broad heads, and they had a prowling, threatening way of moving. And if the animal were old or sick, perhaps it might have been slinking under the hedgerows, and a defensive snarl might easily have been interpreted – by drunken old Toby, who probably wouldn't know a Rottweiler if it savaged him – as a *gargling noise*.

Convinced that at least she had come up with a theory which fitted the facts, Natasha suddenly felt brighter. But although she presented it enthusiastically to Nick, his agreement struck her as slightly false, as though he were humouring her. Instantly, she was cast down, and so angry she could have slapped him. When he suggested, over a late and mainly silent breakfast, that they might go over to Whitby for the afternoon, she could only give a sullen nod.

A north-east wind was blowing, buffeting the car on the unprotected stretches of the North York Moors. Knowing the road, regarding its switchback dips and turns as a challenge, Nick drove fast and well, while Natasha leaned back into the Rover's comfortable seats and gazed at the dramatic views. Just a few hundred feet above sea level and yet it looked like the roof of the world, a great sweeping mass of heather-covered hills, russet and brown beneath a clearing sky. Here and there, groups of horned sheep were cropping small patches of grass; it was peaceful and quiet, with just the rush of the wind and the purr of the engine as the old car ate up the miles. Neither of them spoke, but then Nick rarely did when he was driving, and usually Natasha liked to subside into her own thoughts.

She had tried, with some success, not to think of the events of yesterday; or rather to channel her mind towards the aggressive young tractor-driver, since his anger and those four-letter words were infinitely preferable to her memory of that woman with the men going at her like animals in rut. The terrible thing was that when she did think of it she remembered the silence, the smell of decay, and that sensation of being touched. Despite her revulsion there was a horrible fascination about it, and even a guilty excitement.

What was left of the detached, logical, trained part of her mind demanded an explanation. Freudian psychology would no doubt lay all of it at the feet of sexual frustration; but that, she thought, taking a swift glance at Nick, was her fault, not his. He wanted her willing response, and for her to make some encouraging move towards him; but she could not do it. Pride, that was his problem, but what was hers? She did not know, could not describe it, except that love and need dissipated into chill reluctance whenever he made the smallest of overtures.

Tension, frustration, and an awareness that she was not yet over recent stress, were tempting theories, but she had been in that position before, especially when living alone and working hard. The usual effects followed a recognisable pattern, and did not include seeing things. Imagining things, perhaps; attributing wrong reasons for people's behaviour, even becoming slightly paranoid when life refused to go well; but hallucinating, no.

Was it possible, she asked herself, that traumatic events left an impression on the landscape? She had never thought so, the very idea went against logical belief, and yet it was attractive, far preferable to the only other explanation, that what she had seen and felt was the product of her own distorted imagination.

As they crested the last great rise and began the long drop of almost a thousand feet to sea level, the little port of Whitby came into view, nestling at the mouth of the River Esk and protected by a surrounding arc of cliffs and hills. Over town and sea the sun was shining, the sky an incredible shade of blue. On one clifftop stood the abbey's medieval ruins while on the other a Victorian pile stood like a citadel overlooking the sea. Between the two outposts, everyday life went on.

The town was busy, the harbourside crowded with families enjoying a day out, children, pushchairs, dogs, all jostling for position on the narrow pavements. The cheerful holiday atmosphere, despite it being November, was a tonic in itself. Pushing morbid thoughts aside, Natasha found herself laughing, clinging to Nick's arm as they threaded their way along the quay. The gusting wind brought forth a variety of smells: seaweed and raw fish, a sudden waft of fried food, and the aroma of marine diesel from cobles and trawlers moored alongside. Gulls were everywhere, beady eyes cocked for scraps of food, their raucous cries competing with children's piping voices and snatches of music from the amusement arcades.

By way of contrast, the pier was almost deserted, only a few hardy souls willing to brave that exposed stretch of wall where it reached out into the sea. There, the onshore wind was fierce, driving breakers on to the beach and sending up a fine salt spray to obscure the great dark cliffs of Sandsend and Kettleness. Holding on to the sturdy iron railings, Natasha blinked against sun and wind to look up at the abbey and the church, and the old town clinging to the cliffside. She could see the church steps clearly, winding above the chimney-stacks and steep-pitched roofs, and the gravestones teetering on the cliff edge, needing little more than one bad storm, it seemed, to send them tumbling into the sea.

Pondering that grim thought, she turned and caught Nick's gaze upon her. His expression, serious, slightly questioning, was one she had come to recognise of late; because it made her feel guilty, she pretended to find the antics of the wind amusing. His hair, thick and straight, was whipping across his forehead, revealing a touch of grey at the temples. Pushing it back with one hand, she kissed him lightly and took his arm with the other.

'Come on, let's walk back before this wind blows us away.'

They crossed the swing bridge into the old town, and wandered the tiny cobbled streets, peering into shop windows and quaint little yards with strange-sounding names. They climbed the steps up to the church, edging their way in and out of the old box-pews to read the extraordinary memorials to explorers and whaling captains, fishermen and ship-owners, who had worshipped in this place but mostly died elsewhere. The wind was too strong to wander around the churchyard, however, and they lingered only long enough to watch the light fading over the sea. It was a relief after that to regain the shelter of the town, and to go in search of something to eat.

They had an excellent fish tea in a bright and crowded restaurant by the upper harbour, where the atmosphere was as lively as any continental bistro; but as they came out to return to the car, Natasha suddenly realised that she did not want to go home. She would have given almost anything to stay in Whitby, beneath the clear and star-studded sky. Lights, people, shops and busy restaurants, all reminded her of the absence of such things in

Denton. A sickening reluctance in the pit of her stomach had the feeling of something old and very familiar. It was a similar sensation to the one she used to have as a girl, leaving school and waiting for the bus to take her home. Once she was on the bus it was all right, the unfeeling flatness of resignation set in; but it was hard, leaving the school and the town, watching her friends go off with other friends, hearing them make arrangements for the evening or the coming weekend. She always wanted to leave her sister and the group of country children, leave them to run to the others; but there would have been no point. She could not have stayed, she would have had to go home eventually, and the price of disobedience was high.

Nevertheless, that was how she felt now. She would have liked to say to Nick: 'Don't let's go home yet, let's find a hotel and stay the night . . .' But it was pointless. He had to be in college tomorrow, and anyway, they had to go home some time.

In the car, later, as they came down off the moors and ran into heavy rain near Pickering, Nick caressed her thigh and asked, with a smile in his voice, whether she was tired and ready for bed. Trying not to shrink from his touch, Natasha said that she was tired and left it at that. But it was not just fatigue that dogged her; inside her head the events of yesterday afternoon were playing over and over like a distorted piece of film.

Ten

IT WAS STILL raining the next morning, a steady downpour of grief from a leaden sky. At nine o'clock on the dot, Mrs Bickerstaff arrived, shaking her umbrella and complaining about the weather. Natasha agreed that it was wicked, cold as well as wet, and took the morning's mail from Nick as he edged past on his way out.

There was a redirected envelope from her hardback publishers, which looked like a fan letter, and a large, stiff-backed envelope bearing the logo of Oasis Books. It was weighty enough to cause a flutter of excitement; with a smile Natasha retired to her office.

The fan letter was kind, well written, appreciative of all the salient points of her first novel; it was the sort of letter which made her glad to be a writer. With a smile she set it aside for later reply, and opened the other envelope, containing the jacket proof of a new paperback edition of *The English Lesson*. It was to come out in tandem with the new hardback, and was certainly striking in its design and strong use of colour. With it was a note from her new editor at Oasis Books, expressing his pleasure at the new cover, and hoping she felt the same. She smiled and nodded, aware that the morning's mail had lifted her spirits, setting the rain-soaked yard at one remove and reminding her that there was another world out there. A world of readers and publishers, artists and printers, to whom books were meat and drink. They were important to her; she was important to them; by comparison, what was going on in Denton and its environs was just a pin-prick.

Forget it, she told herself; forget Nick and his moods, forget the woman in the yard and that weird experience down Dagger Lane. Write something, anything, an article or short story, it doesn't have to be a novel.

By late morning, when she was interrupted by the sound of a vehicle pulling into the yard, Natasha was several pages into an account of her walk on Saturday afternoon.She was also in the middle of a sentence, and it was with annoyance that she tore her attention away to peer through the window. The driver of the battered old Land Rover was shadowed by the cab, but as he climbed out Natasha recognised him at once. He had been so present in her mind, she even looked down at the page she was working on; but she had not reached that point yet . . .

Her heart lurched and began to race uncomfortably. Totally bemused, she watched him as he opened the gate, giving the long, low house a single appraising glance. He still looked as though he should have been wearing knee-breeches and a leather jerkin.

She followed him with her eyes as he came up the path. He paused by the porch door and lifted his hand to the bell. As it rang, she leapt up as though stung, banging her hip against the door-jamb in her hurry to answer the door. Mrs Bickerstaff was just coming down the stairs, and she signalled her to wait within earshot as she stepped into the porch.

Her visitor's eyes, she noticed, were blue and deep-set and on the same level as her own. She would have liked to be haughty, but between haste and alarm had difficulty finding her voice. 'Yes?'

'Mrs Rhodes?'

'Natasha Crayke,' she answered automatically.

'Oh.' The dark-blue eyes, flecked like lapis lazuli, hesitated for a second, and then he looked at her directly. It was as though a little dart of fire struck and spread within her.

'But you are – I mean, we did meet on Saturday? Down the lane?'

'I – yes, I'm the person you abused,' she managed breathlessly.

He looked down, pursed his lips, pushing his hands deeper into the pockets of his Puffa jacket. The rain was dripping off the porch roof on to his shoulders. He cleared his throat. 'Yes, well, I'm sorry about that. That's why I've come – to apologise.'

Natasha sensed something forced in his manner, as though the apology was made under duress; nevertheless, instead of accepting it and wishing him good day, she stood back and invited him inside, out of the rain. He stepped into the porch, but with a gesture at his muddy boots, would come no further. From the doorway she glanced back at Mrs Bickerstaff, who raised her eyes heavenwards, nodded, and went back upstairs. Hearing her feet on the boards above, Natasha turned to the young man before her. He was in his early twenties, not unattractive in a roguish kind of way, despite the taciturn manner.

'The name's Morrison, by the way – Craig Morrison. The old man has Forest Hill Farm, and the sheep belong to him, but –' He broke off, and on a note of genuine apology said, 'I'm answerable. That's why I was so . . .'

'Incensed?' she offered, with a tight little smile.

His mouth twitched, and broke into a grin. 'Yeah, I guess you could say that.'

He was definitely attractive, Natasha thought, and he did not sound like one of the locals, his phrasing and intonation were all wrong. But as he glanced back at her and spoke again, the frank appraisal in his eyes sent all other considerations fleeing. 'You know, I'm real sorry for what happened – for what I said.'

She was conscious of physical weakness, a melting of resolve and anger that made her say 'That's all right,' while wondering where her backbone had gone. 'But you know,' she added uncertainly, 'what I find hard to understand is why you thought I should be responsible?'

The dark-blue eyes creased into a smile. 'Well,' he explained, 'you don't often see a woman down there on her own – not without a dog.'

'I'm surprised,' she said challengingly, 'that you haven't seen me before. I often walk down there – or I did, in the summer.'

'I must have been blind . . .'

Unable to look away, suddenly she wanted to touch him, to press her mouth to his, to feel his teeth against her throat and his hands on her body. If she made a single move towards him, she knew it would happen; he wanted her too, she could see it in his eyes, hear it in his breathing, everything seemed magnified. Her throat and chest were tight, and only a distant awareness of Mrs Bickerstaff, cleaning upstairs, made her draw away.

As she turned, blindly, the leaves of a potted geranium brushed her hand, the touch like an electric shock. She jerked back, rubbing the skin; a moment later, however, she was stripping dead leaves and flower heads as though her life depended on it, and crushing them in her palm.

He moved back, towards the open door. She heard him take a deep breath and release it slowly. He said hesitantly: 'I – I don't live with the family, by the way – I've got my own place. At Brickhill. Yew Tree Cottage – it's right by the church.'

Her body knew what he meant, but her mind tried to ignore it. 'Yew Tree Cottage?' she repeated, plucking feverishly at the geranium. 'Well, fancy that – and we're Holly Tree Cottage.' Trying to rescue the inanity, she asked: 'Is that a coincidence, do you think, or were our forebears just unimaginative?'

With a sudden smile, he said: 'Superstitious, I guess. Terrified of their own shadows. Holly and yew are supposed to guard against evil spirits.'

'Really?' She heard the alarm in her voice and shivered suddenly, remembering the woman in the yard. 'I didn't know – at least, not about holly.' Inadvertently, her eyes strayed to the hedge.

So did his. 'It's a fine specimen – been there a lot of years, I'd say. Probably since the house was built.'

'Oh, surely not – '

'Could be – they're very slow-growing.'

'There's more than one – '

'Yes, I can see that. What you've got there will have spread from the original bush.' He looked at her and grinned. 'Don't look so worried – it's only an old wives' tale.'

'I'm not worried,' she answered quickly, but her hands were

trembling and she was thinking about the lane, about the sensation of being invaded and the woman being raped. For a moment, as though he read what was in her mind, his smile broadened, and then to her relief his gaze shifted to the house.

'You've got this place looking good,' he acknowledged. 'It was always a dump when I was a kid. An old guy used to live here – never did a thing, let the place get into a real mess. A crying shame, I always thought.'

'Well, it's been hard work . . .'

'I guess so. I'm still doing my place, but it takes time and money, and I'm short of both!' He laughed, as though it was a matter of no real importance, and let his eyes linger on the array of plants on their shelves, the pairs of walking boots and wellingtons lined up neatly underneath. Suddenly, he turned to her and said: 'Can I see you again?'

Nonplussed, afraid to meet his eyes, Natasha stumbled over her reply. 'Well, I suppose – I mean, you're bound to see me, aren't you? You know, out walking, that sort of thing . . .' Her voice petered out and she felt a fool.

With a slow smile, he murmured: 'Bit cold this time of year . . .'

The sexual connotation brought the woman to mind and blood to her cheeks. For a moment she could hardly breathe. 'I dare say,' she managed at last, 'but at least it's healthy – lots of fresh air and exercise . . .' Too late she caught the double meaning of that and blushed again.

'Sure is,' he agreed, laughing at her confusion. 'Anyway,' he added, pulling a face at the rain, 'I'd better get going – I've some beasts to get to market. Maybe you'll explain about the fresh air and exercise some other time?'

'Yes – perhaps.'

He winked at her and grinned, while she forced a smile and watched him into the Land Rover, grimacing at the way he turned it in the yard. He waved from the cab, and then he was gone, the decrepit vehicle bouncing wildly into the lane.

The conviction that she would indeed see him again produced a mix of alarm and elation. There was something unbridled about him and it had touched a similar vein in herself, one she had not been aware of before. She stood quite still, considering it, and saw again Craig Morrison's eyes, the long mouth with the full lower lip, and his hair, black and curly, tied back in that incongruous red band. The gold hoop earring completed the piratical image, confirmed her suspicion that he was not above taking what he wanted and asking questions later. And what he wanted gave her a sudden shudder of pleasure.

Gulping at the cold, damp air, she stood for a moment in the open doorway and then turned abruptly for her office. It struck her that she had better seek sanctuary there until she calmed down: it would not do to have Mrs Bickerstaff's sharp eyes noticing that sudden flush of excitement.

With the door closed, Natasha sat down at her desk and lit a cigarette. Shaken by the violence of those sexual reactions, she tried hard to think clearly, to detach herself from fantasy and concentrate on the man himself. He was hot-tempered, hot-blooded, and too cocksure by half; but the very fact that he wanted her, and was not afraid to show it, was more than flattering, it was intoxicating. She felt she had had enough of clever men with their convoluted thought processes, their questioning of every motive and reluctance to commit themselves.

She found herself smiling as she went over their conversation, remembering the look in his eyes as he'd said this, or that – but then she recalled the reason for his visit and realised that neither of them had mentioned the wolfhound. She was annoyed with herself; she should have asked about McCoy, put in a plea for the stupid creature before he was shot out of hand. And she should have told him about that bloody stray of Toby's, she thought savagely; that was the likeliest culprit, whatever Nick had to say on the subject.

A tap at the door made her start, guiltily. Mrs Bickerstaff put her head round to ask whether she should prepare some sandwiches for lunch. Natasha glanced at her watch, amazed to see that it was a good half-hour past their usual break-time.

'Yes – yes, please. I'm sorry, I was so involved with this – '

She was gone. A woman of order and routine, Natasha thought, sighing.

'Oh, aye, a real cuckoo in the nest, that one. Where he sprang from, nobody knows – not a bit like the other lads. A real trouble-causer, that Craig.' Mrs Bickerstaff sniffed disapprovingly and dabbed at the corners of her mouth with a paper tissue. 'I'm not surprised he went for you over those sheep – strike first, ask questions later, that's him.'

'Well, he only swore at me,' Natasha said, 'and he did come round to apologise.'

'Aye – it'll have been his dad made him come round, he wouldn't come off his own bat. And there'd have been no *need* to apologise,' the older woman said, clearing the table, 'if it'd been one of the other lads. They'd have *asked* if you had a dog.'

Natasha shrugged. 'Oh, well, no harm done as it happened.' After a moment, she said: 'How old is he, by the way?'

There was a pause while Mrs Bickerstaff thought about that. 'Let me see – he's the youngest of the four, and the oldest is the same age as my Christopher. And then he was in Canada for a couple of years, so I suppose he must be twenty-three or four by now.'

'Canada? Craig Morrison was in Canada?'

'Yes, he's not been back that long.' She ran water into the sink. 'Five or six months, I suppose.'

'I thought he sounded different – that explains it. What was he doing in Canada?'

'Farming – same as here.'

'So what made him go there?'

With a sidelong look, Mrs Bickerstaff said: 'Just let's say things got a bit rough for him round here.'

Intrigued, Natasha wanted to know more, but it took some persuasion to find out that the misdemeanour was to do with a married woman, and a series of guesses and eliminations to discover that this other party was in fact the present wife of their local MP, Major Norton-Clive. After all her years in service with the Major's parents at Sheriff Whenby Hall, Mrs Bickerstaff was reluctant to gossip, but she disliked the present owner of the estate, thought he was not a patch on his father, and could not imagine what had possessed him to marry 'that little trollop', his second wife.

'So how did Craig Morrison get to know her?'

'Worked there. The agent took him on as trainee farm manager after he finished at the agricultural college. Lasted about six months.'

'Until the Major caught him out with the fair Amanda, I suppose?'

Vera Bickerstaff pursed her lips. 'No, it was the agent. There was the devil to pay, I can tell you.'

Natasha could imagine. The Major was a junior minister, and she suddenly began to see why Craig Morrison had been shipped off to Canada for a couple of years. Strings would have had to be pulled, and money paid out, but that must have seemed preferable to having the name of Amanda Norton-Clive linked with that of a farm worker. She could almost see the headlines: the press would have had a field day.

'But you keep it to yourself, Miss Crayke – I never said a thing. And think on – he's a bad lot, that Craig Morrison, no respect for anybody. Give him an inch, he'll take a mile, you mark my words.'

There was warning in her glance, as though she knew only too well what had passed between them in the porch. But, having said her piece, she turned back to washing the crockery. 'If you ask me, the sooner he gets himself a job away from here the better. Although who'd want to employ him, I do not know. And as for his hair and that *earring*,' she added with another sniff of disgust, 'well, he looks no better than a gypsy.'

From a hard-working countrywoman, it was the ultimate condemnation. Picturing the students at the university, remembering herself and how she had looked ten years ago, Natasha suppressed a grin. 'Oh, I expect he'll grow out of it,' she said placatingly, aware that she was sounding like someone's granny. Privately, she did not give a damn whether he did or not. She fancied him exactly as he was, long curly hair, earring and all.

Eleven

It was just after three when Mrs Bickerstaff left, the feeble light of the winter's afternoon already fading to dusk. Natasha went back to her office, switching on lamps against the outdoor gloom. Collecting the loose sheets of paper from her desk, she was struck again by the coincidence. How odd that Craig Morrison should have arrived at the very moment she was writing about that incident down the lane. How odd that he should break it, twice.

Glancing at the pages in her hand, she pulled the other one from the typewriter and hastily pushed them into a drawer. She did not want to think about it.

Her attention went to the new jacket proof and she seized on it thankfully, reminding herself that she really must give her editor at Oasis Books a call. Oliver Duffield was relatively new and she did not know him well; in fact they had met only once, but the peculiarities of paperback publishing meant that there was no real need for them to meet very often. She remembered him as being thirty-ish and rather charming.

The receptionist put her through to his office, and Natasha was struck at once by his voice, well-modulated, with perfect vowels and crisp consonants. There was, however, an underlying warmth which blossomed as they talked about the cover, and became even more intimate as he went on to reveal that he had just finished reading her new manuscript, and was, even now, completing a letter to her on that very subject.

'You liked it?'

'Liked it?' Soft laughter reached her ears, the kind of amusement that said such words were quite inadequate. 'I sat up half the night with it – couldn't put it down – that's how much I was involved – '

Suffused by a glow of pride and pleasure, she pressed the phone more firmly to her ear and felt the smile on her face grow wider. He liked it. The revisions had worked, he had come to it fresh, and the whole book had spoken to him; he had identified with the characters, been moved by their predicament; he'd even felt a surge of pity for the priest.

If Natasha was surprised by that, she was also pleased; not because she liked the priest, but because she'd wanted to describe him as a human being, not a monster. Only in her own private world were priests allowed to be monsters.

'. . . and you know, what I really like is the way you turn accepted ideas upside down. This thing about the countryside, for instance, being a repressing influence rather than a liberating one. We all – well, we city-dwellers, that is – tend to regard the countryside as synonymous with freedom, whereas you describe it as . . . well, almost as a prison . . .'

The word surprised her. Did she see the countryside like that?

'Is that too strong?' he asked.

'Well, yes, perhaps – I don't know,' she laughed, 'I hadn't thought of it in quite those terms, but I think it can be. Depends what you want out of life, I suppose.'

There was a slight pause. 'But living in the country suits you? Being a writer, I mean?'

Again, Natasha found it difficult to reply. Did it suit her? She was not at all sure that it did. Cutting aside the undeniable thrill of Craig Morrison's recent visit, she felt that she would have exchanged everything here for the rather more predictable dangers of life in town.

'I'm sorry,' he murmured apologetically, 'I don't mean to pry. It's just that I'm a great admirer of yours, and so one tends to be . . . well, *interested* . . .'

At the softness of his voice, Natasha was prepared to forgive him anything. Oliver Duffield, she thought warmly, could have talked all afternoon and she would have gone on listening. She found herself trying to remember what he looked like, but could bring only a vague picture to mind of someone with keen eyes and a pleasant smile. She thought she would like to meet him again, if only to discover whether his presence had the same effect as his voice.

As though he read that desire, Oliver Duffield said, 'Natasha, are you planning to be in London soon? I was just thinking how nice it would be if we could have lunch.'

Natasha had not been planning anything of the kind, but the idea had instant appeal. She thought it would be very pleasant indeed to spend a couple of hours or so having lunch with Oliver Duffield, part of whose job it was to make her feel like a treasured possession. She heard herself agreeing, not only agreeing, but suggesting a date for the following week.

As she put down the phone, Natasha stretched and preened herself like a cat. Yes, she thought, it would be very satisfying, and do her a power of good to be fussed and praised after all the hard work she had put in over the last few months. She needed it, deserved it, and was determined to have it.

The ringing of the telephone intruded upon that sense of her own importance. It was Nick, enquiring about her plans for the evening. Giles wanted his advice on a period play the students were producing; if it was all right with Natasha, he would stay on and have a meal with Giles, and maybe a drink afterwards.

She said yes, of course it was all right, but felt unreasonably let down by the suggestion. All very well for Nick, she thought, surrounded by people all day, while she, Natasha, was stuck here in this god-forsaken place, with nothing to do and nobody to talk to. There was a distinct edge to her voice as she asked what time he thought he might be home.

'Look, if you don't want me to stay for a meal, I'll come straight home.'

'No, don't bother – I don't have any plans, you might as well stay.'

'Natasha, are you all right? Nothing else's happened today, has it?'

'Not a thing, no. And I'm fine, just fine.'

There was a lengthy pause. 'OK, then, I'll see you later. About ten, I expect.'

Which probably meant eleven, she thought as she replaced the phone. For a moment she was grossly tempted by the thought of Craig Morrison. Should she or shouldn't she? The question was momentous, laden with betrayal and a host of shattered principles; the fact that she wanted him so much left her feeling exposed and vulnerable. All at once the night seemed to be pressing against the window-panes like a voyeur, and she hurried to shut it out.

He was not in the phone book. There was a number listed for Morrison at Forest Hill Farm, but nothing listed for Brickhill; she even tried Directory Enquiries, but drew a blank there too. It was fear of looking a fool that prevented her from pursuing it further, from driving down to Brickhill, for instance, and knocking on his door. She was not quite prepared to go that far.

In the end, Natasha phoned Fay, in the hope that she might be at home and doing nothing. Fay was discreet and non-judgmental, and if Natasha could not see Craig Morrison, it might help to talk about him.

When she said where Nick was, and what he and Giles were supposed to be doing, Fay laughed sympathetically and invited her down.

'Have you eaten yet?' Natasha asked as she followed Fay into the house. 'We could go out, if you like.'

'Darling, I've been studying all day – another course I'm doing, and I look a fright, in case you haven't noticed! I haven't eaten, but I'll knock something together for the two of us, and open a bottle of wine – how's that?'

'I brought some anyway,' Natasha laughed, producing, like a magician, a bottle of Australian sauvignon from a supermarket carrier.

Fay had recently bought a small Victorian terrace house which Natasha loved to the point of envy. Just outside the city walls, it had a fine view of the Minster from the main bedroom, and such a wealth of original detail that Natasha was quite prepared to overlook the nightmare of damp-proof-coursing, rewiring and kitchen-fitting that Fay had just endured. The house reminded her of the one she had owned before marrying Nick, but hers had been modernised previously, whereas this one still possessed its period charm. Each visit brought forth such a wave of longing and open-hearted admiration that Fay shook her head in amazement.

'But your house is *beautiful*, Natasha – all those oak beams and floorboards – and the renovations must have cost a small fortune. I know how much this place has cost me, and the work's been nothing in comparison with yours. You've just got straightened out too – aren't you happy there?'

Natasha paused in the act of tossing the salad. 'I don't know,' she said slowly, 'probably not.'

Giving her a keen look, Fay said, 'Oh, dear, what's wrong? Is it the house, or is it you and Nick?'

They talked, over dinner and afterwards, mainly about the problems that had beset Natasha since finishing the book. She suffered sharp pangs recalling those highly charged moments with Giles, but carried on, judging that he would not have mentioned anything to Fay. There was, after all, nothing to mention. Endeavouring to keep things light, Natasha made quite a joke of her first meeting with Craig Morrison, and the fact that he had virtually propositioned her at lunchtime today. Although she admitted that she had been unnerved on Saturday afternoon, she did not mention what had happened just prior to that meeting, nor her earlier sighting of the woman on Friday. Fay was a kind and sympathetic listener, but Natasha was afraid of the assumptions she might make. It might seem that sexual deprivation was inducing fantasy and hallucination; or, even worse, that she was going mad.

What Natasha would have liked, of course, was a woman-to-woman agreement that men were impossible to live with, marriage was a ridiculous and outdated institution, and that there was no reason whatsoever why she should not have a bit of fun on the side with this randy young farmer who obviously found her so attractive. Or even with the rather more cultured and sophisticated Oliver Duffield.

But in that respect, Fay was a disappointment. She put forward the opinion that Nick was not having an affair, on the basis that Giles would have been sure to know about it, and Giles being Giles, he would have told Fay.

'Not necessarily – he'd be afraid you'd tell me. Anyway,' Natasha pointed out, 'it doesn't have to be an affair, does it? How about a one-night stand?'

'Oh, come on, this is Nick we're talking about – that's not his style at all!'

'You weren't at that bloody Hallowe'en party! I still say he took that creature in green up to his study for a quick bonk – and I'm just as certain Giles knows he did.'

With a sorrowful sigh, Fay reached for the wine and topped up her glass. 'Well, as you say, I wasn't there. Wish I had been – if I'd seen him, I'd have sorted him out in no time flat.'

Natasha grinned, albeit ruefully. 'Yes, I'm sure you would. Not like me, rooted to the spot . . .'

'Look,' Fay said, squeezing her hand, 'they all play at being silly buggers sometimes. If he did get carried away that evening – and you don't know that he did – I'm sure it's over and done with. Nick thinks the world of you – he wouldn't risk his marriage just for a few cheap thrills.'

'Wouldn't he?'

'No, he wouldn't. And I don't think you should, either. You've got too much to lose.'

Natasha left with mixed feelings, happier for that talk with her friend, but aware that Fay had not the slightest idea of the strength of her desire for Craig Morrison. According to Fay, the best way of dealing with such situations was to flirt a little and enjoy the thrill; and unless you were serious, to leave the rest alone.

But she hadn't been standing next to him in the porch at lunchtime . . .

Natasha drove at speed along the country roads, enjoying a fantasy which was pleasurably heightened by some heavy rock music. Only as she coasted through the village did she turn down the stereo and slow for the roughness of Dagger Lane. Ahead of her, on the crest of the rise, she noticed a sudden flash of light, the eyes of some animal crossing the lane. For a moment, remembering the other night, she was alarmed and braked; she thought she saw a movement under the hedge, a shadow blacker than the rest, and her heart leapt – but when she stopped to look it was nothing, just a shadow.

With her heart thundering, Natasha accused herself of too much imagination and drove on, past the house wall and the holly hedge, and into the yard.

Nick came striding out of the house as she pulled up by the gate.

'Where the hell have you been?' he demanded, yanking open the car door. 'I've been worried sick about you!'

Recoiling a little, she said defensively: 'Well, since you were out having dinner with Giles, I thought I'd pop into town and see Fay –'

'You might have phoned, or left me a note! Christ, why didn't you?'

Natasha clung to the steering wheel. 'I'm sorry, I forgot.'

'Forgot? Jesus Christ . . .'

He slammed her door and strode back into the house. Trembling, Natasha drove into the barn, switching off the engine and headlights. As she stepped out, something soft and furry brushed against her legs; with another start of alarm she looked down to see that it was only one of the cats, giving a low purr of satisfaction at the enticing warmth of the car.

Before Nick left for college the next morning, he looked into the spare bedroom.

'By the way,' he said brusquely, 'we're out to dinner tomorrow evening. I thought I'd better remind you, in case you wanted to organise some flowers or chocolates or whatever, for Nancy Fish.'

Natasha blinked and rubbed her eyes. 'All right – I haven't forgotten,' she said; but she had.

A few minutes later, as the car drove noisily down the lane, she pulled herself up against the pillows and tried to remember what the dinner was in aid of, and why they had been invited. She staggered through into Nick's study and looked at the appointments diary. Against Wednesday, 27 November, he had written in his neat italic script: *Graham Fish, Charlie Cramp, etc.*

'Oh, *God* . . .'

Twelve

'In my opinion,' said Charlie Cramp, swirling the brandy in his glass and propounding on the oral examination which had taken place earlier, 'in *my* opinion, his only weakness lay in minimising the social conditioning behind the movement, and in over-playing that of deference. But, subject to the revisions I've outlined – a copy of which you'll be sure to let him have –' He turned his gimlet gaze upon Dr Fish, 'I must say I've no hesitation in recommending the award of the doctorate. All in all,' he finished expansively, 'an excellent thesis.'

Thank God for that, Natasha thought, since the gathered company – and in particular, Graham Fish – had been waiting on this judgement for several hours. Suppressing a yawn, she looked up as the department's most senior lecturer rose from his seat.

'. . . and I'm immensely gratified, so if the Professor will excuse me, I'll go now and phone him. He'll be delighted by the news.'

'By all means.' Professor Eric Benson, stooped and wizened, was stuffing tobacco into his pipe-bowl, 'I thought he handled the viva very well . . .' He seemed to be addressing the company in general, but grinned at Natasha in a conspiratorial way, as though he understood exactly what she was thinking.

She liked the Professor. In spite of his age and chronic arthritis, he always had a sly twinkle in his eye, as though the world with all its warts gave him much secret enjoyment. And, unlike Charlie Cramp, he was a man of few words. Nevertheless, he had complimented Natasha on her outfit and insisted she sit next to him at dinner, which had thrown Mrs Fish's table-plan completely. The subsequent small kerfuffle had hardly improved Nick's mood. Just prior to leaving home, when she was finally dressed and ready, he had criticised her outfit. That short black velvet dress, those long suede boots, were totally unsuitable for a gathering which consisted mainly of senior academics and their wives. Since Nick was the most junior, and Natasha the youngest by some twenty years, he was anxious not to offend in any way, but she was not in the mood for compromise. When he accused her of looking like the principal boy in a Christmas pantomime, she had retorted that if so, she should be well-dressed indeed, since academic dinners bore a similarly poor relation to reality. Despite the fact that she had enlivened the Professor's evening, Nick remained unamused; Eric Benson was about to retire, and his eccentricities were now tolerated rather than deferred to.

Eyeing the pipe with alarm, Nancy Fish tried to tempt him to more pudding, but Professor Benson had eaten well and now wanted nothing more than coffee and a postprandial smoke. At the look on their hostess's face, Natasha was torn between sympathy and amusement. The old gentleman might be endearing, but his brand of tobacco was powerful and the aroma could last for days; however, Mrs Fish was bound by the laws of hospitality to nod her head, smile, and invite him to carry on. As he leaned back in his chair and touched a match to the tobacco, pungent clouds of smoke issued forth; it was a cue for the other smokers to light their cigarettes, and Natasha did not hesitate.

Nick was tempted, she could tell; his fingers fiddled with a teaspoon in the way they had been used to play with a packet of cigarettes. He sighed and turned to Dr Cramp. 'Do you think there'll be a chance of publication?'

'Well, he throws a considerable amount of fresh light on the period,' the older man conceded, 'quite apart from the specific issues of the movement. I think, shorn of its appendices and so forth, that it might well be publishable.' He thought for a moment. 'He would need a respectable house, of course. We shall have to see what we can do for him . . .'

Was that the royal 'we', Natasha wondered, or did he mean Nick? From what she knew of Charlie Cramp, either interpretation was possible. He had been Nick's mentor in the early days and still took a proprietary interest in his career, for which beneficence he expected favours, both large and small. In academic circles, such behaviour seemed *de rigueur*, although Natasha found it objectionable; what irritated her most of all, however, was Charlie Cramp's tendency to refer to Nick – and in his presence, too – as *my former pupil*. It was so belittling. But then, she reflected, it was Charlie Cramp's habit to belittle just about everybody, especially women. She was not at all surprised that Dr Elizabeth Powell, well known throughout the department for her feminist principles, had declined this evening's invitation.

As a consequence, they were an odd number at table, but Professor Benson seemed not to mind, he had patted her knee three times already. It amused her to imagine him patting Mrs Cramp's knee, but Mrs Cramp was seated in what should have been Natasha's place, next to Dr Fish's presently empty chair. She was an odd little woman with cropped, frizzy white hair and huge myopic eyes, which, when they were not fixed adoringly on her husband, glanced nervously around the table. At the touch of Professor Benson's hand, she would probably have yelped like an overbred poodle.

Shifting her gaze back to Dr Cramp, trying to envisage what had attracted one to the other and sustained the relationship throughout thirty years of marriage, Natasha decided that it could not have been good looks. His narrow skull with its high, sloping forehead, broadened into wide, prominent cheekbones, then tapered to an even narrower jaw; he had no neck to speak of, and the hunched shoulders of a tall man who has spent a lifetime crouched over a desk. But it was his mouth, small and slightly petulant, that revealed his true character; and his eyes, which were bright and very hard.

Lost in contemplation of that relationship, aware of no more than a wash of words, Natasha was just wondering what he was like in bed when she realised that Dr Cramp was actually addressing her. As those penetrating eyes looked directly into hers, the little mouth curved into a smile. The lustful message found its mark, striking hard below the waist, rousing her to shocked and horrified awakening.

Swallowing hard, Natasha shook her head and attempted to smile while stammering her apology. She had no idea at all of what had been said.

His smile broadened, like that of a cat with a plaything; his voice was almost a purr. 'You were miles away, my dear.'

Her heart was hammering like that of an imprisoned bird, and she had about as much hope of rescue. 'Yes,' she whispered, 'I'm afraid I was.'

'Oh, don't look so alarmed, my dear, it was nothing of any importance . . .' His eyes lingered, predatory and amused, and it seemed to Natasha that he stripped her to the bone, while she shivered and shook like a hungry victim, longing for the game to be over. '. . . I simply remembered that you do a bit of scribbling yourself, and –' he gave a smirk in Nick's direction, 'my former pupil here informs me that your publishers are really quite respectable. They have an educational branch, I understand?'

'I believe so.' She was instantly suspicious. For a moment, beyond that sense of panic and those leaping darts of need, she wondered at his interest. Then it dawned on her that he could be looking for an introduction for the young man whose doctorate had just been confirmed, or worse, for information about other authors. From Nick she knew that her publishers handled the work of two quite eminent historians, ones whom Charlie Cramp had already dismissed as 'courting public acclaim'. Not that *he* would reject it, she thought, should the opportunity ever come his way.

'It strikes me that they might take an interest in young Mountfield,' he observed, musingly. 'I think he has a future. What say you, Professor?'

Natasha did not linger to hear what the Professor might have to say; released from the grip of Charlie Cramp's insolent gaze, she quietly excused herself, almost stumbling on her way up to the bathroom.

It was a relief just to sit on the toilet and let her throbbing muscles relax. Cold water helped, and fresh air blowing in from the open window. She hung over the windowsill for a minute or two, letting the damp night air cool her face and shoulders. She was horrified by her body's response to Charlie Cramp; even the thought of his touch made her shudder with revulsion.

Questions, aversions, disgust and more questions, all flitted through her mind as she struggled to regain composure. There were no answers, however, and it seemed to Natasha that only in avoiding eye contact might it be possible to avert those sudden, lustful urges. She steeled herself to return downstairs and to spend the rest of the evening studying the tablecloth. If she seemed bored and miserable, it would not be far from the truth.

At the foot of the stairs she almost bumped into Nancy Fish, coming out of the kitchen with a fresh pot of coffee.

'Oh, sorry, dear – after you. I say, are you all right? You look a bit pale – I hope nothing's disagreed with you?'

'No – no, really, Mrs Fish, the dinner was superb. I just felt rather warm, that's all.' She forced a light laugh. 'I've been cooling off in the bathroom.'

With a searching look as they paused in the hallway, Mrs Fish said: 'Take no notice of Charlie Cramp – *scribbling*, indeed! I read your novel, and I thought it was *wonderful*, couldn't put it down.' She laughed and shook her head. 'I don't know how you do it – I have trouble writing letters!'

'It's an obsession,' Natasha said, smiling. 'Once the characters come alive, they won't leave me alone.'

'And how's the next one coming along?'

'Actually, I've just finished it – it should be out in May.'

'Oh good – I can't wait!'

Her unfeigned enthusiasm was warming, in a pleasant, wholesome way, and Natasha thought, not for the first time, that Nancy Fish must come close to being the ideal university wife. She was kind, she was sensible, she had endless patience and she loved entertaining, and it seemed to matter not at all whether her guests were lowly students or university dons.

'I'll open another window,' she said, leading the way into the dining-room. 'It's a bit smoky in here . . .'

As Natasha returned to her seat, she noticed that Professor Benson's pipe had gone out, but he was using it to emphasise a point, one that fortunately diverted attention away from her.

'I read that review of yours in the *TLS*, Charlie – and I must say I thought you were less than generous to young Sharpe. What he had to say about the rebellion was refreshingly new. To me, at least.'

'Original and old-fashioned all at the same time, if I remember rightly,' Dr Cramp retorted. 'And as for his sniping at me in Chapter Nine – well, that was utterly unsubstantiated. It relied entirely upon what I felt was a misinterpretation of what has long been familiar to all of us.'

'Nonsense,' Professor Benson declared, 'you were settling old scores.'

Just for a moment there was silence. Not daring to look up, Natasha was aware of Charlie Cramp's fury. Then he gave a sudden bark of laughter, and there came relief in coughs and sighs and little chuckles from around the table.

'Well,' he said expansively, allowing Graham Fish to refresh his glass, 'we all do that, don't we? It's just part of the game . . .'

Involuntarily, Natasha nodded. It was a game, one that certain writers and critics also indulged in, and one that she despised. She might have been tempted to make some personal comment, but Nancy Fish intervened, in a cheerful but determined effort to change the subject.

'I want to hear about Nick's strange beast,' she said. 'Graham was telling me about some odd coincidence he'd come across, and I've been longing to see you, Nick, just to hear the rest of the story.'

Natasha was sure he was about to refuse, but with an encouraging smile, Nancy Fish overrode his evident reluctance. With an apologetic gesture towards the distinguished company, Nick began his story hesitantly, with a brief description of old Toby Bickerstaff, who seemed to have been the first person to see the large, black, unidentified creature by the wood on Dagger Lane.

No he wasn't, Natasha thought; I saw it first, and it was a

dog. But then she realised that Nick was right in describing the sequence of events, and she was somewhat relieved that he glossed over the incident in the car. Mrs McCoy's encounter was described in detail, while the dinner guests listened in flattering silence. After a brief pause, and a quick, doubtful glance in Natasha's direction, Nick then mentioned his discovery of an account in Beauchamp's *History*, which concerned a black hound seen in Brickhill church in the 1630s, a hound that eluded capture and, before the entire congregation, disappeared through the church wall.

Remembering Craig Morrison and his casual comments about evil and yew trees and his cottage by the church, Natasha was unpleasantly impressed by the connection. The others were obviously intrigued, all except the Professor, who sucked on his pipe and looked dubious, and Charlie Cramp's wife, who seemed disturbed.

Nancy Fish thought it a wonderful story for a winter's night and said so, demanding to know what anyone could make of it; as might have been expected, it was Dr Cramp who responded, and with all the smug assurance of an expert.

'Padfoot,' he said crisply.

'Sorry?'

'Padfoot, that's what he's called. In my neck of the woods – that is, where I was born in Norfolk, not where I live now – there was a spectral beast that fits your description, Nick. It might have been a dog or it might have been a cat – but I suppose,' he added with a smile in his voice, 'that being spectral, it could have been either or both!

'It used to be seen in the country lanes towards Happisburgh, which was seawards of my parents' farm – and as I recall, some people who went looking for it actually claimed to have seen it. In fact my father saw it, but in his case it was quite by accident.'

'*Really?*' Nancy Fish was satisfactorily mesmerised, and Charlie Cramp waited to be encouraged. He was.

'Well, you see, he was cycling back from Home Guard duty – it was during the last war, and the Norfolk coast was particularly vulnerable – and he said the thing appeared before him quite suddenly, on the path. He braked hard and almost fell off his bike –

but he didn't brake soon enough, he went straight into the beast and beyond it. Of course, it wasn't really there, but when he cycled on and looked back, there it seemed to be again, standing where he first saw it.'

Natasha went cold, the blood draining so fast from her extremities that for a moment she thought she might faint. She looked at Nick and he held her gaze, his thoughts mirroring hers so obviously that there was no need to speak. He was thinking of the dog she had braked so hard to avoid: the dog she thought she had run into, one which disappeared so completely that he had doubted her word.

Almost imperceptibly, he shook his head. Not here, he seemed to be saying; not in front of these people.

'I was about eight years old then,' Charlie Cramp went on, 'a gullible age you might think, and you'd be right. But my father was a farmer, not given to telling tall tales, and he always maintained that he had seen Padfoot that night, cycled through him, and lived to tell the tale.'

In the silence that followed, Nick cleared his throat. 'I don't quite follow?'

'Well, the story was, you see – locally, that is – whosoever saw Padfoot was to suffer gross misfortune, even death. It was, anyway, regarded as an evil omen in Norfolk.' He sipped his brandy as if to control a sudden chill; or perhaps to conceal the seriousness with which he still regarded the incident. Then he said lightly, looking at Natasha, who quickly averted her eyes: 'I'm surprised you haven't a similar story to tell, my dear . . .'

From a constricted throat, no sound would come. She stared at him then, knowing that she must look as she felt, like a terrified rabbit.

'Coming from the Fens, as I believe you do?'

How did he know that? sprang to mind, but the question remained unasked. 'I never heard of it,' she managed to say at last, 'but there again, my father disapproved of superstition.'

'Oh, I think you'll find, my dear, that there's rather more to it than that . . .' With a smirk he raised his glass to her, but it was empty.

Under the table, Professor Benson patted Natasha's knee. Then, having refilled his pipe and clamped it threateningly between his teeth, he said: 'Are you being quite serious, Charlie? I mean, well, really, ghosts and all that.'

'Yes, Eric, I rather think I am.'

Nick chipped in quickly: 'Do you know of any specific accounts? Giles Crowther mentioned the Whitby Barguest, of course, but I'd be interested in any others.'

'Oh, good heavens, Nick, there must be dozens – folklore's a blossoming industry these days, rather as it was in the last century. Can't say I've ever bothered to look into it myself. However,' he added with a dismissive laugh, 'if you should happen to run into Padfoot yourself, you must be sure to let me know!'

Thirteen

PATRONISING OLD bastard, Nick thought, recalling that conversation. Trust Charlie Cramp to have an answer for everything, and to cap the story so effectively. He was as much irritated by that as he was by the older man's conceit. Five years ago, when they had been in almost daily contact, that pupil–master nonsense had been something to be endured, a relic of the past to which some senior academics still clung, simply because that was the way things were in their day. But it was dying out, thank God, and since Charlie Cramp's departure Nick had been his own man, looked up to by some, and no longer beholden to anyone. He had indeed made his own small mark on the academic world, might even make a larger one yet, but he resented the implication that he owed everything to his former mentor.

Natasha had been more succinct than that on the way home, but by the time they were alone together in the car that night she had marshalled her defences again. He knew with absolute certainty that old Cramp's story had frightened the wits out of her at the time; that she had put the pieces of the jigsaw together and believed the picture they presented, just as he had. But she would not discuss it. Not then and not since. It was by far the most infuriating part of a most unsatisfactory evening.

But if Nick despaired of his wife, he was also highly irritated by the way Charlie Cramp had identified, filed and dismissed Nick's little mystery as being of no account. He was stung enough to pursue it in earnest now, and wished he could get a sight of the beast if only to settle his own curiosity. But even so it would be satisfying to do a bit of digging, collate the tales, identify the sources, and then write up his own conclusions. Let Charlie Cramp sneer then!

On Saturday morning, after a late breakfast, he went outside to have a look at the weather and the state of the lane. The day had a bleak, inhospitable look to it, the fields colourless and oppressed beneath a weight of dense grey cloud. He had thought of walking down to Brickhill, but three miles there was also three miles back again, and that sky was threatening something, probably heavy, torrential rain. His car, warm and convenient, was sitting in the barn, and Nick weighted temptation with the thought that the trip to Brickhill might turn up nothing at all. It was simply a place to start, an obvious place to be eliminated quickly before he turned his attention elsewhere.

He went back inside for his coat and car keys. Natasha was cleaning the grill.

'Going out?'

'Yes. Thought I'd just pop down to Brickhill – I won't be long.'

She stopped what she was doing. 'Why Brickhill?'

He shrugged. 'I want to have a look at the church – the memorials,' he extemporised, since he was unclear as to what he was looking for.

'Oh, well,' she said, with a sudden, rare smile, 'I think I'll come with you – that is, if I'm not going to be in the way. I could do with a breath of air.'

As she went to fetch a warm jacket, Nick sighed. He would have preferred to be alone.

The journey, along the narrow, hedged road from Denton, down part of the B road towards York, and then back on to another hedged lane towards Brickhill, took about fifteen minutes. Nick had been to the church before, some years previously, and remembered that in those days the key had been kept at the village post office, some yards down the main street from the steep rise which led to the church itself. The main street was, in fact, the only street, and the post office was the first of a row of cottages which ended adjacent to the church gates.

With the key in his possession, Nick returned to the car, which he had parked outside the gates, and opened the passenger door for Natasha. He thought she seemed abstracted, staring back down the village street at denuded gardens and that rather featureless row of brick-built cottages. To him, the farmhouses set back in a line from the broad green verge were far more interesting.

'Don't you remember? We've been here before, a couple of times at least.'

'Once,' she corrected him, 'last summer. We had a drink at the pub.'

Nick smiled, rather bleakly, as memory clarified. 'Yes, of course, so we did.' Early summer, he thought, a long and beautiful day, the majority of which had been spent cooped up in the house, sanding and waxing floorboards. Around four, he had downed tools in protest, insisting they go for a walk. So they did, just as they were, in paint-stained jeans and tatty shirts, and the air was so warm and intoxicating, so full of the scent of blossom in the hedgerows and the satisfied drone of bees, they had continued all the way to Brickhill, ending their walk at the pub. They had drunk lager in the cool bar, and persuaded a sandwich from the landlord, who said he didn't normally do meals; and then there had been the long walk home in the dusky twilight.

'That's Dagger Lane, isn't it?' Natasha asked, breaking into his reverie.

He turned and looked. Across the road, between two farmhouses, a muddy lane emerged into the village street, while directly facing it, to one side of the churchyard, was the old continuation, now blocked by a field gate about thirty yards along. 'Yes, that's it,' he said, 'the old road to York. Before the turnpikes came, of course . . .'

She seemed strangely fascinated; even went to look down the grassy stretch, which ran between the churchyard and the row of cottages. Eventually, he said: 'Do you want to see the church? It's a bit of a disappointment really. Wonderful Early English doorway, but not much else.'

'Why not?' she replied with a shrug. 'That's why I'm here, isn't it?'

He turned abruptly and led the way between the avenue of yews which dominated the churchyard. The church had been built upon a promontory of rock overlooking the Vale of York, but not, curiously enough, at its highest point. That vantage had been claimed, in the century before this church was built, by some obscure Norman baron seeking to protect his interests. Whether his castle had ever been built of stone was, Nick thought, rather doubtful, but local legend had it that when the castle was abandoned, its stones were used to rebuild the original timber church. Certainly, the castle had long since disappeared, and only the grassy mounds of broken and eroded earthworks now remained to mark the position of the bailey.

But this locality was dotted with such remains, and Nick gave them no more than a cursory glance. Weighing the great iron key in his hand, he did pause to gaze up at the magnificent doorway, which must have been protected for a greater part of its existence by a medieval porch. The porch, like so much else of architectural interest, had been removed about a hundred years ago, probably by some local gentleman of great wealth and limited vision. Nevertheless, the dogtooth indentations, the carvings of grotesques and human masks, were still remarkably clear. He gazed at the tiny human heads, complete with bonnets and wimples, and realised with a surge of pleasure, that he was looking at caricatures of local people who had been alive in the thirteenth century. A sensation of a different kind touched him when he noticed, among the imps and devils, a mask remarkably like that of a snarling hound.

With a grim smile, he pointed it out to Natasha. 'There's your Rottweiler – or is it a mastiff? Not a bad likeness, though, is it?'

She pulled a face and pretended to snarl back at it, but he had a feeling the snarl was really for him. He fiddled with the key in the lock, searching for the turning-point; he found it at last, lifted the latch, and the massive oak door swung back, pulling him across the threshold even as he tried to restrain it. A shiver of anticipation – or was it merely the dank, cold air, smelling of hassocks and dust? – caused him to pause before moving into the nave.

'There must be light-switches somewhere,' he said softly to Natasha. 'Can you find them?'

She did, and the church's uniform gloom was suddenly transformed by patches of light and vast areas of shadow. For a little while they wandered about, separately studying the memorials, their footfalls echoing across stone floors. Her voice, with all the force of a young curate preaching hell-fire and damnation, reached him unexpectedly from near the pulpit. 'What, precisely, are you looking for?'

Startled, he swung round, his hand still on the smooth marble effigy of a bewigged and pouting local worthy. 'I'm not sure – nothing specific.'

'Well, if you don't mind, I think I'll have a wander through the graveyard. I swear it's colder in here than it is outside.'

Relief washed through him, leaving warmth in its wake. 'Oh, well, if you like . . .' He watched her go and, with the door closed, his movements became more decided. For some reason he found her presence inhibiting.

He paused briefly to admire the cut and mutilated figure of a fifteenth-century gentleman in armour, and was just as taken by the exquisite nineteenth-century graffiti carved into the same tomb. The other memorials were more recent and less interesting; nothing to help him there. What was he looking for? In truth, he did not know, but something in the back of his mind was nagging, prompting, and he did not want to leave until he had identified the cause.

A few minutes later he was ready to give up, and retraced his footsteps to the door. There, on a small table beside the charity box, he noticed a printed guide to the church. Expecting no more than he knew already, Nick picked it up and scanned the first of a series of cheaply produced pages. According to the brief introduction, the information contained within had been written as long ago as 1923; it was possible that he had picked up a copy on his previous visit but did not recall doing so.

It was all fairly standard, and his eye ran down each page

quickly until it was arrested, on the third, by an extraordinary reference:

> *Of Brickhill castle, built by the brigand baron, Reynald de Briec, canis venaticus of the old chroniclers, nothing now remains, but the stone of it formed the major part of the present church, erected around 1250* AD.

'Well, I don't know about that,' he whispered, lowering himself into the nearest pew, 'but as for Reynald de Briec – well, I'll be damned!'

He read the paragraph again, and almost laughed aloud. *Canis venaticus* – it was by no means good Latin, it was almost – and here he checked himself at the pun – poor dog Latin, but its meaning was quite distinct. Reynald de Briec, founder of the settlement of Brickhill – another corruption there – was also known as *the hunting dog*.

Why? It was a strange appellation, even for the time. During the period of the anarchy, when Stephen and Matilda were battling for possession of the throne, there were plenty of lawless barons around, with names like 'the wolf', or 'the hawk', or simply 'the black'. But 'hunting dog' was specific, Nick thought; it implied something about the man himself, probably that he was somebody's pet strong-arm man, a killer at the beck and call of a more powerful overlord.

Still, it was a curious link, definitely something to pursue. He could try to find the source for that name, and also have a look at the old parish registers to see what references, if any, they contained.

As he left the church in search of Natasha, with the guide clutched in his hand, Nick stood back to look again at the grotesque carving of the snarling beast. 'Now who put you there?' he wondered aloud. 'And why?'

His eyes scanned the ancient stones of the church wall, and for the first time he wondered whether Reynald de Briec's castle had in fact been more substantial than was usual for the time. But if so, why had it been abandoned?

The yews formed such an effective screen that he could not at first see Natasha, and had to go back, circumnavigating the church in his search for her. He thought she might be hidden by the few remaining upright stones in the graveyard, or walking amongst the trees which crested the hill, but she seemed not to be there. Feeling mildly irritated, he returned down the path to the car. To his surprise, he saw that she was some way up the narrow, grassy lane which divided the churchyard from the first cottage.

'Natasha!' She looked round, startled. 'What are you doing?'

Pulling a twig from the shrub which overhung the garden fence, she ambled slowly back to the car.

'Winter jasmine,' she said, a little defiantly, he thought. 'If I can get it going, it will look nice against the wall.'

'Were you talking to someone?' he asked, scanning the cottage with its one massive yew tree in the front garden. He thought he had seen movement inside, but could have been mistaken.

'Who would I be talking to?'

'I don't know,' he responded irritably, 'whoever lives here, I imagine.'

She shrugged and climbed into the car. Annoyed, with all his pleasure at those discoveries gone, Nick turned up his coat collar against an increasingly bitter wind. He took the church keys back to the post office, a bell jangling inside as he opened the door. The woman who had handed them to him earlier came through from private quarters at the back, shivering as she greeted him.

'By, it's turned cold this last hour. I think it could snow!'

He thought, privately, that it was too early in the season for snow, but agreed that winter was setting in with a vengeance. As he handed the keys across the counter she asked whether he had managed to find what he wanted, and he said that he had, assuring her that he had also locked up properly and turned out the lights.

'That's good. Some don't bother, or can't remember, and I don't fancy trailing up there myself this afternoon. *He* won't go,' she laughed, indicating the back parlour, 'he's watching the racing!'

Nick nodded sympathetically, and put in a request for the

local newspaper. 'Tell me,' he asked as she folded it for him, 'are there any strange stories connected with the church? You know, ghost stories, that sort of thing?'

For a moment, she looked startled; then she laughed. 'Been seeing shadows, have you? Mind you, I'm not surprised, that old church'd give anybody the creeps, specially this time o'year. He –' She indicated the back room again, 'he's been sidesman, sexton, everything up there, for forty years or more, and *he* don't care for it after dark, I can tell you. He's funny like that. Mind you, some folks are. I've heard all sorts in my time, and I'm not saying I believe it, but there again, it makes you wonder . . .'

Somewhat bemused, Nick nodded and agreed that it did.

'I said to the rector, not that long back – I said, Rector, when television came in, ghosts and that vanished. And do you know what he said to me?' Nick shook his head and she leaned across the counter, confidentially. 'He said, no Mrs Peckitt, they didn't – they're still here, but they can't compete with it all!'

Her knowing, satisfied smile seemed to invite some sort of comment, so he nodded again and said: 'He's probably right.'

'Aye, he is that.' She tapped the counter with Nick's change, and he began to wonder whether he would ever get it; he was also beginning to regret starting this conversation. 'But if you want to know about that there church, you want to talk to the Rector – I'm sure he could tell you a thing or two.'

But Nick rather doubted that. The rector of Brickhill parish was also the incumbent of Denton and Sheriff Whenby, a busy man whose chief concerns, of necessity, seemed to be the crumbling fabric of his three medieval churches. Nick's acquaintance with him was small, but he had already placed him as a jovial and energetic organiser, rather than a spiritual shepherd of his flock. Aware that his own spiritual life these days might be described as arid, Nick nevertheless regretted the lack of that quality in his local rector; and he did not at all think that such a practical man would welcome a discussion on ghosts.

Taking one last chance, he said to the woman: 'So you don't know anything yourself, anything more – specific?'

There was a pause in which each eyed the other speculatively. 'Well, no,' she said at last, 'not really.'

It was the *not really* that made him decide to give her a lead. He had heard that phrase too often from the lips of students who were generally more confused than ignorant. He said: 'You see, I read somewhere, just recently, about a black dog that appeared in the church – a long time ago, of course. You've never – ?'

'Black dog? You mean, like a ghost?' As he nodded, her bosom and shoulders heaved with amusement. 'Oh, not that old tale! It's as old as the hills, that one. They used to frighten us with old Reynard, when we were kids.' At his bemusement, she added: 'You know, Reynard, like the fox.'

'Oh, yes, of course – like the fable.'

She laughed again. 'Horror story, more like! Terrified the life out of us, when we were little. *Be good, else Reynard'll get you!*'

The similarity of the name alerted him. Anxious to have this clear, he asked: 'But your Reynard wasn't a fox, was he? He was a dog – the dog in the church?'

'That's right. Not just in church, though – roamed all round these parts, so they say. Never knew anybody who claimed to've seen it, mind – just an old wives' tale, I expect.'

Picking up his paper and his change, Nick smiled and shook his head. 'Ah, but you never know,' he said, making a jest of it. In truth, he could not get Toby out of his mind.

With his hand on the door, he turned back. 'Just one thing – when they said Reynard would *get you*, what did they mean?'

For the first time, he thought the woman looked uneasy. 'Well, you know, it was just to frighten children, make them go quiet to bed.'

'And if they didn't,' he persisted, pretending ignorance of the phrase, 'Reynard would come and take them away?'

'Aye, something like that.'

Having resurrected the fears of childhood, she was reluctant to put them into words; Nick sensed it, and experienced a profound sympathy. When he was a child, the phrase, *I'll get you*, was a dire threat. It meant to damage, or to kill.

With a bland smile and another rueful comment on the weather, he thanked her and stepped out into the teeth of a bitter wind. But the certainty that he was on to something made him impervious to all else; there was a lightness in his step as he returned to the car.

Natasha was white-faced and shivering, huddled deep into the collar of her padded jacket. Just for a second, as he slid into the driver's seat, he was transported back to the university library all those years ago, and she was the beautiful girl with whom he had fallen in love. The urge to hold her, to kiss warmth and smiles back into those perfectly sculpted lips, was irresistible.

His arm was halfway towards her when she said, ungraciously: 'Lord, you took your time, didn't you?'

'I'm sorry,' he said stiffly. 'The woman in the post office was talkative.'

'Oh, yes – young and blonde, was she?'

Nick gritted his teeth. 'Grey and middle-aged, I'm afraid.' He started the car, refusing to be provoked. 'Straight home?'

'No, I need a drink to warm me up. I'm so cold I could be sick.'

They drove along the village street. The pub, Nick felt, should have been called The Black Dog, but the sign swinging in the wind depicted three fat cattle crossing a ford. It was called The Drovers.

In bed that night, relentlessly wakeful, he tried reading one of his favourite novels, but not even Wilkie Collins could hold his attention for long. Instead, the mystery of *The Woman in White* set his mind wandering over mysteries a little closer to home.

At one o'clock, he got up and went to his study. If the problem of Natasha refused to be solved, then it might help to set down, on paper, the main points of the other puzzle.

Nick was no medievalist, and his vast collection of books – only part of which lived in his study – contained little other than secondary texts on certain aspects of the period, chiefly to do with chivalry and knighthood. Briefly, he was distracted by a few titles, but then he sat at his desk and began jotting down the clues.

(a) *Natasha sees black dog in headlights of car on Dagger Lane, between house and village.*

(b) *Toby reports encounter with large black beast on track by World's End.*
(c) *Mrs McCoy sees black beast in fog, this side of the wood.*
(d) *Toby and Nick find clear print of large animal by elm stumps. Could be dog, but has 5 pads not 4.*
(e) *In 1630s, a large black dog or hound is reported as being in Brickhill church – makes popular press.*
(f) *The story is known in Brickhill, where the dog or hound is known as Reynard – as in fox.*
(g) *The castle at Brickhill was built by one Reynald de Briec, temp. Stephen.*
(h) *A chronicler alluded to this Reynald as 'the hunting dog.'*

Reynald = Reynard???

He sat and looked at his notes for a minute, then added:

(i) *In early seventeenth-century France an official of Cardinal Richelieu encountered a black beast near V-Bocage. Written description tallies with T's verbal account.*

Is it possible, he thought, for a legend associated with a twelfth-century baron to survive for 800 years? Surely not. But if, he silently argued, Reynald equals *Reynard*, then it seems to have done.

Is there a link, he asked himself, between the baron's nickname and the reported sightings of the seventeenth century and now? Could it be possible?

'It's not possible,' he said aloud. 'For a folk legend to survive that long, it has to have something to feed on . . .'

And in this case, he reasoned silently, that something has to be sightings of the 'beast' more frequently than once in three hundred years . . .

Momentarily appalled by what he recognised in himself as the beginnings of an obsession, Nick thrust the paper aside and went back to bed. As he drifted into sleep, he was remembering a conversation he had had with Natasha earlier in the day.

'. . . just a little bit of historical detective work . . .'

'. . . which won't produce a corpse or a culprit, or even a crime . . .'

Fourteen

SOMETIME DURING the early hours of the morning, there was a heavy fall of snow. Recalling the woman in the post office at Brickhill, Nick pulled a face; with regard to the weather at least, she had been right.

The wind, which had abated, had piled the snow in substantial drifts against the barn and garden walls, although it did not appear to be freezing. Beneath a pale sun the hedge was dripping, and, where a tractor had passed up the lane, the fragile whiteness was despoiled with mud.

It was warmer out of doors than he had imagined, and he stood for a moment, feasting his eyes on the transformation around him. Snow made a wilderness of the yard and surrounding fields, lending an unaccustomed beauty to the plain face of the house. The old bricks were mellow, the pantiled roof ridged in terracotta and white, while the ancient holly, with its dense, dark green, provided the perfect foil. Gazing up at the house, he found himself thinking, yet again, about the man who built it. He kept meaning to investigate, but that kind of task was always lengthy and generally frustrating, and more important things had a habit of getting in the way. Nevertheless, when he had searched the parish archives for Brickhill, Nick thought he would have a look at those for Denton-on-the-Forest too. Something might turn up.

He went in, made some breakfast and glanced through the headlines of the Sunday newspapers. By the time Natasha came down the outdoor brightness had gone, and the cloud, thickening in the south-west, held the promise of more snow.

'Did you say you were going to London tomorrow?'

'Tuesday.'

'Hmm. If this little lot gets any worse, you may have to cancel. In fact,' he added, lowering his newspaper and peering at the sky, 'if it decides to snow again tonight, I may not get into college.'

'Nonsense. They'll be out clearing the roads before dawn, you know they always do.'

'Always?' he repeated mildly, surprised by her vehemence. 'We were blocked in last February. Two days, if you recall.'

'Snow never stays in November, it's too early.'

Irritated by her determination to argue the point, Nick handed over the review sections and said that he had work to do.

On his desk were the notes he had written the night before. He glanced through them, paused at the note: *Reynald = Reynard???*, and pulled his typewriter towards him. He had an old friend from student days, now a medievalist at Bristol, who might be able to help. After the usual polite enquiries with regard to health and family, he wrote:

> *I am doing a little incidental research into Brickhill village, which lies to the south of us, and am particularly keen to know what there is on Reynald de Briec, who built the castle there, probably during the twelfth century. I know nothing more about him, except that in the guide to the church he is referred to – without source – as canis venacticus, which I interpret as 'hunting dog'. I hope that helps.*

He paused for a moment, wondered whether he could add anything to that, decided not, and then closed with a few more personal sentences. A couple of minutes later, looking for David's address, he came across another that gave him food for thought. Sally Armitage, he knew, had moved on from the Castle Museum, to Ghylldale on the North York Moors. If it was possible to speak to her, she might be able to help with the folklore aspect.

Making a note in his diary, Nick suddenly wondered at the

wisdom of contacting her again. Still, he reminded himself, almost five years had elapsed, and on the rare occasions that they had met since then, she had treated him amicably enough.

After lunch, during a fierce flurry of snow, Natasha began to wonder whether Nick might be right about the weather. By late afternoon, faced with the boring bits of the newspapers and an old film on television, she thought it might be a good idea to investigate the state of the roads. Agreeing with her, Nick went to fetch his coat.

Where the snow had drifted under the arms of the hedge it was soft and deep, supported by brambles and pierced by the rusty spikes of dock and willow-herb. Nick tested the depth of it in his boots and found it almost knee-high in places, while Natasha walked where the tractor had been, leaving a trail of muddy brown footprints all the way down the lane. What remained of the day was fading fast and ahead of them, in the village, lights began to appear like yellow stars between the trees.

The air was still and not particularly cold. Along the pronounced curve of the Green the beck gurgled noisily, while a solitary car crept slushily past, sure signs that the snow was melting. They continued up to the road, where enough traffic had passed to make the metalled surface visible; they agreed that by morning it would probably be clear.

With that reassurance they walked on a little way, returning via a narrow lane which served a group of cottages behind the church, and cutting back through the graveyard to reach the Green. Unlike Brickhill, most of the memorial stones here were in their rightful places, those in the northern shadow of the church still covered in snow, like upright corpses in their winding sheets. All was silent, with an indigo blueness to everything, and nothing stirred. There had been no service in Denton that day, and it seemed a desecration to mark the snow-covered paths, to speak in more than a whisper. Creeping past the church they stopped simultaneously as the sound of a drunken voice, raised in snatches of song, reached them from beyond the gate.

Toby, glancing to neither right nor left, his face flushed with effort and drink, was heading homewards after a protracted session in some local pub.

'Where's he been?' Nick asked. 'Can't have been the Half Moon, it shuts early on a Sunday.'

'Must have been to Sheriff Whenby – that's the nearest.'

'Lord, you've got to admire his dedication,' Nick breathed, 'it must be all of three miles.'

Toby spotted them and hesitated, walked on for a few yards and then waited while they caught up with his progress across the open expanse of the Green. In the middle stood a large snowman, its cap and slightly leering expression so evocative of the old man that Natasha almost laughed.

'What are the roads like further down?'

'They'll do. Not bad, considering. I should've taken the bike.'

'Are you keeping all right, this weather?' Nick asked.

'Aye, not so bad.' Wheezing as they started the slight climb up Dagger Lane, he said: 'Morrison lost another sheep last night, killed stone dead it were, just like t'others.'

'Where was this?'

'On that grassland t'other side o' World's End. He's been out this morning with his lads, looking for a dog. He says it was had by a dog.'

'Does he know which dog?' Natasha asked.

'Nay. Thinks he does. Thinks it's that there great Irish thing.' For a moment it seemed as though the old man was about to expand on that, but whatever opinions he had were lost in a bout of coughing.

'It's that bloody stray again,' she said, but Nick shook his head.

'Do you think it might be the creature you saw?' he asked directly.

Toby sniffed and wiped his nose with his sleeve. 'Thing that size, if it got hungry it could do it. But them sheep weren't etten, just had their throats ripped out.'

'To kill a sheep,' Natasha said, 'it would have to be flesh and blood itself, wouldn't it? It's got to be a dog.'

The old man ignored her. 'Came in the pub, they did, just as I were leaving – been out looking all day. I told 'em it were no use.' He shook his head. 'Turned warm, now.'

'Thawing,' Nick observed, kicking at a soft bank of snow.

'Aye, could be worse. No doubt will be, afore we've finished.'

He left them by their gate, whistling tunelessly as he trudged on in gathering darkness towards his lonely habitation.

'Dead sheep . . .'

'Doesn't mean a thing,' Natasha said repressively, irritated by the old man's drunkenness and the fact that he had ignored her. 'He's enjoying himself though, you can see that. Sinking pints on the strength of what he saw – or what he *thinks* he saw.'

Nick regarded her curiously, and with some distaste. He said: 'Don't be so bloody hard, it doesn't suit you,' and went inside.

As had become usual, they ate their evening meal in comparative silence while watching television in the kitchen. Afterwards, Nick said that he had some work to do, and disappeared upstairs. Natasha watched a play on BBC 2, but it failed to hold her attention completely. She kept thinking about sheep with their throats ripped out, and Craig Morrison, leaping down from the tractor and stepping into the porch. She thought about Oliver Duffield too, with that wonderfully sexy voice; but unlike Craig, he would be smooth and sensual . . .

Just after ten, Nick came down to pour himself a nightcap. He sat beside the stove for a little while, and then, with a theatrical yawn, said he was going up to bed. Although he paused in the doorway and looked back at her, he no longer asked which room she intended to sleep in. Of late it had become accepted between them that she preferred to be alone.

With his going, Natasha felt the tension seep out of her. It was a distinct physical sensation that left her more aware than ever of how much she resented his presence. Over the past few days that feeling had been building up, so that she could barely look at him now without wanting to push him out of her way. She was no longer jealous and insecure, she felt quite impervious to him. He could have his women if he wanted them; in fact she wished he would. If only he would leave, go for good, then she might be free to conduct whatever business she fancied, whenever and with whom she liked.

She thought of Craig Morrison, imagined him taking her, time after time; pictured herself, responding to his lustful aggression. Such imaginings excited her, and in the last three or four days they had increased to the extent that she could barely think of anything else. She was under such compulsion that she hardly dared leave the house for fear of losing control with a perfect stranger.

For the moment, those prurient fantasies were centred on Craig Morrison, but the unwelcome truth seemed to be that almost any man would do. Only the other day, in town, she had noticed a man in the street, and at the unexpected meeting of a glance had suddenly been stricken with desire. A tourist, obviously not English, the man had stopped and turned, and for a moment she'd thought he was about to grab her arm and usher her down the nearest alleyway – and she'd wanted it, that was the awful truth! It was as scaring as it was thrilling, like leaning into the wind to look over the edge of a cliff. But that day, the man's laughing companion had dragged him back from the brink.

Yesterday, infuriatingly, Nick had managed to do the same. Another minute and she'd have been inside Craig's cottage, the compulsion was so strong; as it was, he'd whispered, 'Monday afternoon . . .' and she pulled at the jasmine and walked back towards Nick. And then, seeing the snow this morning, Natasha had thought his presence would frustrate her plans again.

Desire, dark and unsettling, possessed her. Unable to concentrate on the tepid drama on screen, she switched it off and went up to bed. The main bedroom light was still on, but she did not even bother to look in to say goodnight. Almost any man would do, but not Nick. She did not want him at all.

She stripped off, sliding naked between cold sheets, shivering for a moment before running light, teasing fingers over her own body. Thinking of tomorrow, of Craig Morrison's careless arrogance, added a certain *frisson* to the pleasure. Hot and sweating, a few moments later she relaxed; breathing deeply, she drifted into sleep.

The hooting of an owl disturbed her. Roused from a dream, she was aware of it close by, just outside the window, probably in the hedge. Without opening her eyes she listened to that repeated call and willed it to go away, to shut up and leave her in peace. After a while it did, the long, broken cry fading into the distance. Natasha turned on her side, settling more comfortably into the narrow bed. Then, just as she was beginning to relax, there came another sound from outside, a low, subdued growling, not that of an angry dog, but something softer and more fluid, like the magnified purr of a cat, eating . . .

It was very close, if not in the garden then in the lane, horribly near to the house. She lifted her head to listen, wondering what on earth it could be, while her mind leapt to dead sheep and Toby's stray dog, and the five-clawed creature which had left its marks by the wood. With her heart pounding, she thought of calling Nick, but her breath seemed stuck in her chest, and she dared not get out of bed. The sound became intermittent, then seemed to be lessening, growing fainter as though the creature was moving away from the house and down Dagger Lane.

As her heart and breathing slowed to more acceptable levels, Natasha relaxed against the pillows and tried to blank out the grisly image of a huge black hound slavering over its freshly killed prey. She had a brief moment of horror, thinking about the cats in the barn, but there had been no sudden screech, no indication of a fight; and if there had been, Natasha was not sure she had the courage to investigate.

Anyway, Colette was indoors. After a while, waiting and listening, Natasha began to wonder whether she should go down anyway, but the thought of putting on lights and maybe attracting that creature back again was unnerving. Clinging to the warmth and safety of bed, she wondered about Nick. But there was no sound from the next room; obviously he was asleep.

Just as she was beginning to relax, the noise came again, more clearly this time, so close that it seemed to be inside the house, inside and coming closer, an animal with great, gaping jaws, its breath gurgling in its throat as it came padding up the stairs.

She wanted to scream but could not; wanted to leap up and

hide, but the bedding was like lead, pinning her down. The gurgling noise came closer, she could hear the scratching of claws on oak treads and floorboards, the nuzzling of something against the door. It opened and she stared, eyes starting out in a paroxysm of terror; stared at a shadowy form that seemed to be rising up, changing shape, until what threatened her was not a hound but something with the form of a man. Everything was moving, like shadows on the wall; the features were in darkness, but the eyes held her transfixed, halting the heart in her breast and the breath in her throat. Lust was in those burning eyes, and a sadistic, leering amusement; she saw a reflection of her own fantasies and they were fantasies no longer.

The creature seemed to be struggling to maintain its shape. As it lurched towards her, Natasha edged away, finding the wall at her back, kicking to free herself of binding sheets so that she could run –

But as she drew breath to scream, the woman came. The woman was there in the modest dress with the apron and big white collar. Except it wasn't a collar, it was a sort of shawl, the ends tucked into the front of her dress. Natasha watched her pull it away, at the same time releasing her hair from its cap, long, light-coloured hair that shimmered as she shook it free. Very slowly, moving between Natasha and that horrifying phantom, she freed her bodice and cast off her skirt until she was standing there in her shift. For a moment, the creature hesitated between them, then incredibly, the form it had been struggling to achieve was suddenly wavering no longer. It became dense, three-dimensional against the darkness, a tall, gaunt figure of a man swathed in some kind of robe. The face, blessedly, turned away from her then, the eyes followed the woman as she raised her shift and retreated against the wall.

As he closed in on her, the woman's face was blank, devoid of emotion. He raised her up and thrust deep, and Natasha saw her face over his shoulder, the mouth agape, the eyes shut as they had been before, in the lane down by the wood.

She woke in a cold sweat, sheet wrapped around her ankles, quilt kicked to the floor, her naked body twitching and shivering as though she herself had been raped. The image of those faces – the woman's so cold and hard, the man's so dark and insubstantial – were imprinted so clearly it seemed they were before her still. And the action of their bodies! A conjunction of hatred; cruelty taken with contempt.

Whimpering, Natasha reached for the bedside light, flinching even as she welcomed its brightness. Grabbing the quilt she wrapped it around her, hugging her knees, forcing those faces away as she made herself look at every familiar object in the room: pictures, wardrobe, the mirror on the wall. This room was light and bright, with white walls and white plaster between the beams; nothing like that dark, louring room of her dream. Even the door was in a different place. Thank God, she thought, thank God for that.

Just a dream, she told herself over and over; a nightmare, that's all it was. But it took some time to calm down, and when she did, Natasha was frightened to go back to sleep. Tying her dressing-gown securely, she went to the door and reached for the light-switch. Only when the long landing and stairs were fully lit did she venture out, pausing for a moment by Nick's door as she struggled with the temptation to wake him. Eventually, telling herself that he would think she was mad, she went downstairs. In the hall, she reached for the kitchen switch before stepping through the doorway. Colette, she was relieved to see, was quite safe, sitting on the windowledge and peering out at the garden.

Natasha made a drink and found her cigarettes, together with a novel she had been trying to read earlier in the week. She read until her eyes would no longer focus on the page, and then, yawning and stumbling, finally made her way back to bed about five o'clock.

A little after eight, Nick disturbed her with a cup of tea. 'Thought I'd better wake you, Mrs B.'s due at nine.' He went over to the window and drew back the curtains. 'Snow's gone – more or less, anyway.'

As she struggled into her dressing-gown, Nick turned to face her. 'By the way,' he said, 'when I got up this morning, all the lights were on.'

His words hurt, like sunflashes on a migraine. Wincing, she raised her hand, but the dream was still with her, clearer behind closed eyes, evoking fear afresh. Nausea threatened; forcing it down, she clutched at the quilt and stared, wide-eyed, around the room. 'Yes,' she said faintly, 'something woke me – a horrible noise outside.' She shuddered and reached for her cup of tea. 'I don't know what it was – a fox, probably, killing a rabbit. Then I fell asleep again, and – and then I dreamt about it. Awful, a nightmare really . . . so I got up and made some tea.'

'You should have come in and woken me.'

'Don't be silly – there was nothing you could do.'

'So you left the lights on, instead.'

She looked up, unsure whether he was chiding her, but it seemed not. He was wearing a tracksuit, the soft material clinging to his shoulders and thighs, emphasising the long, clean lines of his body. By sheer contrast, it made her think of that other figure last night, skeletal yet amorphous. Horrified, she blinked and looked away.

'Have you been out?'

'No, I'm just on my way – round the village, I think. The lane'll be too slushy this morning.'

But he lingered a moment longer, his eyes on the open V of her dressing-gown, where her breasts were partly exposed. Prudishly, Natasha pulled it together and he turned away, his stockinged feet silent on the stairs as he went down. A couple of minutes later she heard the door slam as he set off for his run.

A little later, over breakfast, she mentioned that she might go into town that afternoon, maybe have tea with Fay if she was around. Without lifting his eyes from the *Guardian*, Nick said in that case he would probably stay on after college and have a game of squash with Giles.

'What time will you be back?'

'Around seven, I expect – maybe a little later.'

'Well, if you should decide to stay on for a while, please don't come back drunk at midnight – I'm supposed to be going to London tomorrow.'

He paused in the act of eating his toast. 'When have I ever

come back drunk at midnight?' he demanded, glaring at her. Pushing his plate away, he added resentfully: 'Anyway, I haven't forgotten your trip to London. I shall be up early, as usual, ready to give you a lift into town.'

As Mrs Bickerstaff turned in at the garden gate, Nick disappeared upstairs to shower and change. Twenty minutes later he was on his way, in dark-green shirt and tie, Harris tweed jacket and black trousers, with his overcoat slung over his shoulder. In his wake lingered the distinctive fragrance of Paco Rabanne.

Fifteen

NICK'S MOOD was not improved by spending an hour with a group of first-year students whose joint attitude, even at this late stage of term, remained steadfastly morose. Heading back upstairs at lunchtime, he was depressingly convinced that everything in his life was a waste of time. Indulging his bitter mood by mentally composing a letter of resignation, he barely acknowledged the greeting of a colleague, ignored the students hanging around in the corridor, and proceeded towards the haven of his own room.

Fortifying himself with a mug of instant coffee, he turned to the window, staring out at the dull, gunmetal surface of the lake. But even the ducks had abandoned it, squatting disconsolately on the grass. Turning back to his desk, surveying the bulging folders awaiting his attention, he could have binned the lot. Paperwork, he thought disgustedly; how the hell did Admin. expect research to be done? They expected academics to work like office managers, while the bloody government were insisting on more and more research, as though each university was no more than a factory production line. Quality, value and originality no longer mattered; visible results did, and the pressure to produce something, anything, in order to keep up the department's output was phenomenal.

His own research was lagging behind. That book he had been so excited about was going nowhere at present, and he knew why. He felt old and tired and past it, morale and enthusiasm on a par with that of the first-year students, which seemed to him at an all-time low.

But that was a general problem, not something he could conquer single-handedly. Could he conquer anything, though? Even his personal problems seemed mountainous, this thing with Natasha rising like the north face of the Eiger whenever he tried to survey it. He could not get close to her, that was the trouble. She was holding him off, both physically and emotionally, with ice building up by the day.

If only he could talk to her; but conversation, even on the most mundane of levels, was practically impossible. In the last few days there had been sharpness and cynicism, even moments of active dislike, and yet until about a month ago they had been so close, easy with each other in spite of some strong external pressures.

What had gone wrong? Did she really think he was having an affair? Surely she wasn't still making a melodrama out of that ridiculous incident at the party. He had told her there was no one else, told her clearly and honestly, yet it had made not a scrap of difference. That lack of trust was destructive, it made him feel like a criminal.

For someone who prided herself on calmness and logic, he thought, Natasha was behaving like an irrational child. Perhaps stress was playing havoc with her imagination at the moment, but Nick knew to his cost that she had a strange way of reacting sometimes, and what appeared on the surface often bore little resemblance to what was going on underneath. He had only to think of Natasha as she had been when he first knew her, to realise that.

He looked across the room and sighed. The furniture which had been quite new in those days was considerably more battered, and the coffee table fit only for the nearest bonfire; but he remembered her coming in for her first tutorial and sitting down over there, and he remembered his reaction. She was dressed entirely in black, and looked more like a groupie from a heavy metal concert than a serious student of history. Social sciences might not have objected to chains and safety pins, but he did; and the fact that she was aiming for a combined degree of English with History, rather than the more disciplined course of History as a single subject, had irritated him further. Every time he looked at her – and he had tried not to – he wanted to tell her to go away, to wash her face, comb her hair, and find some more suitable clothes.

It had not made for a good beginning, and that she had very much disturbed him while he had been busy terrifying her was afterwards obvious, even though he'd not realised it at the time.

Looking back, he thought that if it hadn't been for Giles, Natasha would probably have abandoned his course and those agonising tutorials, and that would have been that. End of story, without either of them being any the wiser. He would never have known the girl behind the mask, never have discovered the fascinating mind or her complex and vulnerable personality; never have known the heights of happiness or the appalling depths of despair into which she could fling him . . .

He closed his eyes and rubbed his forehead, trying to ease a pain that was intensified by the memory of old wounds. For a moment he half wished that Giles had stayed out of it, and that he might have been spared the subsequent involvement. The thing was, so much of it had been good, and he could not regret that.

But Giles, concerned about the pupil they shared, had intervened; and because they had argued about her, because Giles had told him he was being pompous and a fool, and that it was about time he stopped venting his personal problems on his students, Nick had been forced to examine his own attitudes. He hadn't liked what he had seen; but there again, he had been angry with himself and what was going on in his life for quite a while before that, so it was no great surprise. It was just unpleasant to realise how irritable and ill-tempered he had become, and how many people had noticed it.

He could see now that there had been a real danger of that attitude becoming permanent; but Giles had brought him up short, made him understand that he owed the girl an apology, and that he should do his utmost to see that she stayed on the course. Which had been vital to her study of the links between Hardy's novels and the agricultural economy of the period.

He too had been a lover of Hardy in his youth, so he had thawed a little, made a special effort to show that he could smile occasionally, especially when his pupils responded with first-class essays.

And she did. Oh, yes, she did. He half-smiled, recalling that first essay and the tingle of excitement it had provoked. He had been astonished to discover her grasp of the problem, her command of language, the ability with which she could convey an opinion on paper. She was not always right – in fact she was very often wrong – but her reasoning was always admirable. That was what made her so special, what attracted him to her; and yet every time they met he was dismayed afresh by the ferociously spiked hair and heavy make-up, the monosyllabic replies that made communication so difficult.

Frustration was what he remembered about that time; which was ironic, he thought, since that was precisely how he felt now, longing to get to grips with the problem, yet unable to find an approach.

Then, his opportunity had come by chance. It was a day towards the end of February when snow was on the ground. He remembered it well because there had been something wrong with one of the boilers, and in the main library it was very cold; only a few determined souls were in there, most of them looking for books rather than working. Needing to check a reference, Nick had headed for the appropriate section and been surprised to see Natasha at one of the tables. For a moment he'd barely recognised her. Half hidden behind a pile of books, she was bundled in scarves and sweaters, her face paler than ever in the white light reflected from a sky full of snow.

She didn't appear to have noticed him, and for a moment or two he watched surreptitiously as she pored over the pages. She looked so different without all that heavy make-up; dark hair, dark eyes, and the luxuriant sweep of lashes were all untouched. In that harsh, unforgiving light, her face was a study in monochrome, the planes of nose and cheek and brow as perfect as a Beaton photograph.

For the first time he noticed how vulnerable she seemed.

Before, she'd always struck him as having too many sharp angles, but in that moment she was relaxed and unaware, there was a fragility about her which brought out all his protective instincts. He could not imagine how he had ever viewed her as a threat.

And yet she had been a threat, when all was said and done. Over the next few months she had turned his life upside down, in good ways as well as bad. Not from any wilful desire on her part, but just by being what she was: awkward and enchanting, challenging and beautiful.

So beautiful. She looked up from her books that day and met his gaze, and those pale cheeks were suddenly suffused with colour. Aware of a corresponding warmth in himself, aware too that she was struggling with something and needed help, he had gone across to speak to her. So simple, and yet it had changed everything. Nothing was acknowledged, he never tried to touch her, and for months their relationship remained that of tutor and pupil; but from that point on everything was different. She seemed able to talk to him at last, he looked forward to seeing her, she grew in confidence. And with that blossoming of her personality, her appearance became less artificial, there was a softness about her that spoke of satisfaction and enjoyment rather than the edgy suspicion which had enveloped her before.

He was happy too, extraordinarily so. After all that had occurred in the months before he met Natasha, he felt he deserved the innocent pleasure she gave him. Self-delusion, of course, but without it he would have had to acknowledge the danger he was in, and once he recognised the danger, he would have had to walk away from it.

Giles, who might have issued another warning, raised no more than a quizzical eyebrow now and then, and in the meantime winter turned to spring, and the spring became early summer.

Had he been less determinedly blind, and Natasha less innocent, then surely he would have realised sooner; but when the time came, when his emotions finally caught up with him in what seemed a tidal-race of love and knowledge and desire, it was already too late.

There were regrets still, particularly when he thought of the boys. Because he loved them, because he did not want them hurt by his mistakes, he had tried when it was over to pretend that the affair with Natasha had never happened. But that was easier said than done, and in the following three years he paid every day for the pleasure of those few weeks with Natasha. In truth, he had been paying ever since through his relationship with his sons; less directly perhaps, but just as painfully. Bernice saw to that.

But what had destroyed him when Natasha ended their affair was that she did not explain why. All right, he was married, that was obvious enough; but they had never really discussed it, either then or since. When he was with her, he was happy; he did not want to share with her the anguish of his sleepless nights. In those short, glorious weeks of early summer, all he had wanted to think about was Natasha; and then she ended it, it was over, and without explanation.

Her novel was revealing, but as a piece of fiction not even that provided the ultimate answer. When he read it, more than six years after the event, he had felt crucified by the emotion. But the conclusion was wrong, and he had never understood why.

Nick looked out at the flat surface of the lake, and wondered what was to be done. Thinking about the past had made him no wiser, but it had certainly raised questions that should have been answered a long time ago. But in the last two years, in the midst of happiness, such questions had seemed like sleeping dogs, and best left alone.

Well, they were stirring now, and he thought it was time to give them an airing. He might get bitten for his pains, but anything was better than this current estrangement.

The more he thought about it, the more vital it seemed to tackle things now, at once, before anything else could get in the way. He glanced at his watch and reached for his diary. He had a tutorial at three, one which could be postponed, but he had also made arrangements to play squash with Giles.

There was no reply from Giles's number. He was just about to call the departmental office when someone knocked at his door.

With an exclamation of annoyance he put down the phone

and called out for his visitor to enter. His heart sank as Jane Bardy walked in. For the past few weeks, in spite of every discouragement, she had been covertly pursuing him. Unlike Natasha, who had been intimidated by his stern looks, and would have shrivelled with dismay at any recrimination in those days, Jane Bardy seemed impervious. She was a bold, physically striking young woman with something actressy about her; and while he could picture her declaiming from behind the footlights, Nick found that he could not seriously imagine her with a degree in single-subject History.

As she relinquished the folder she was clutching and placed it on his desk, Nick's eyes were level with the front of her blouse. He saw at once that beneath the loose, baggy cardigan and man's white shirt, she was wearing little else. The outline of her breasts, even to the darkness of the nipple, was perfectly obvious.

He was aware that his glance lingered just a fraction too long. Looking down, resisting the urge to clear his throat, Nick picked up the folder and opened it. The essays that he had been waiting for, and had not expected to see before Christmas, were now before him. Flicking through them, he allowed himself a small, throaty rumble of approval at the neatly written pages. Content was probably debatable, but at least the work was here.

'You *have* been busy . . .' With his eyes and thoughts once more under control, Nick risked looking up, to meet a most self-satisfied smile.

'I thought you'd be pleased.'

Refusing to respond to that, he said: 'Am I to take it that you're now up to date with all your outstanding work? Dr Fish mentioned an essay . . .?'

She looked away, her full mouth making a small moue of dissatisfaction. 'Well, I still have a couple more to finish, but – '

'In that case, I should get on with them as quickly as you can. Now, Jane, I really must – '

'Actually,' she interrupted, 'it wasn't just the essays. I was hoping to see you today because I wanted to ask you something . . .' She hesitated under the sharpness of his gaze, and then rushed on: 'I – we – sort of wondered whether you'd like to come to a Christmas party. It's in college,' she went on hurriedly, 'and a few of us decided to get together and organise something before the end of term. It's a week on Wednesday . . .'

His mouth relaxed, very briefly, into a smile. 'That's a great idea, and it's kind of you to ask me, but I won't be able to come. You see –' He made a play of looking up the date in his diary, ' – that's the day my sons come home for the holidays, and I shall be picking them up from school.' In fact the boys did not finish for Christmas until early the following week, but Jane Bardy was not to know that.

Nick stood up, moved round his desk and paused, extending his arm in the direction of the door. 'Anyway, I wish you every success with the arrangements. Have a – '

'But you don't understand – '

As he turned, she launched herself at him. The next instant her arms were around his neck and her mouth on his. Instinctively, he grasped her arms, but even as furious indignation took hold, he was torn between two forms of violence, the urge to thrust her away, and the desire to clasp her to him. He could so easily have pushed her down on to his study floor and relieved every last ounce of his frustration.

He forced himself not to respond in any way. He stood, rigid, until she drew away of her own accord; and when she did, she rubbed her arms where his fingers had bitten deep, an expression of pain in her eyes.

'I'm sorry,' he said curtly, 'I didn't mean to hurt you.'

'That's all right,' she muttered, hanging her head so that he might not see her embarrassment, 'my fault, anyway . . .'

On a sharp release of breath, he said, 'Perhaps. But I think it's time you put the matches away, Jane, before you burn yourself.'

She was suddenly close to tears. 'God, you really are a shit, aren't you?'

'I would be,' he said grimly, 'if I took you up on your invitation.'

Sniffing, pulling her cardigan across that revealing white blouse, she said accusingly: 'I thought – I honestly thought . . .'

'But I told you two weeks ago that this must stop!'

Christ! he thought furiously, longing for a cigarette to relieve some of his tension, that bloody Hallowe'en party! Would the consequences never be over? He wanted to tell her to get out, leave him alone, he had bigger problems than her sexual fantasies to worry about; but he knew that the fault was his. He had started this ball rolling by acting like a fool at that party. The stupid, utterly incredible thing was, he hadn't even recognised her in that green wig, and under all those vivid bands of make-up. If he had known who she was, he would have stayed well clear. But drunk, having such a good time, it hadn't crossed his mind at first that she might be one of his own students, and that she was out to seduce him. She'd damn nearly succeeded, too. If it hadn't been for Liz Powell, the department's resident feminist, glaring at him as he steered Jane Bardy towards the door, Nick might well have been guilty of far more than a passionate embrace and a few devouring kisses.

What was it Liz Powell had said? 'I should wash your face, Dr Rhodes – it's horribly *green* . . .' She had read the situation in one single disparaging glance, and the contempt in her voice had sobered him at once. At that point, fortunately, his companion had been overtaken by her friends; so Nick had made his excuses and slipped upstairs to the Gents. A little while later, with his face cleaned up, he had run into Giles, who had instantly jumped to the same conclusion as Natasha.

It seemed that no one wanted to believe the truth about that night, including Jane Bardy. He had tried talking to her after Graham Fish's subtle hint, but had been too soft, obviously. She hadn't flung herself on him then, but had evidently expected him to weaken under the force of her misplaced adoration.

The trouble was, he still felt guilty about that night, and loathed having to explain himself. He took a deep breath and moved away from her, retiring behind the safety of his desk. 'Jane, this is a difficult situation – you know it as well as I do.' He indicated the chair she had just vacated. 'Please won't you sit down a moment?'

She did so reluctantly, hiding her face behind a straggling curtain of hair.

'You're a most attractive girl, and I'm sure you realise that. You also know that I'm married, and just about old enough to be your father.' The clichés rolled off his tongue, mocking him with their reality; but if he had been gentle with his explanations before, this time he was curt. 'I've already apologised to you for my behaviour that night of the party, so I won't repeat myself. Except to say that if I'd known you were one of my pupils, it would *never* have happened. Do you understand that?'

'Yes,' she whispered, barely audible.

'Good,' he said briskly, feeling that at last he was making some kind of progress. 'So you must see that you're wasting your time on me – precious time that should be spent on your work. It really isn't so brilliant that you can afford to neglect it.' He paused to let that sink in. 'If I'm to continue as your tutor, Jane – and I'm not at all sure at the moment whether that's a good idea – then we must get back to a more professional relationship. As I said before, this sort of thing simply will not do, and I don't want any more of it. So I suggest,' he added, standing up, 'that we forget that party – at which we *both* had far too much to drink – and put this afternoon behind us. As far as I'm concerned, it's already forgotten. All right?'

With a grudging assent she rose and went to the door. She flicked back her long hair and gave him a tight little smile. 'Thanks for the lecture,' she said bitterly, 'I dare say I'll forgive you one day, but I doubt if I'll ever forget . . .'

It was a dramatic exit line, which part of his mind appreciated even though it made him grind his teeth. Under his breath, as the door closed, Nick gave vent to a string of profanities.

Looking at his watch, he realised that almost half an hour had passed. If he was going to catch Natasha before she left for town, he would have to hurry. Grabbing his coat and briefcase he strode out of his room and almost walked into Haydn Parker. The chaplain was in his usual camouflage of jeans and sweat-shirt, and carrying a bundle of posters.

'Hey, Nick! I was just coming to see you,' he laughed. 'Have you got a minute before you dash off? It's about the charity match on the 14th . . .'

Although Haydn was a few years younger, the two men had played rugby together and were still great friends. Normally, Nick would have been pleased to see him, but today he was anxious to get away. 'Haydn, I'm sorry – can it wait? I'm in a bit of a hurry –'

'Of course, but –' he broke off, glancing keenly at Nick. 'Are you all right? You look a bit –'

Nick laughed, but without amusement. 'No, I'm not all right, to tell you the truth – but I'll survive. Just had a bloody awful morning, and I want to get home. I need to catch Natasha before she goes out.'

A sympathetic, steadying hand gripped his arm, and Nick felt the warmth of it through his jacket. 'Anything wrong at home?'

'No – really, Haydn, everything's fine.' Even as he framed the words, Nick was aware that Haydn knew he was lying. And that was the thing with Haydn – he was a very difficult man to lie to.

'Come and see me, when you've a minute,' the younger man said. Then he grinned. 'We need to talk about this charity match!'

'Okay, will do – later in the week, all right?'

'Fine. You know where I am.'

Sixteen

'ARE YOU ALL right, Mrs – Miss Crayke?'

Startled, Natasha looked up. She had not heard Mrs Bickerstaff come into the office. She pulled her hands from the typewriter and clasped them in her lap. 'Yes – yes, just struggling with this – this article.'

'Well, I knocked twice and you didn't seem to hear.' She set the cup of coffee down on the desk. 'Are you sure you're all right? You look a bit peaky to me – not going down with something, are you?'

'No – no, I don't think so.'

'I've nearly finished now – just the ironing to do. I was going to say that if you wanted to get off into town, you could go now. I can lock up.' She gave Natasha a look of almost motherly concern, then glanced out at the rain. 'But if you don't have to, I wouldn't bother this afternoon . . .'

'Well, yes, you might be right,' Natasha agreed faintly, wishing Mrs Bickerstaff would just go.

'I should leave it. Why don't you get yourself off in the morning, first thing? Then you'll have the day.'

Natasha nodded and said that she would, not bothering to explain about the trip to London. Anyway, she might cancel that. And as for the mythical shopping trip, it was no more than an alibi to cover her visit to Craig Morrison's cottage at Brickhill.

As the door closed, she slumped in her chair for a moment, burying her face in her hands. What on earth was going on? The past few days had been spent in a fever of lustful anticipation; only last night –

Last night –

Her mind sheered away from that, and with a shuddering chill she clutched at the radiator, hugging it until the fit of trembling passed. She was being haunted, not by ghosts and ghouls, but by her own subconscious. It was horrifying to think that her love for Nick, which had been a prime force for almost a decade, was fading so fast that she hardly cared what he thought of her, or what might happen to their marriage. She barely recognised herself; her personality seemed to be fragmenting by the day.

Was this the onset of madness, she asked herself; the beginnings of schizophrenia? She chewed frantically at a fingernail, feeling the knots tighten in her stomach, the bubbling rise of panic. The urge to flee was almost overwhelming.

She flung herself out of the chair and paced the room, up and down, one window to another, as she had been doing at intervals all morning. She had tried to make a start on last week's correspondence, but for a whole hour, every time she turned to the typewriter, there was but a single phrase hammering at the forefront of her mind: BY THE GRACE OF GOD AMEN. Utterly meaningless though it was, she had typed it, in capitals, at the head of innumerable sheets of paper, all of which had been ripped out and destroyed. But it kept coming back. She had even gone into the kitchen to listen to the radio, had looked at the newspaper and talked to Vera Bickerstaff, but as soon as she returned to her office and the typewriter, out came that phrase again: BY THE GRACE OF GOD AMEN.

She heard it, in the same way as she 'heard' dialogue when she was working on a novel; but this was uncanny, far more compulsive than anything she had ever known before. The voice was female, and inevitably the woman sprang to mind, the woman of the dream and of World's End Wood, the woman Natasha had seen so clearly in the doorway of the barn.

That idea brought forth a renewed sense of panic, destroyed hard-won control, and reduced her momentarily to helpless tears. 'Oh, God,' she muttered in unconscious prayer, 'don't let me go mad. Please don't let me go mad . . .'

Feeling like a prisoner, Natasha went to the window which overlooked the village. Opening it, she drew in great breaths of dank winter air, finding solace in the redolence of earth and leaves and rain, in the evidence of habitation just a short distance away. She weighed Craig Morrison against London and Oliver Duffield, and both against the typed sheets on her desk. She felt sick, not at the conflict of interests, but with a sense of revulsion at what she had been planning and contemplating for days. Craig Morrison's eyes; Oliver Duffield's voice; she had been obsessed by both of them, envisaging sexual encounters so lurid that it appalled her to think where such ideas originated. And now this – this voice, this woman, this sense of being manipulated in another fashion . . .

Turning back to her desk, she took a mouthful of coffee and reached for her cigarettes, gazing all the while at the half-written page in the typewriter. It was like reading someone else's work. She was barely conscious of what she had been typing for the past couple of hours, and that first-person narrative was not her style at all.

The sound of a car dragged her attention from the page. She looked up as Nick's Rover pulled into the yard, swishing through the heavy rain. For a moment she stared like someone paralysed, then, as Nick came down the path and into the porch, she snatched at the sheet in the typewriter, pushing it into a drawer with the rest.

She opened the door. Almost thirty feet away, in the hall, he turned to hang up his coat, pausing as he caught her eye. Something in his stance, in the way he looked at her, sent her heart plummeting. She felt that he could see right through her, that he knew what was happening, what she had been doing. Then Mrs Bickerstaff spoke and he turned away; a moment later, with another glance at Natasha, he went upstairs.

She wondered what could have brought him home in the middle of the afternoon, when he had said he would be late. Beset by guilt and alarm she went up to his study. He was standing by the desk, looking out of the window.

'You're home early,' she ventured.

'Yes. I suddenly realised that I'd had enough of this situation, that it was about time we talked.'

He glanced at her and away, staring out at the rain as though it, rather than Natasha, held the answer to his problems. In that faint, watery light, his skin had a greenish tinge. She thought he looked ill, but did not want to acknowledge it. Nor did she want to talk. Her hold on normality seemed possible only if she did not talk, did not attempt any kind of explanation.

Striving for lightness, she said: 'Well, you certainly pick your times, with Mrs Bickerstaff here . . .' But it came out wrongly: even to Natasha, her voice sounded brittle.

'Sod Mrs Bickerstaff,' he said tersely. 'We have to talk, Natasha, and we have to talk *now*.'

'What about?'

He turned then and looked at her, a bright glitter of fury visible behind his eyes. 'What about? My God, after the way you've been behaving in the last few weeks, do you really have the temerity to ask me that? Something's going on that I don't understand, and I think I deserve an explanation!'

She fumbled for the doorknob. 'Don't talk to me like one of your bloody students!'

But as she got the door open he slammed it shut, leaning over her as he held it, his breath coming short and fast. His face was only inches away, and in the half-light she could see her reflection in his eyes.

'You're not my student – not any more. You're my wife. Have you forgotten that, Natasha? *My wife*. Doesn't that mean anything to you?'

Closing his eyes, he leaned his forehead against hers; she could feel his breath on her cheek and the powerful grip of his fingers against her collarbone. She wanted to scream at him to leave her alone.

'Natasha,' he murmured huskily, 'I'm sorry, but I can't live like this . . .'

For a passing moment she was hurt for him, and frightened by what was happening to them both. But, when she could find her voice, some devil of perversity made her say: 'I suppose you're referring to your *conjugal rights*?'

He drew back, his hands falling away. The pain and shock she inflicted seemed to rebound on her, and for a moment they stood apart, scarcely breathing.

Defying her trembling limbs, Natasha grasped the doorknob and turned it. 'We're no longer living in the nineteenth century, Nick – if I don't want to sleep with you, I don't have to. All right?'

He simply stared at her, slowly shaking his head like someone stunned.

'And now, if you'll excuse me,' she said brusquely, 'I was just about to go out. I have some shopping to do.'

After that exchange she had to leave the house, grabbing her things and diving through the rain to the car. She drove badly, shaking with fear and remorse, direction no more than automatic along those winding roads that led towards town.

She passed the road to Brickhill with a shudder of revulsion and drove on, knowing that she could not see Craig Morrison now. The Minster's twin towers were looming above street level before Natasha realised where she was, and it was no more than a reflex which made her turn off to find a parking space. After that the only option was to walk, to make a pretence of the shopping that she had told Nick she needed to do.

Dragging a scarf over her hair, Natasha dodged a stream of oncoming traffic and entered the heart of the city through Monk Bar. Although she tried to ignore the rain, the cars splashing past, and pedestrians bumping by with umbrellas, she felt wounded and vulnerable; when a woman with a child in a buggy tutted and made a performance of avoiding her, Natasha could have burst into tears on the spot.

With a muttered apology she hurried on, her misery accentuated by the glow of windows decorated for Christmas, the scent of oranges from a street-stall, and spices from the doorway of a herbalist's. It was a time of year she had always loved, and she had loved it best in York, where there were no garish decorations, only the brilliance of tiny shop-windows in medieval streets, and Christmas trees above the doorways. A wave of nostalgia swept over her, as strong as the desire for home from abroad. She had missed York, missed it dreadfully, and was tempted to believe that all her current ills were to be blamed on that decision of Nick's to move away.

She walked on, glancing up and around in spite of the rain, until the smell of freshly ground coffee slowed her steps and took her into an old-fashioned, bow-fronted shop which had a café upstairs. It was busy, but by the window there was a seat at a smoking table, and with relief Natasha removed her wet coat and lit a cigarette. She was cold and her hands were shaking, and a woman nearby let her glance linger with curiosity before returning to her perusal of the menu. Natasha turned to the window, from which she could look down on the shoppers in Stonegate, the passing raincoats and umbrellas, the little children in boots and sou'westers, couples pausing to look at the array of gifts in shops across the way.

The buildings here were steep-gabled and timber-framed, with leaded lights in the upper windows; above the doorway of one shop hung a great bible, while squatting beneath the jettied eaves of the shop next door was the bright-red figure of a devil. Ancient signs from the days before people could read: a bookseller's and a printer's. To Natasha's eyes, however, they seemed oddly appropriate to the moment. Good and evil, truth and lies, love and lust; but in life, it seemed, those sins and virtues were never as clear as the words that named them.

Under which sign, she wondered, had Nick kissed her for the first time? It had to be one or the other, since the doorway into which they had retreated was facing her now.

It seemed ironic that she should be reminded of it today, although when she cast her mind back she remembered that they had had an argument then. Well, not strictly an argument, since in those days she had been in no position to dispute his opinions. It was simply that he had managed to upset her, and very seriously, over what she intended to do once she had her degree. He wanted her to stay on, felt she could make her mark as an academic, but Natasha had never been ambitious in that direction. For her, university had been a means of escape, not an end in itself.

When she finally admitted to him that she wanted to be a novelist, he had been appalled. '*Fiction*?' he had demanded, as though the very word was a disease, 'you want to write *fiction*?' She could hear that tone now, still see the darkening glance, the sheer disbelief as he began to remonstrate. And he had been far from convinced when she said she would work in journalism in order to keep herself and gain experience; in fact he had smiled that slow smile of his and explained that failed writers were ten a penny, that it was a craft more difficult to master than most people realised. 'Fleet Street, my dear, is full of aspiring novelists; and so are the English departments of most universities. Ask Giles Crowther – he'll tell you.'

But she had not wanted Giles's opinion, she had hoped for Nick's backing and approval. The lack of it, the implication that she was aiming for the moon, had been very distressing. A long time afterwards, it had been the goad she used to keep herself going, part of her determination to prove that she could do it. To prove to *him* that she could do it.

And she had. To give him credit, he had needed no prompting to apologise, and his admiration of her achievement was quite unstinted. But at the time, when his encouragement was so important, Nick had been busy mapping out another future for his protégée, and his disappointment was all too clear. Looking back, it was hard to say which had wounded her most: his disparagement of her precious dreams, or the awareness that she had let him down, revealed herself as ordinary and unoriginal, not worthy of his interest.

She managed to avoid him for the best part of a week, but then he came looking for her, in his eyes a mixture of contrition and exasperation. 'You know,' he said, 'you're going to have to do better than this. Do you think a reporter from the *Mirror*, or even the *Guardian*, is going to run off in a sulk just because somebody says he doesn't like what she's doing? Hmm?'

And then she had known she was forgiven, because he had asked her out that evening for a drink and a meal. The invitation was unusual. Sometimes she had lunch with him, followed by a browse round the bookshops, and she often saw him in the pub for a while after college; but he spent his evenings at home. She had wondered whether his wife was away for a few days, and recalled taking an age over the decision of what to wear. In the end, because it was summer and the evening was warm she had decided to wear her favourite dress – actually her only dress – which was in a light, silky material, and had a fashionably tattered hemline. It was black, of course. In those days just about everything she owned was black; even her naturally dark hair was dyed.

Amused by the memory, Natasha smiled. Black hair, black dress, a new pair of fine black stockings, and a pair of high stiletto heels she had bought, ridiculously cheap, from a nearly-new shop. The only serious concession she had made to Nick was in her hair and make-up. Although she had toned things down considerably during the previous few months, that evening she felt she had managed to achieve the perfect balance between drama and subtlety. Even her flatmates stood back and told her she looked great.

Nick was obviously of the same mind. Although he made no more than a couple of references to the way she looked, Natasha could see the approval in his eyes, hear it in his voice, and the masculine admiration went to her head a little. For the first time she was conscious of being on an equal footing, and for some reason that evening was not afraid of making a fool of herself. To begin with, Nick even seemed a little in awe of her; he kept looking at her and smiling, and then looking away again. But after a glass or two of wine he relaxed, and they talked about all kinds of things, most of them light and inconsequential, certainly nothing as serious as her future. He laughed a lot too, and she remembered that he'd suddenly seemed much closer to her in age. With the barriers down, Natasha found herself telling him how much he had scared her when she first knew him, how utterly conventional and forbidding he had been. They had both laughed at that, but then he raised his glass to her and said, 'All part of the image, Natasha – I hide behind it, just like you do.'

At the time she had thought that he was joking. Now she knew otherwise. There was still so much of him she did not know, and yet that evening she had felt quite secure, imagining she knew him very well indeed.

He was in good spirits, his green eyes smiling as he looked at her. They finished their meal and the last of the wine in an atmosphere almost of celebration, and the Italian waiters, sensing the aura of romance more keenly than she did herself, made a fuss of her as Nick paid the bill.

Once they were outside, he took her hand and squeezed it. 'You're so lovely,' he said impulsively, 'I just wish I were ten years younger and starting all over again.'

In genuine astonishment, she laughed. 'But why?' she asked, pausing to look up at him. 'You have so *much* . . .'

'I haven't got you, though, have I?' He said it so softly, she was not sure whether he was serious or joking or even slightly drunk. He stood quite still for a moment, gazing at her, and she saw that, drunk or not, he was very serious.

'But – '

'Yes, *but* . . .' He shrugged and smiled and tugged at her hand. 'Never mind. Come on, I'll walk you home.'

He said nothing more until they were well clear of the restaurant, but she was aware of his breathing, as sharp as her own, punctuated by the staccato tapping of her high heels. In the narrow, shadowed reaches of Stonegate, he suddenly said: 'It's as well I'm not driving, I've had too much to drink. Do you want to go straight home, or would you rather walk for a while?'

Thinking of the friends she shared with, Natasha did not want to ask him in for coffee, but on the other hand, her flat was only minutes away, and she did not want to cut the evening short. 'I'd be glad to walk,' she said, 'but can we go a little slower? These shoes – '

'Oh, of course – I'm sorry.' He stopped – just there, across the street – and looked down at her black shoes with the pointed toes and silly, three-inch heels. And then his glance travelled up, slowly, taking in the shape of her legs and her slender figure with its small breasts and too-long neck. Meeting her eyes, moving closer, he said: 'I'd forgotten about your shoes . . .'

They made her taller, and easier to kiss.

She remembered that moment as though it were yesterday, the smooth fabric of his shirt and the silkiness of his hair as she placed her hands, tentatively, around his neck. She had never been so close to him before, hardly ever touched him except accidentally, and the difference between imagination and reality surprised her so much, she barely had time to notice the first light touch of his lips. His flesh was so much firmer than she had imagined, his arms and shoulders quite solid in comparison to her own soft pliability; and as he held her close, she could feel the rapid beating of his heart, feel the warmth of his breath against her cheek.

It came to her then that this was real, that this was her tutor, Dr Nicholas Rhodes, the man she had been so terrified of in the beginning, and had worshipped so romantically ever since; and she was in his arms and he was kissing her . . .

The next moment, she was very much afraid that in her surprise she had missed the best part of the experience, and that it might not be repeated. When he drew back to look at her, he smiled ruefully at the expression on her face.

'Oh, dear,' he murmured, 'am I so out of practice? Then for heaven's sake come here, and let me kiss you properly.'

And in the shelter of that deep, unlit doorway across the road, he had done just that, with a tender, persuasive sensuality that made her head spin, that was unlike anything she had ever experienced before. Here was no rough force, no quick, hot stabbing of a repulsive tongue, or the slavering of a wet mouth against her face while she struggled to extricate herself from an unpleasant and unwanted situation. This man touched her as though she were infinitely precious to him, and with his fingertips traced the soft fullness of her mouth before he kissed it. The taste and smell and feel of him were so good she wanted it to go on for ever.

How long they stood there, in that dark little doorway, she had no idea. Quite a while, she suspected, since her lips were bruised and burning, her body on fire, as he must have known, before they parted. He seemed, she thought, as shaken by the experience as she was herself; certainly his hands were unsteady as he lit a couple of cigarettes, and when he spoke his voice was husky. With no apology or explanation, he simply said that he must take her home.

The street, which had been deserted, was suddenly echoing

with voices and laughter; people leaving the Olde Starre and the Punchbowl were heading towards them. Nick slipped his arm around her shoulders and drew her close beside him, apparently without a care for who might see them together. In that brief moment she was intensely happy; loved and in love, she had a sense of having joined the human race at last. Nothing else mattered.

It mattered later, of course, because that euphoric feeling did not last, doubts crept in, huge enormous doubts that centred on his wife and children, and the life he shared with them.

In retrospect, she could see how unprepared she was for the dizzying emotions of a sexual relationship, especially with a man of Nick's age and experience. Academically speaking, she might have been clever and perceptive, but she was emotionally immature, she had no secure base from which to conduct this new relationship, and nothing to fall back on when it became too much for her, which it very quickly did. She was alone and the changes scared her; Nick scared her sometimes, and not just in the chances he took. It was the power he had over her, the fact that her own will was so subservient to his; and once they had been to bed together, it seemed that sex was all he wanted, he could not get enough of it, could not get enough of her.

He never realised how guilty she felt afterwards, how often she thought about his wife.

And he never knew how much she worried about him being in the flat. Her friends knew, of course they did, he was there so often during the day; she worried about what they might say, and to whom they might say it.

But in spite of that, she loved him. So much, it was unbearable. Waiting to see him, she was like a junkie waiting for the next fix, and hating herself because of it. The summer was coming, the long, long summer, during which she had to go home, find a job, while Nick went on holiday with his family, took a research trip to France, immersed himself in his work. He was talking about taking her to France with him, but that was pie-in-the-sky, there was no way she could have gone.

Towards the end of term, he organised an informal lunch at

his home, for the Hesketh students who had been in his care, and for those who, like Natasha, had been on that year's courses. It was something that he'd always done, and he was keen for her to attend, overriding all her objections until she promised to be there. It was a mistake, of course, but although she had known that beforehand, Natasha was unprepared for the agony of seeing him in his home surroundings.

The house was part of an early Victorian terrace near the river, with light, airy rooms and a beautiful garden. There were walls full of books and comfortable furniture, and the evidence of children in toys and pictures and scribbled drawings. In different circumstances, Natasha would have loved it, but that Sunday her vision was clouded by envy and a sense of inadequacy. How could she compete with that? It was impossible, and his wife merely reinforced that awareness. She was tall and well-built, with good features and long, red, curly hair.

Natasha had met her before on a couple of occasions, and had disliked her on sight, long before she had much to do with Nick. Nevertheless, there was no denying her physical attributes and, with a wife like that, Natasha could not help wondering what on earth Nick saw in her. With no chance of competing, she had stuck to jeans and a T-shirt, and had spiked her hair in a gesture of defiance. At least she blended in with the other students, smoking too much, drinking too much, eating little and saying less. Three solid hours in which she prayed to be ignored and overlooked, although Nick, in his role of genial host, did neither. He talked to all his guests, he played with his children, he even carried one of them in his arms while he talked to her, and, under the pretext of finding a book she had asked about, showed her his study.

He sent the little boy out and asked what was wrong; he even kissed her. It was unbearable. Soon after that she left under cover of other departures, smiling her thanks to his wife, avoiding his eyes, hating him so much she was almost blind with it.

Two days later she ended the affair. Harshly, even cruelly, but that was only because she distrusted herself to end it effectively in any other way. At the time she had thought that a clean break would be better than that agonising see-saw of pleasure and pain; but she was wrong. It hurt more than anything she had ever done, before or since, and only the fact that it was the end of the university year, with no opportunity for going back on the decision, enabled her to keep to it.

That summer had seemed endless. She would never forget the long days, the sticky heat, the sick sense of loneliness; nor that job in the burger bar. Still, all these years later, the smell of fast food cooking could bring back those unwanted memories on a surge of nausea.

The acute stage passed eventually, until, like someone with arthritis, she grew used to it. The pain was no longer life-threatening, just a nagging limitation. She gained her degree the following year, an adequate one, not brilliant, and a couple of years after that, in an attempt to cure herself of a recurrent sense of longing, she had embarked upon her first novel. It was as much about this city and university life as it was the story of an innocent and unworldly student away from home for the first time. Thinking about it now, remembering the poky room in which it had been written, the tough environment in which she had worked as a junior reporter, Natasha thought she should have been glad of the home she had now. But she was not. That sense of peace had been seriously disturbed; quietness had become a blanket of isolation; she was in danger of losing her hold on reality.

Seventeen

ALONE IN THE house after Mrs Bickerstaff had gone, Nick sat at his desk, staring at the lamp's reflection in the windowpane. Every few seconds, clusters of raindrops gathered, sliding down the glass like illuminated tears.

His body felt as though he had just played a vicious game of rugby, as though it had been repeatedly kicked and trampled on. There was, however, no alleviating sense of satisfaction at a game well played, and no one with whom to commiserate after being soundly beaten. And in this game, apparently, there were no rules and no referees.

Her callousness had stunned him, and with a return of feeling he still had to keep reminding himself that she really had said those words, and in such a way that he could not mistake their meaning. His wife had just made it very clear that she did not desire him, had no wish to sleep with him, and, presumably, no longer cared.

Why? Had he really hurt her enough to deserve that?

The questions went round and round in his head, battering at sense of *déjà vu*, that feeling that he had been in this position before. What was it she had said then, that day in his office? He could not remember the context – shock had taken care of that – but he recalled one word very clearly, simply because it was so old-fashioned, so unexpected from a girl of her generation. *Besmirched*, that was it; something about not loving him, and feeling besmirched by their relationship. And she had delivered it with such precision that there had been no doubting that that was exactly how she felt.

Then, and now. Such pain. Why? For God's sake, what was the matter with her? Was she mad? Had she decided that work and marriage did not mix after all, or had she met someone else? That thought made him feel slightly sick, but then he considered it logically, and shook his head. It was, after all, unlikely. With whom would she have an affair? She never went anywhere, didn't know anyone locally, and anyway, Natasha was a woman who lived for her work. An affair, he decided with an ironic twist of the lips, would be regarded as too much of a distraction.

But whatever the cause, he was destined to remain in the dark until she chose to enlighten him. That realisation made him angry, and anger alleviated some of his pain. She must please herself, he thought bitterly, and no doubt would; but in the meantime she would find that his patience was not endless, and that he had no intention of pandering to any more nonsense. It was time she grew up, stopped being such a child. And, if she was indeed so heartily sick of him and their marriage, let her do the leaving. He would stay.

Fortified by that decision, he took another cigarette from the packet he'd found downstairs, and lit it with a sense of defiance. He drew the smoke into his lungs, enjoying the taste, the smell, the blessed release from tension that cigarettes provided.

It was almost half-past four. If he tried Giles's number, he might just catch him. What he needed now was a hard game of squash; and afterwards, a drink.

Apart from the porch light, everything was in darkness when Natasha returned, with no sign of Nick's car in the barn. For a moment she almost panicked, wondering whether he'd left for good; then, remembering that there had been a mention of Giles that morning, her misery hardened into painful cynicism.

'You bastard,' she muttered, staring at the empty, rain-lashed house, 'you don't give a damn, do you?'

She sat there for a moment, with the Peugeot's engine running, wondering what to do. It was with something of a shock that she realised she was actually nervous about entering the house on her own; and that she was even more reluctant to park the car in the dark and empty barn. For a moment she even considered driving back to York to ask Fay if she could have a bed for the night; but that seemed so peculiarly defeatist that she felt ashamed. In the end she reached a compromise, left the car to the mercy of the weather and dashed through the rain to the house.

Instantly it seemed her damp clothes were wet again; she was shivering by the time she opened the door. Colette came out to greet her, sniffed the air, and then skipped off into the darkness. Natasha called her back, but she had already disappeared. 'Oh, bugger you then!' She closed and locked the porch.

It was warm in the kitchen, wonderfully so. Stripping off her outer clothes, Natasha set the kettle to boil and looked in the fridge for something to eat. She didn't feel like cooking, but there were plenty of eggs and some cheese, so she whipped up an omelette and ate it with a stack of bread and butter while sitting in her dressing-gown in front of the stove. After that, she felt considerably restored. Recalling the lurching, veering emotions of the day, she wondered whether the violence was not an over-reaction to recent stress and a particularly bad night. It was comforting to think that she might have been imagining much of it.

But at nine o'clock, bored with the television, she began to feel unsettled again. She thought about having an early night, and started to look for something to read; then she remembered the story, that collection of typed pages that she had shoved into her desk drawer, unread.

There was a surprising number of them, Natasha realised as she shuffled them into order. Usually, she was a slow, painstaking worker, but this seemed to have rattled out of the typewriter with no effort at all.

BY THE GRACE OF GOD AMEN: strange words, part entreaty, part-commendation, whose significance was still unclear . . .

But it was chilly now in the office. She took the sheaf of papers into the kitchen, and lit a cigarette as she began to read.

I was baptised Sarah Mary Kirkham at All Saints Hammerford, on the River Nidd, two days before Christmas in the year of Our Lord 1695.

My parents had been childless for nigh on a score of years, so my birth astonished everyone, my mother being over forty at the time and so sick with me it was feared she was dying. No one suspected a child, but I was born at last after thirty hours' labour, to confound doctors and family alike.

Joy was followed by grief, since my mother died anyway, being too old to withstand the birth after all those barren years. My baptism was preceded by a funeral, but I was too young to know such things, and never having had a mother did not unduly miss her.

My father grieved, I suspect, and showed a tear in his eye whenever he spoke of my mother, but he was sanguine by nature, a man who looked for the good in life and generally managed to find it. By the time I was old enough to understand, his sadness had largely been replaced by joy of a child. That I was female may have been a disappointment, but he never said so, and I was fussed and petted as only a daughter can be – an only daughter, at that!

But if he indulged my female whims, my father also taught me well. I must learn to read and write, to figure accounts, to ride a horse and master servants. In the house I took my lessons from the cook, and for at least part of every day accompanied my father on his rounds.

The house, and most of the land we farmed, was held in tenancy from the lord of the manor, a distant, often absent man, whose interests lay more in buying and selling than in the time-honoured tradition of farming. Our landlord's father had declared for Parliament during the Civil War, which did not make him popular locally, but explained – or so my father said – his lack of interest in the land. He cared about its productivity only in terms of the wealth it provided, and, so long as his rents were paid, was happy to leave it in other hands.

By contrast, my father was a farmer born and bred, as eager to see his rented acres produce good crops as he was his own land in an adjacent parish. Some of that had come to him through his own family, some through marriage to my mother; yet more had been acquired in the intervening years. All in all he was middling wealthy, respected for his careful husbandry as well as his invariable good humour, and a welcome guest at most of the tables in the neighbourhood.

At fourteen years of age I was still sufficiently a child to regard my father as the centre of the universe. If I thought of the future at all, I suppose it was to imagine us going on much as we were, happy, companionable, planning the next season's work, calculating our revenues, discussing newsletters as they came, and visiting our friends and relations. It never occurred to me that my father was growing older, that he must think and plan for my future, to secure what he had acquired in the hands of an honest and reliable son-in-law . . .

Despite my efforts to ignore the fact, I was growing up. Tall for my age, angular in build, I had rarely suffered a day's illness in my life. I prided myself on my ability to give a hand in the fields when help was needed, as well as mastering the usual domestic skills in dairy and stillroom. My sewing and weaving perhaps left room for improvement, but I knew my herbs and could provide a fine meal even in the depths of winter.

If my days were full from dawn to dusk, leaving small time for reflection, the work was not always hard, and we had our entertainments. In the summer of 1710, we were invited to the wedding of my youngest cousin, Elizabeth Piper, at Holy Trinity Goodramgate, in the city of York. In company with a groom, we travelled the eight miles on horseback a couple of days before, our finery carried behind on a pack-horse. My father had purchased a new coat and breeches, and wore his best full-bottomed wig, while I had a new petticoat and bodice, made for me by Widow Dennison, one of our neighbours in Hammerford.

I was excited, not least by the new clothes. The outfit made me feel grown-up, even though I was in awe of the fine silk and satin and wondered how I should manage to eat in the tight bodice. Widow Dennison had thought to show off my figure to advantage, but in truth it was as flat and unyielding as a boy's, while the narrow, pointed stomacher had the effect of making me look thinner than ever, despite the soft yellow ribbons. But my discomfort was less than the novelty of the occasion and my pleasure at spending three nights with my cousins.

Aunt Margaret Piper was my father's sister, essentially kind if something of a bustling busybody. She it was who tutted and sighed next morning over my rough hands, the broken nails and freckled brown skin, and my wiry hair, bleached yellow by the sun.

'So unfashionable,' she declared with a sigh, trying to cover my hair with a piece of lace from her clothes-press. 'She's no beauty, Jack,' she muttered to my father, 'and if you let her work in the fields, she'll end up looking like a labourer! It'll not be long before she's thinking of marriage herself, and a man likes something to cuddle in bed, not a bag of skin and bone!'

My father laughed his hearty laugh, but as the implication dawned, I felt myself blush to the roots of my unfashionable hair. Aunt Margaret was plump and deep-bosomed, with two fine sons and three daughters living, so I presumed she knew these things. Evidently, she expected me to marry, and within the next year or two.

On impulse, I said my looks did not matter, that I would not marry, but stay with my father and help him run the farm.

'Mercy, child, but you won't! There's no need for you to be an old maid, not with your prospects. You'll marry and have children of your own, as all good women should.'

She hugged me and patted my shoulder, but I caught the look she gave my father and felt crushed by it. She seemed to be saying that I was too thin, too plain, and that

I was attractive only for the wealth that would come to me on my father's death.

And that was not to be thought of. Struggling free, I rushed to my father's side and demanded to know who would look after him if I should marry and leave home.

Aunt Margaret said he might marry again if he wished, but while my father protested, laughing, he did say that he would be content with our servants, and was sure he would want for little. He tried to reassure me by saying that when the time came he was sure I would marry well, to a man who would love me for myself, but I was in no mood to believe him.

Indeed, I felt intolerably let down, as though even my father had betrayed me. It spoiled my enjoyment of the wedding, made me prickly with everyone, and ruined what should have been a happy and exciting day. Even my fine new clothes irked me. They made me fidget, yet aided the illusion that I was too old to be comforted. My cousins saw my sour face and left me to sulk. The only person who took much notice of me at the wedding breakfast was a married cousin on my Uncle Piper's side of the family, a young woman of eighteen or twenty, who seemed as much in need of a quiet corner as myself. Her name was Caroline Stalwell, a dainty creature as fragile and pretty as I was plain and robust.

After we had been talking a little while, discussing the bride and groom and where they were to live, Caroline confided in me that she had been married just over a year, and was expecting a child in the fall.

I was surprised, and looked at her more keenly. The month was June, and there seemed little to show for her condition. Caroline Stalwell was not like the farm-girls, stout and big-bellied; but there again, she was a lady, and they were not. I imagined that must make a difference. I asked after her husband, and it chanced that when he was pointed out to me, Richard Stalwell was in conversation with my father. I was not aware that they had met before, yet they were talking like old friends.

'No doubt discussing pigs and heifers,' Caroline remarked.

'But that's the way of farmers,' I declared, surprised by her tone. 'They must worry the subject – their lives depend on it.'

She laughed at that, and tapped my hand. 'Ah – I perceive you to be a farmer's daughter, and more fortunate than I, since I know nothing of crops and cattle! I fear poor Richard finds me ignorant,' she admitted a moment later, though without much apparent regret. 'But he is tender towards me, I will say that . . .'

Her secret smile, and the way she placed a hand over her stomach, made me blush and look away, although I could not have said why at the time. As ill-luck would have it, I glanced towards her husband, inadvertently caught his eye and felt my blush turn to crimson. He was very handsome, and with the bluest eyes I ever saw . . .

Well, Natasha thought, it seemed innocuous enough, the beginnings of an historical romance perhaps, or even something a little spicier. Not really her sort of thing, and certainly not written in her usual style, but it was nothing to get worked-up about. Her earlier fears seemed suddenly misplaced, exaggerated, and she wondered why she had felt so alarmed. This story could hardly be billed as *a new and exciting contemporary novel* – which was how the *The English Lesson* had been marketed – but did that matter? For her it was different and intriguing, and she suddenly wanted to know where it was going.

As a writer, she reflected, it was something of a novelty to be so much in the dark.

Natasha was busy typing, so deep in the story of Sarah Mary Kirkham that the shrill summons of the telephone came as a shock. Jerked back to reality, for a moment she hardly knew where she was; with her heart pounding like a steam-hammer, she grabbed at the phone to silence it. It took her a moment to answer.

'Yes?'

It was Giles and he was drunk, she could tell from the careful way he enunciated his words. Out of the verbiage, she gathered that Nick was also drunk. 'He's in that wonderfully mellow state, you see – not inebriated, no, but not *strictly* in a condition to drive. You know how *particular* the police can be, nowadays . . .'

'Yes, Giles, I do. You mean Nick's pissed, and he's staying at your place tonight.'

He sounded pained. 'Natasha, darling, don't be like that – '

'Well, Giles, it's difficult not to be, at this time of night. But anyway,' she added, relenting a little, 'thanks for letting me know.'

'Just a moment – just a moment –' He turned from the phone, and she heard the muffled murmur of voices. 'He wants me to say that he's sorry – sorry about the morning and – and your lift into town . . .'

With a little dart of alarm, Natasha realised that she had completely forgotten that luncheon date with Oliver Duffield. She would have to phone, make some excuse, first thing. 'It's all right, Giles – tell him it doesn't matter. I'm not going to London, after all.'

No, she thought, returning to the typewriter, she would not be going to London. There were more important things to do.

Eighteen

COFFEE AND aspirins staved off the worst of Nick's hangover, but did nothing to alleviate the cause of his misery. The only cure for that, he decided stoically, was work. For the time being he could not bear to think about Natasha, or the ramifications of yesterday's argument; instead, he set his mind to other problems.

At lunchtime, pondering on Reynald de Briec, the builder of the castle at Brickhill, and his possible connection with Reynard, the legendary hound, Nick reached a decision. The other day he had been hesitant about calling Sally Armitage; today he told himself that he was being over-delicate, that he needed to explore every avenue if he was to get at the truth. With that in mind, he rang the museum of country life at Ghylldale, just outside Whitby.

It was a small place, staffed mainly by volunteers, but no less significant for all that. As he waited for the curator to come to the phone, he wondered what his reception would be.

'Sally? It's Nick Rhodes . . . Yes, I know, it's been a long time – how are you?' He grinned at her sardonic response, a grin which broadened as the exchange between them became bantering. 'Yes, I know I only call you when I want something, and I'm sorry for that . . . No, really, I'm desperate for information, and it's much more your field than mine. Folk tales, legends, that sort of thing . . .'

He outlined the facts, such as they were, and could tell at once that he had caught her interest. She was able to provide a potentially helpful name and telephone number, and promised to look out for anything further. After that, the conversation became more personal, and she demanded to know why he had not been up to Ghylldale since her appointment as curator. She had, she said, made a lot of changes, and it was just the place for a day out with his sons.

Nick laughingly promised to bring them during the Christmas holidays, and, as he said goodbye, realised that it would make a change for him too. It would be good to see Sally, she was humorous and forthright, possibly a little too frank at times, but she could always make him laugh.

He retained an image of her in his mind: well-built and capable, thick fair hair braided out of the way while she tinkered with an ancient tractor engine, or fought her way through a collection of rusty farm implements. They had met years ago, while she was working at the Castle Museum, but he had always felt that she was wasted there. A curious mix of intellect and physical competence, she was the sort of woman who loved getting her hands dirty, who could have worked as a garage mechanic while running an extremely successful chain of filling stations on the side. Certainly, during the period of their relationship five years ago, his car had never been so well looked after.

There remained in him a fondness for her, since she had helped him through a difficult period of his life; but once he ceased to be a lame dog, the relationship foundered. He could not be sure whose fault it was, or whether there had been a fault at all. It seemed, looking back, more a question of having answered each other's needs for a while, and once that time was over . . .

But they had parted without recriminations, and for that he would always be thankful. He was grateful too for the information she had given him. Dr Betty Wills – a retired *medical* doctor, Sally had been quick to point out – sometimes did lectures for the WEA on folklore, myths and legends, but the subject was more of an obsession than a hobby.

'She's a bit odd,' Sally had said, 'comes here sometimes to root through our library. I keep dropping huge hints that we could do with someone to catalogue the collection, but she doesn't take on, in spite of being more *au fait* with it than anybody else . . .'

Ah, well, he thought, odd or not, she was worth trying.

He dialled the number Sally had given him, and it rang a while before being answered. At first he thought that young, light voice belonged to someone else; but no, it was Dr Wills, who informed him a moment later that they had met, three or four years previously, at a university function. For a second he wondered whether to lie and say he remembered, but then admitted he did not, and went on, quickly, to state the reasons for his call.

There was a short pause. At first she said she didn't think she knew anything about spectral hounds, but then went on to mention the legend of Prince Rupert's poodle, killed during the Civil War battle of Marston Moor. But Nick knew all about that, and didn't believe it anyway.

'Well, no,' he said patiently, 'Marston Moor's virtually the other side of York. I was thinking more of the area around Sheriff Whenby. You haven't heard anything about spectral hounds in that area?'

Again there was that hesitation. Nick wondered whether it was a case of knowing nothing at all, or knowing a lot and being very reluctant to share it.

'Well, I'm not sure,' that light, feminine voice said in his ear. 'Not sure it can be called folklore, that is. I did come across a story to do with Brickhill, but I think it had ceased to be common knowledge by the time it was recorded – about 1800, or perhaps a little later . . .'

Ah, he thought, that's more like it. He glanced at his watch: he had a lecture very shortly. 'That sounds promising, Dr Wills,' he said warmly. 'Do you think we might meet – perhaps over lunch one day soon – and have a longer talk about this?'

She was slow to agree, but eventually said that she had to return some books to the university library, and perhaps they could meet then?

Pleased by that, Nick said he looked forward to it. Feeling rather better than he had first thing that morning, he gathered up his notes for his lecture on field systems, and hurried downstairs.

On the way home he suddenly felt exhausted, and found himself hoping that Natasha would not be sitting at home nursing a barrage of grievances about last night. All he wanted to do was have something to eat and go to bed; if she had anything to say, he hoped she would leave it until tomorrow.

His wishes were granted. She was quiet but perfectly civil; she cooked dinner for them both, and, when he ventured to ask why she had changed her mind about going to London, she said simply that she had not been in the mood for London. The business could be postponed, or discussed over the phone.

Contrary to his expectations, Nick was neither pleased nor relieved by that studied politeness. It seemed unnatural. He even wished, irrationally, that she would berate him, criticise him for his shortcomings as a husband, tell him, for God's sake, what was so wrong that she couldn't sleep with him.

The questions plagued him. He was so tense that a nerve started twitching below his eye and would not stop; he put a finger over it, but still it leapt. After rubbing it for a while, he said quietly: 'Do you want to talk?'

She sighed and put down the magazine she was reading. 'Not just now. I'm too tired, I didn't sleep much last night.'

'Neither did I.'

'But for different reasons, I imagine,' she countered sharply.

He gave up and went to bed.

The next morning, in pursuit of necessary diversions, he telephoned the Borthwick Institute for an appointment to view the parish registers for Brickhill. Although he was also tempted to ask for the will indices for Denton, he resisted it. Just checking the names of all those who had been resident in Denton at the time of death, and had been wealthy enough or important enough to leave a will, would take him a couple of days at least, and at the moment he did not have that kind of time at his disposal. Besides, the house could prove to be a major project, and it was worth doing well. For the time being there was enough to occupy him in this matter of Toby's dog and its possible connection with Reynald de Briec.

After lunch he drove into town, parked his car and walked to the fifteenth-century building on Peasholme Green that housed the Institute of Historical Research. Before the Reformation, St Anthony's Hall had been a hospital for the poor and aged; since then it had been variously an arsenal, a workhouse, a prison and a woollen mill, and in more recent times had functioned as a school for poor boys. The entrance hall, with its polished tiles and worn stone steps, always reminded Nick of his own schooldays, even though his school had educated the sons and daughters of what would now be termed middle management. Nevertheless, quite a few from the working classes, including himself, had managed to dazzle the examiners sufficiently to obtain entrance. He smiled wryly, recalling the ambivalent relationship he had enjoyed with school, that awareness of being different, of not quite fitting in, which had spurred him to succeed, to prove that he could be just as good as the rest, if not better.

But as he passed onwards and upwards – rather as he had through life – that awareness faded. The upper floor of the Borthwick Institute was completely different; with soaring roof-beams and broad, creaking oak boards, the character was that of a medieval hall, the atmosphere as hushed as a library in an ancient monastic house.

It would have been more fitting, Nick felt, to have been able to browse through the vellum pages of the original registers, enjoying that sense of direct contact with the past. He would, of course, have taken hours over the task, making notes on the comments scrawled in the margins, absorbing small, irrelevant details recorded more than three hundred years before. Instead, he was faced with the cold, technical efficiency of a viewing screen and a reel of photographic evidence. Microfilm offered no temptations, esoteric or otherwise, but it fulfilled its functions of protecting the original manuscripts, and it was quick. Nick loathed it.

Nevertheless, his sense of distaste was overcome by the satisfaction of discovering that the parish registers proper for Brickhill, not merely the bishop's transcripts, had survived for the period immediately prior to the Civil War. During those chaotic years, when records were inadequately kept, or even abandoned altogether, the registers for many churches had been destroyed by excesses of Puritan zeal; but those for Brickhill must have been hidden, or respected, or simply ignored.

Winding the film forward to 1635, the year of that reported incident in Beauchamp's *History*, Nick concentrated upon the cramped and spidery handwriting. There was, however, nothing beyond the usual offices of baptism, marriage and burial, no comments or asides. He was seized by irrational disappointment, a feeling that he had been conned by Beauchamp and deliberately led astray. He sat for a moment, staring at the screen, and then wound the film back to the very beginning of the register, finding there a note of tithes due to the rector, scribbled in shortened form and dated 1662. Heartened again, he wound the film forward, to the very end of the register this time, which, according to the details on the box, continued to 1688, after the inevitable gap for the Civil War, from 1643 to 1656.

He found three blank folios and then felt a surge of excitement. On the last endpaper were a series of entries, headed: *Tithes wch are owed to mee A.D.1636*. A later subheading read: *List of Papish recusantes in ye Parrishe in ye year 1662*, and beneath that, faint but discernible, and partly overwritten by that list of names, he found:

Martinmas A.D.1635

Itm: *that ye dore keys be changed.*

Itm: *that Goodye Tesseyman be admonyshed fr. railinge at the clerk in seruice times.*

Itm: *that in diuine seruice Master Yokham being to preche, a grete blacke dog cam in at ye chancel and ran through ye body of ye chirch and escap owre handes so that some sayd the divil hisself did not byde the scriptures and Master Yokham sayth, some poor puritan was losed upon ye earth for a tyme, and made light of mens fears. This mch I saw and heerd, and set it down herein.*

Jn. Cartwrighte
Rector's Warden
1635

Nick smiled, grimly, If this was the bare bones of the story in Beauchamp, then for once it would seem that the popular press of the time had barely exaggerated. In pensive mood he copied it down, word for word, spelling for spelling; then he rewound the film, boxed it, and returned to the campus.

At the end of the week, very much to his surprise, there was a letter waiting for Nick in the departmental office. It was from his old friend David, the medievalist. Opening it in his own room, Nick's smile broadened as his eyes travelled down the page.

> *Dear Nick,*
>
> *It was good to hear from you, I've been wondering how you were – good, I presume, since you didn't say otherwise!*
>
> *Your letter intrigued me – an unusual request from you – and since I guessed you wanted an answer quickly, here we are. I've looked at everything I have here, and at some volumes in the library. There isn't much about Reynald de Briec, but I give you the sum of it.*
>
> *He held land of the Honour of Mowbray at about the time Stephen ascended the throne, in 1135. He came from Normandy, where his father had land held directly of the dukes, but he was rather a minor figure there. He acquired various manors from the Mowbrays, all of which they held of the crown as tenants in chief. But in 1139 Reynald acquired land south of Deynton Sub Galtris from the Paynels of Drax, and made it his principal residence as far as can be determined.*
>
> *There is a single charter that may bear his seal, what seems to be a running dog, heraldically a talbot, I suppose, can't say for sure. He was mixed up in some local warfare that had precious little to do with the struggle between Stephen and the Empress, although he fought for Stephen at the Battle of the Standard in 1138, and was associated by the chroniclers with the household of the Earl of Albemarle.*

I did come across one curious allusion to him, although not as a hunting dog! In the chronicle of the monk of Nostell, who wrote (and this is verbatim but transcribed by Clay in the nineteenth century): 'Now amongst them at this time (he doesn't say which time!) was Reynald de Briec, a black and savage man more merciless than a horde of northmen, and one said by his enemies to have made a league with the devil and spirits too about his castle, insomuch as it was said *(this is my emphasis)* that his unnatural hunger for things of the flesh left no man or woman safe who came by mischance into his hands, and that he did ride forth when there was no law, and seize upon victims for his privy desires, *but some good priest prevailed against him by prayer.'*

Sounds quite a character! It's very vague, I know, but it's the best I can do. There's nothing else that I'm aware of, but the links you can make from this will be self-evident, even to an early modernist! His seal was that of a hound or talbot, and the chronicler's remark indicates that he was a hunter, hence your Latin.

How or when he died or was killed, I have no idea, nor do I know how the priest's prayers were answered! (But maybe that's fiction.)

I checked on Brickhill as a manor in the Paynel Fee, and find that in 1150 it was in the hands of someone else, although whether related to Reynald or not I can't say. But it proves the Paynel–Reynald association was broken by then, and the Mowbray documents show that Reynald had been replaced in all their manors by at the latest 1154, the year of Henry II's accession.

This is the best I can do for the moment. You could however, have a look at the charters yourself . . .

Shaking his head at that suggestion, Nick knew he would have preferred a look at that monastic chronicle, in spite of needing someone like David to translate it for him. But still, that was pure curiosity, and Clay was reliable.

As he read the letter through again, Nick was aware of a surge of gratitude. David's information was very much more than he had expected, and he had obviously put himself out to supply it in double-quick time. The facts made the link between Reynald and Reynard tenable, and offered more than a little scope for speculation. Nick found it extraordinary that Reynald de Briec, for all his short lease of something like a decade, should have left such a powerful mark on the locality that his manor had been known, ever after, as *de Briec's hill.*

But why was his lease so short? It was more than possible, in those violent times, that he had been killed in battle; but on the other hand, Nick reasoned, if Reynald were as noxious as the monk of Nostell Priory suggested, it was equally possible that he had been murdered. Or perhaps his war-weary overlords, the Paynels, found de Briec's activities too much to swallow, and drove him out, back to the Mowbrays or even back to Normandy.

Perhaps not, though. A violent death for a violent and rapacious man, that would be fitting. And if murder was more often than not a domestic matter, then perhaps de Briec's assassins were members of his own household, the act committed locally, his body buried in unconsecrated ground. Was that not the reason, in myth and legend, for the haunting by unquiet spirits?

Nineteen

Caroline Stalwell, cousin of my cousins on the Piper side, died that October in childbirth, and the poor sickly baby, a boy, died three days later.

My father was summoned to the funeral, and was away for two days. I stayed at home, riding out over the cropped, rain-swept fields of Hammerford to shed a tear or two for that poor girl and her baby. Her fate disturbed me, for she was not much older than myself. If I should marry, I thought selfishly, that might easily happen to me. I did not want to die, I had not yet begun to live: the tears, I think, were as much for myself as that distant cousin.

I was fifteen that December, and at Christmas we were invited to stay with my aunt and uncle in town. Although my father had to return home between-times, we were all together again for Twelfth Night, when Aunt Margaret laid on a banquet for as many of the family as were able to attend. With sons and daughters, spouses and children, various cousins and their offspring, the number was approaching two score, all gathered in the lofty, raftered hall of their old house on Goodramgate. The trestle tables were set out, and we were all squeezed on benches in descending order of age and relationship, with the older children, like myself, at each foot. The little ones were all in bed, or supposed to be: I caught a glimpse of eyes and noses peeping down from the gallery.

To my surprise, Richard Stalwell was there, and seated next to my father on the top table. Surely he doesn't deserve that position, I remember thinking; and then I checked myself, feeling sorry for him as Aunt Margaret must have done. No doubt she had seated him next to my father because they had so much in common: even my father found the talk of city merchants beyond him sometimes.

Amongst the gaily-coloured finery of the other guests, Richard was as distinctive as a Puritan in black, with only plain white linen at his throat. He wore no wig, either, but his own hair, sleek and dark, tied back in a simple ribbon. His face was pale and serious but, it seemed to me, not unduly morose; I even caught him smiling at my father's jests, and laughing, like the rest of us, when the game of snap-dragon commenced. Later, while the tables were being cleared away for the music and dancing to follow, Aunt Margaret beckoned me away from the boys and girls and said my father wished to speak to me. For a moment I was afraid I had done something to offend, but no, he seemed as surprised as myself, just recalling himself sufficiently to introduce me to his companion. Tongue-tied, I hardly knew what to say to Richard Stalwell, whether to wish him a merry Christmas or condole with him on the loss of his wife and child. In the end I did neither, simply bobbed a curtsy to his smiling bow, while my father did all the talking, explaining to my embarrassment that I was his only child and the comfort of his old age.

Until you see fit to marry me off, I thought rebelliously, giving him a sidelong glare. To my consternation, Richard Stalwell saw that look, his eyes dancing with laughter as I chanced to meet his glance.

He recovered himself quickly. 'Your father,' he said, 'tells me you are exceedingly accomplished for so young a maid.'

My cheeks grew hot. How dare he laugh at me? 'I try to be of use, sir.'

'You read and write, I believe? Might I ask your reading matter?'

I felt he was staring at me like a freak in a side-show. In fact I read as much as time and opportunity allowed, and by then must have been familiar with almost every book in Hammerford, including my father's dozen, the rector's two shelves, and Widow Dennison's collection of transcripts. She could not read the poetry so beloved of her late husband, but she liked to listen to me. We were both enamoured of Robert Herrick, to the extent that I knew his words by heart; but I was unsure how wise it was to admit that.

'I read my bible, sir, and such newsletters as come our way.' That sounded modest, I thought, and those items were safe enough.

My father laughed. 'She reads everything, Richard – history, poetry, political tracts – although I question sometimes how much she understands those!' He laughed again, heartily, showing me off like the curiosity I surely was. My smile, I felt sure, was more of a fixed grimace, but there was compassion as well as interest in Richard Stalwell's eyes.

'Your father is fortunate,' he said kindly, 'in having so lively a companion.'

'You are generous, sir.' I bowed my head modestly, and studied my clenched hands while the men continued their conversation. Torn between manners and a need to get away, I wondered how to take my leave of them; but as the musicians began to tune their instruments in preparation for the dance, Richard Stalwell murmured regretfully that he must leave.

'In other circumstances,' he said to me, 'it would have given me great pleasure to join the frolic, but alas . . .'

He indicated his state of mourning, and I was constrained to murmur some words of sympathy on the loss of his wife. 'She was so kind,' I said, 'and so very pretty . . .'

'Yes,' he agreed stiffly, 'she was.'

In the short silence which followed, I feared I had said the wrong thing, but then my father caught the eye of his sister, and advised Richard that he should take his leave while she was presently disengaged. Richard bowed to me and turned away, but in the few minutes that he remained in the hall, my eyes never left him. I was burning with shame for my youth and plainness and lack of pretty conversation, and how I wished that I had not mentioned his wife . . .

It was the mention of Christmas, rather than Caroline Stalwell, that made Natasha pause. Taking a break to stretch her limbs, she moved to the far window, but the view from there, if slightly more interesting, was no less bleak. Below the broken terrace lay a wilderness of bleached grass and dead weeds; even the oaks were denuded now, their gnarled limbs like arthritic arms raised to some oblivious god.

Christmas, it would be Christmas in just four weeks, and for the last few days, while Nick was out of the house, she had done nothing but write. She was becoming obsessed with this Sarah Mary Kirkham, the intricate detail of her life, her friends and relations, the girlish passion which seemed to be developing for Richard Stalwell. It was certainly far more interesting than her own life, Natasha thought wryly, and a sight more colourful. Sarah Mary Kirkham had conversations with her father and servants; Natasha Crayke had barely exchanged a word with anyone since Mrs Bickerstaff's departure on Monday afternoon.

She sighed, thinking of Nick. He was making a virtue of work and lofty forbearance. They watched the news together, ate mostly in silence, and then departed for their separate rooms, separate worlds. The atmosphere within the house was as bleak as it was without; had it not been for the rapid approach of Christmas, Natasha told herself that she would have walked out and left Nick to it.

In spite of her lack of religious belief, there was something about the festive season which made the idea of leaving then particularly cruel. It even brought a ridiculous lump to her throat, especially when she thought of the twins, and how wonderful life had seemed a year ago. The house had been barely livable, the renovations less than half complete, yet the boys had loved that sense of camping in, it had quite taken their minds off the idea of being awkward.

But if the indoor temperature had been cold last year, with frost outside and no central heating, this year's atmosphere was likely to be colder still, in spite of hot pipes and two roaring fires.

With a sudden shiver, she went through the house to the kitchen. The stove was glowing but in need of fuel. She sighed and switched on the kettle, then went outside to the little lean-to fuel store at the end of the house. Hearing the sound of a tractor coming up the lane, she turned guiltily, thinking it might be Craig Morrison. She hesitated, wanting to hide, not sure which way to go; then the roaring blue tractor appeared and it was too late. It was Craig, and he had seen her, and he was stopping in the lane.

Returning his wave, she carried on, shovelling coke into the brass coal scuttle as though stoking a boiler.

He came and peered at her round the open door. 'Need a hand?'

'Yes – thanks.'

He picked up the heavy scuttle and followed her into the house, kicking off his muddy boots in the porch. In competent, proprietorial fashion he fuelled the stove, then turned to face her. 'Well,' he said, 'if the mountain won't come to Mahomet . . .'

'Craig – I'm sorry. I should have – '

'Yes, you should.' Regarding her with a crooked smile, he said: 'But I might let you off if you tell me what happened . . .'

'I – well, you see –' She broke off again, indicated a chair, and asked him whether he would like some coffee.

'Yes, I would – and yes, I'll sit down if you give me a newspaper to sit on.'

She passed him yesterday's *Guardian*, and he glanced at it with amusement before laying it carefully on a dining chair. 'I've been expecting to hear from you,' he said reproachfully, 'ever since you didn't turn up on Monday. I thought we had a date?'

'I didn't *say* I'd come.'

'Well, maybe not in so many words – '

'I couldn't come,' she said quickly, remembering Nick, 'my husband arrived just as I was about to set off. And you're not on the phone, are you?'

'You could've dropped by – sent a note.'

'I've been busy,' she said, turning away to make the coffee. 'Work got in the way, I'm afraid – deadlines and things – you know how it is.'

His smile became even quirkier. 'No, I don't. I haven't a clue what you do for a living.'

'I'm a writer.'

For a moment she thought he did not believe her, but then he suddenly relaxed, making quite a play of being impressed. He asked what sort of things she wrote, and was honest enough to admit that he had never heard the name Natasha Crayke other than from her own lips.

Studying him as he talked, she suddenly thought how young he looked, more like a student, with his long, curly hair free of that red band, not like a pirate at all. That she had ever seen him in such a light was now rather embarrassing. Her glance slid away.

'You're different today,' he said suddenly.

That startled her. She ran a hand over her unwashed hair, imagined her face's pallor, and without looking down took mental stock of her old jeans and leg-warmers, the warm but baggy sweater which had been through the washer too many times. But, she reminded herself, she had hardly been dressed for seduction the first time he called at the house. 'Am I?' she forced a laugh. 'Well, I dare say it's because I'm working – I always look a slob when I'm working!'

'No, I don't mean that,' he said cryptically, and continued to stare.

'In what way, then?'

'I don't know – you just are.' He shrugged and looked away,

then, meeting her eyes again, he gave her the benefit of that rather wolfish grin. 'You're not giving me the old come-on, for a start!'

Natasha felt herself blushing, a thing she rarely did, and that set him laughing. With a sidelong glance, he said: 'I could still fancy you, though . . .'

She laughed then, relieved that he seemed to be taking the change of heart so well. 'What?' she demanded, 'looking like this? That is a compliment!'

'It's a fact.' His eyes lingered appreciatively for a moment, and then he said: 'I don't understand it though. When we talked that first day –' He broke off, shaking his head in sudden bemusement.

Watching him, she saw the sudden change from good humour to intensity, and when he shifted position to look at her more directly, there was even a spark of anger in his eyes. 'That first time – the whole time we were talking,' he said tersely, 'there was enough heat coming off you to set a wet fleece alight. And last week was no different,' he went on relentlessly. 'For Christ's sake, you even had your husband in tow that day. How the hell did you get out of that one? I heard him calling you, and he didn't sound exactly pleased.'

'I don't know,' she mumbled. 'His mind was on other things, I expect.'

'Good God Almighty! He must spend a lot of time thinking of other things! Is he blind, or what?'

'No, he's just an historian,' she said bitterly.

'Oh, I see. Poor sod.'

That took the wind out of his sails, Natasha thought. Releasing a pent-up breath, she realised that the atmosphere between them was suddenly lighter. She offered him a cigarette, but he did not smoke; lighting one herself, she said: 'I'm sorry, Craig – really, I am. I don't know what got into me the other week. Something did, that's obvious. But whatever it was –' she shrugged and spread her hands ' – seems to have gone.'

Digesting that, after a moment, he said: 'You're all contradictions, do you know that? I mean, for God's sake, there I was, convinced I was on the promise of a lifetime, and now here I am, sitting in your kitchen, drinking bloody coffee and wondering who's crazy – you or me?'

With a feeble attempt at a smile, Natasha tried to take the jest in good part, but he was alarmingly close to her own suspicions. Raking up an old, jokey response, she said: 'I'm a writer – they're all crazy, didn't you know?'

'No, I didn't. I thought that was artists?'

She laughed. 'Yes, them too.'

'And musicians?'

'Why not?' Laughing again, deciding that he was quite likeable after all, Natasha changed the subject. 'Anyway, that's enough about me. What about you? How are the sheep? I heard you lost another one last weekend?'

His expression darkened. 'Too bloody true. And the weekend's coming up again.' Deep in thought for a moment, he worried a mark on the table-top. 'I tell you what though, that bastard of a dog's going to get his come-uppance soon. I'll make bloody sure of it.'

'It might not be the wolfhound,' she said quickly.

'No? Then tell me what else leaves paw-marks that size!'

Natasha held his gaze unflinchingly. 'There is another dog on the loose, you know. A big black dog – it's been seen a few times.'

He laughed derisively. 'Oh, no, not you too! I heard enough from old Toby Bickerstaff last Sunday – all this bloody nonsense about phantoms and whatever. I'm telling you – whatever's killing my sheep is flesh and blood, and it's got paws the size of that Irish thing.'

'Yes, I know – Nick saw its prints – but they weren't McCoy's.'

'Oh, don't tell me – it had five pads, not four.' He shook his head. 'I wouldn't put it past that old idiot to have made everything up – including the prints. He's crazy enough!'

That aspect was one Natasha had not considered before; but Nick was surely too astute to be taken in by manufactured evidence. 'No, I don't think so. Anyway, old Toby's not so bad when you get to know him.'

Craig Morrison shot her a look of amused disbelief. 'Not so bad? You must be joking! I'll lay you a tenner to a 10p coin that you don't know him *at all*.' Regarding her steadily, all amusement gone, he said: 'He killed a man once, you know. Caught him down in the wood, fucking his woman – knifed him, then cut his balls off. He did fifteen years for that.'

Natasha stared in horror. 'He did *what*?'

'It's right, he did. Why do you think he lives in that bloody old caravan? Nobody else'd have him when he came out. Anyway, he's a nasty old bugger, especially in drink. Or he was – he's past it now.'

There was something appalling about that matter-of-fact tone, in the way he unconsciously answered all the questions she and Nick had asked themselves about the old man, and all without batting an eyelid.

'How do you know all this?'

'How do you think? I was *born* in Denton – I've lived here most of my life. Anyway, I remember him coming out – must have been ten or eleven at the time, and the whole village was talking about it. They still do sometimes – whenever anybody sees old Toby with a skinful, they all stand back and talk about what he did that afternoon, when he'd left the pub . . .'

Shivering again, she asked about the woman, whether Toby had done anything to her. But as far as Craig Morrison was aware, she had been unharmed; she was, apparently, the chief witness at his trial.

'Who was she? What happened to her after that?'

'God knows – she was just some woman he'd shacked up with. She wasn't local.'

So she didn't really matter, Natasha thought ironically.

'No, he's a crazy old bugger – you want to be careful, up here on your own all day. Maybe your husband thinks he's all right, but he doesn't know him. I wouldn't encourage him, and that's a fact.'

That dire warning reminded her of Mrs Bickerstaff and her cautionary words about Craig Morrison. Another irony. She was also reminded of the other woman's refusal to talk about her husband's cousin. What was it she had called him that day? *A dirty, disgusting old man.* At the time, Natasha had been unsure whether the epithets were intended to refer to his bodily state or suspected sexual inclinations, either of which might have given Mrs B a severe shudder of distaste; but now that she knew the reason, Natasha could sympathise. Perhaps if Nick had a murderer in his family, she reflected, he would feel the same way.

It would be difficult, however, to explain any of this to Nick without revealing the source of her information; she was not good at lying, and he was clever enough to worm things out of her if he thought she was being evasive. That thought made her glance, guiltily, at her watch. It was past three already, and possible that he might soon be home.

Craig Morrison stood up. 'Yes,' he observed dryly, 'it's time I was going – I don't want to bump into your husband, do I?'

As she rose to see him out, her eyes were on a level with his. For a long moment they regarded each other, she slightly apprehensive, he considerably amused.

Moving closer, he said: 'I'm sorry you changed your mind . . .'

She was suddenly afraid that he was about to kiss her, and equally certain that this time she did not want to be kissed.

As she stepped back, he gave her a cold, appraising look. 'Anyway, thanks for the coffee. And don't forget – if you should happen to change your mind, you know where I live . . .'

Watching him cross the yard, Natasha felt the tension begin to ebb; as he started the tractor and roared past in the direction of Denton, she released a long, trembling sigh and glanced at her watch. Almost an hour, and if Nick had come home . . .

She shivered and went back to the kitchen, her former concentration gone. Needing to get a grip on herself, Natasha set about preparing the evening meal, but as she chopped up meat with a large French cook's knife, she could not help thinking about old Toby Bickerstaff and the murder he had committed almost thirty years ago. The knife in her hand, the stickiness of blood on her fingers, managed to conjure up some grisly pictures. Revolted, she finished the job hastily, and shoved the casserole in the oven.

Twenty

To Nick, the following week seemed to be one of endless meetings, backbiting amongst colleagues whose favourite projects were being reshuffled and relegated, cliques forming and disintegrating, and a general hair-tearing feeling that nothing would ever be settled for the following term. Mountaineering through memos from Heslington Hall simply added to the frustration, while the students' faces seemed to grow longer and longer as the present term dragged on.

Even the weather was atrocious, national news reporting the wettest autumn for fifty years. November gave way to December in a deluge that went on for days; Wales and the South-West were apparently swamped by it, and the new flood-barriers in York did not prevent the Ouse from overflowing through all the riverside streets. Over the campus, the rain swept in like a monsoon to seek out every weak point in flat-roofed buildings. One of the lecture halls had to be closed, while several rooms in Hesketh College were affected by water seeping in from above; students in residence were being shifted to temporary accommodation elsewhere. On the most mundane level, just walking from one college to another guaranteed a drenching; the lake was like a miniature, storm-tossed sea, and even the ducks were seeking shelter in the shrubberies.

On Thursday, Nick returned to his room in time to meet Dr Wills, and hoped she would provide a little light relief from more besetting problems. She arrived on time, and as soon as the door opened he remembered seeing her before, although the circumstances continued to escape him. He was also sorry that he had asked her to climb all those stairs, since she was both elderly and overweight.

Crossing the room to greet her, he helped Dr Wills divest herself of a plastic raincoat, a paisley shawl, and an Aran cardigan that must have weighed several pounds. Her ample breast was heaving and her pale skin flushed, but she thanked him briskly enough.

After her apparent reluctance to share information on the phone, Dr Wills surprised him by launching immediately into the reason for her visit.

'You were asking me about spectral hounds and suchlike in the area of Sheriff Whenby. Well, I'm still not sure whether this is what you're after, but it seems there was a legend of sorts connected with Brickhill, which isn't far from there . . .'

'Ah, yes – Brickhill,' he murmured, trying to preserve an attitude of calm as his guest fished in a capacious shopping bag.

She brought out a sheaf of papers. 'I've sorted out some old notes for you to go through – you can return them any time, they're not pressing. Anyway,' she added, handing them across to him, 'I can give you the gist of them now. The written evidence, as you'll see, dates back to the 1720s – '

'No, the 1630s,' Nick said impulsively, but a second later, meeting a very icy glance, he wished that he had held his tongue. Dr Wills, it seemed, did not care to be corrected. 'I'm sorry,' he added, smiling, 'it's just that I've been working on this for a while, and . . .' He went on to explain in tones of gentle apology, about the parish registers and Beauchamp.

Her expression relaxed. 'I didn't know about that,' she admitted, her interest eager and undisguised. 'The earliest reference I have – as you'll see from the notes – is from the journal of a local cleric, written between 1720 and 1728. But I'm afraid that's in manuscript form only.'

He asked whether she knew of any subsequent references, and she mentioned three separate accounts published in the ninteenth century. 'Chambers is the most informative, which suggests an independent source unknown to me. But the story's quite interesting,' she went on briskly, 'because it falls into what you might call a *Beauty and the Beast* pattern. That is – and forgive me if I'm being too simplistic – the beast at Brickhill isn't the ghost of an animal, it's the ghost of a man *appearing* as a beast.'

Releasing a sigh, Nick nodded; his own suspicions had led him to a similar conclusion. 'Go on.'

'Well, if we can get back to the cleric – in his journal, he dismisses the story as being unworthy of enlightened minds. But he does imply that it was believed in the neighbourhood, and he hints – only hints, mind you – of a recent appearance in 1723. Tongues were apparently wagging about it, and he noted that the superstitious locals regarded the beast as some sort of ill-omen. What he found curious, however – and so do I – is that their animosity was directed not so much at the beast, but at someone living in the neighbourhood.

'She was a widow, this woman. The rector mentions her several times, and then, towards the end of 1723, he refers to the mystery of her disappearance. According to the locals, she just upped-sticks and left.' Dr Wills paused again. 'But it's perfectly obvious he suspected foul play. Conducted his own limited investigation, it seems, but couldn't prove a thing.'

Unsure what to make of that, Nick shook his head. 'But you say the beast was supposed to be connected with her?'

'That would appear to have been the sum of popular opinion, yes – at least, that's why the rector was getting so hot under the collar.'

'This is the rector of Brickhill, I gather?'

She looked surprised. 'Oh, no. The beast is always referred to in connection with Brickhill, certainly, but the cleric was rector of a neighbouring parish. Denton-on-the-Forest.'

Nick felt his jaw drop. For a moment he was speechless. 'I presume,' he said at last, 'that the widow was one of his parishioners?'

'Oh, yes indeed. That's why he was so concerned by her disappearance.' Regarding him intently, Dr Wills waited for an explanation of his surprise; when none was forthcoming, she continued rather shortly: 'Chambers, who is of course more reliable, calls the beast's appearance an infrequent occurrence, not confined to any season of the year, and attributable to some disturbance in the life of the community. He also gives the beast a name.'

'Reynard?'

Meeting another of those chilling looks, Nick decided that Dr Wills was not the nice old dear her appearance suggested. She was probably, he thought, the kind of doctor who loathed it when her patients gave voice to what they thought was wrong with them.

'Yes, that's right,' she said, as though the admission pained her. 'Reynard, like the fox.'

Deciding to make her wait for the fruits of his own research, Nick asked whether she had done many investigations into this kind of phenomenon. He mentioned Charlie Cramp's beast, Padfoot, and she responded with a few other names of elemental beasts – Gytrash, Skryker, Barguest – and said that the stories were common to virtually all isolated parts of the country.

'In a way,' she went on, 'the Brickhill Beast – which is what I called him in a lecture I gave to the Folklore Society some years ago – fits in with these creatures, in that he appears to be confined to isolated roads and footpaths. He's never, for instance, reported as being seen in open country, fields and so on. But I have to say,' she added slowly, 'that in my opinion there's what I would call another dimension to him. Or should I say *it*.'

'So it would seem,' Nick acknowledged, glancing at his watch. 'But I think we should go down for lunch now, while food's still available . . .'

He picked up her scarves and cardigan, and opened the door. As they went down, she said: 'Obviously, I missed the incident in the church, and so probably missed other things as well, but I did turn up something else about the widow.'

'Oh, yes – what was that?' He nodded to Flora, coming up the stairs, and paused to let a bunch of students pass.

'Well, she was up before the church courts shortly before her disappearance, and the charge was fornication . . .'

Passing them, Flora caught that word and stared hard, then, with a quizzical smile for Nick, went on up the stairs.

'. . . and would you believe she was released without penance. How would you interpret that?'

'Influence?'

'I think she fornicated with her judges.'

Nick raised his eyebrows. 'She must have had a powerful sex-appeal,' he commented with a grin.

'Oh, yes, I think she had.'

Smiling he led the way to the nearest refectory, choosing a quiet corner table. When they were settled – he with a portion of shepherd's pie, she with something that purported to be moussaka – Dr Wills said: 'As I see it, this case falls into a rare category – it may even be unique.'

'Really?'

'Yes, really,' she repeated, her pale eyes fixing him again. 'You see, it's not something restricted to a precise location, or even to specific seasons or days of the year. Chambers thought this thing manifested itself according to a prevailing mood in the community – but I think it was called forth, probably without intention, by somebody in the village.'

Keeping his eyes on his plate, Nick suppressed a smile. 'And what makes you think that?'

'Oh, I haven't a shred of proof,' she admitted, her soft, powdery cheeks quivering with annoyance, 'it's just my diagnosis based on the slender facts.' Irritably, she attacked her vegetables, and a moment later, asked: 'Do you know why the beast was called Reynard?'

'Yes, I think I do.' After a slight hesitation, he felt in his pocket, extracted David's letter and showed it to her.

As her eyes travelled down the page, he watched the faint arch of her brows lift with delight. 'But this is – well, it's the link, the connection! It reinforces everything I've said!'

Nick frowned. She had said nothing, as far as he was aware, that was more than supposition. He needed a lot more than that. Perhaps her notes would be more revealing. Pondering for a moment, he said: 'I think you should know that the thing's been seen recently.'

Her eyes and mouth formed three small circles of astonishment. 'By you?'

'No, not by me. By someone who lives close by. My wife and I live in Denton, by the way – I don't think I mentioned that before. Anyway,' he went on, pushing his plate aside and reaching for his cigarettes, 'the old character I'm talking about has lived in or around the village for most of his life. He saw it one evening at dusk, at the beginning of last month. A couple of days later, this creature was seen again, by a woman walking her dog. It terrified the woman and her dog as well. It was daylight, but foggy, so we have to take imagination into account, I'm afraid.

'And it is possible,' he added cautiously, 'that my wife saw it too, although she swears it was just a black dog – a labrador, or something like it – at the side of the lane. It was, however, after midnight, raining and blowing like mad . . .' He thought for a moment, then shrugged. 'She's probably right – I dare say a dog was all she did see.'

'And where were these sightings? In relation to the village, I mean.'

'All along Dagger Lane – which runs from Denton to Brickhill.'

Her eyes widened. 'Obviously, you believe these stories, these people who said they saw it?'

With a shrug, Nick admitted that he did. 'I can't find a single piece of evidence to support my belief, but yes, I do.' For a moment he wondered why he was so reluctant to describe the paw-prints discovered by the wood, and then decided he could save that information for later.

Dr Wills dabbed her mouth with a paper napkin and sipped some water from her glass. When she said that she would like to come over and see the area, he was not surprised.

'Yes, by all means, I'd be pleased to show you. The only thing is, it's almost three miles from Denton to Brickhill, over some not very good terrain. The first part's all right, down as far as the wood, but after that it might be difficult.'

'Right, then, we'll do the easy part on foot, and Brickhill by car. What about Saturday morning?'

A little taken aback, he heard himself saying: 'Well, I think I'm free, but what about the weather?'

'Goodness me, what's a drop of rain? We won't melt!'

He laughed. 'No, I don't suppose we shall. All right – I'm game if you are. Shall we say eleven? Then we can repair to the pub afterwards, for lunch.'

'My treat, in that case,' she declared, her eyes sparkling with coquettish good humour. Smiling back, Nick suddenly realised that he rather liked this unusual woman. He watched her gathering her bags and scarves together, then scribbled his home address and phone number on a piece of card, together with directions to the house. In the meantime, he said, he would look at her notes.

They parted company by Hesketh College. When she was gone, he went back upstairs to leaf through the dossier on his desk. There was certainly plenty of material, although as he scanned a selection of pages, much of it seemed repetitive. Sighing, he wondered what to make of her. It was hardly surprising, he thought, that Sally described her as odd.

By the end of the week, Natasha was feeling tired and a little overwrought. She was not pleased by Nick's announcement that Dr Betty Wills would be calling on Saturday morning, and even less by the reason for her visit. Although he did not go into detail, she knew why Dr Wills was coming and thought the visit pointless. Stray or spectre, nothing had been seen for weeks, and even the sheep remained unmolested. Nevertheless, when Nick said that he had offered to walk the lane with his guest, Natasha forestalled any invitation by saying that she would be busy on Saturday.

'Anyway,' she added, 'I'm sure you don't want a sceptic like me present while you're busy comparing notes.'

Nick's jaw tightened but he made no further comment.

The rain cleared by Friday evening, and Saturday morning dawned clear and cold. The sky was a delicate, eggshell blue, with not a raincloud in sight; the woods were dun-coloured smudges on the horizon, fields and hedgerows a bleached patchwork of ochre, beige and brown. Looking out of her window, Natasha was aware of a most unworthy sense of annoyance. She would have enjoyed a walk herself today, but wild horses wouldn't have dragged her out with Nick and Dr Wills. Heading for the bathroom, she told herself that she needed a day off, and that a trip to town was necessary, as much for essential groceries as Christmas cards and presents.

An hour later, ignoring Nick's dark looks, she left him cleaning his car and waved a determinedly cheerful goodbye. Let him have his obsessions, she thought as she bumped along Dagger Lane and out on to the Green; as long as he left her free to pursue her own, he could do as he pleased.

Twenty One

DR WILLS rearranged her scarves over a voluminous thorn-proof jacket, and reached into her car for a sturdy walking-stick. On her feet, Nick noticed with approval, she was wearing a stout pair of leather shoes over woollen stockings. Faintly flushed with excitement, she looked ready for anything.

On the way down the lane, he told her about old Toby. She said that she would like to meet him, ask him for a direct account of what he had seen that evening at dusk. Nick tried to dissuade her, for the simple reason that Toby was not keen on strangers, but Dr Wills would not be put off; to his relief, however, when they reached the caravan it had a still, deserted look, and there was no answer to his call. The old man, he said, was probably in some local pub, which was where he seemed to spend most of his weekends.

She was obviously disappointed, answering his questions regarding her research in an off-hand fashion. He had gone through her notes the night before, and had found them interesting, referring to accounts he had not seen. Much of the material was secondary, and less valuable, but he was intrigued by her reference to the journal kept by that erstwhile rector of Denton. Not that he expected it to reveal much about the beast, but it might well mention names, families and properties which were pertinent to his own interest in Holly Tree Cottage. Dr Wills, however, was reluctant to reveal its whereabouts. She kept saying that it was unpublished, exceedingly difficult to read, and that when she had seen it, some ten or twelve years previously, it had been in private hands.

'Whose hands?' Nick pressed, feeling like a policeman interrogating a particularly cagey informant.

'Well, if you must know,' she said crossly, 'it's with the Norton-Clive papers at Sheriff Whenby Hall. At least it was. But if you've ever met the Major, you'll know very well that he has little or no time for the likes of you and me.'

Nick smiled, but did not dispute that. Major Norton-Clive was very fond of declaring his interest in the future, and of saying the past must take care of itself. It was, no doubt, a good political statement, but since his past had been secure for many generations, and his future was assured because of it, he could afford to be dismissive.

'So how did you manage to get a look?'

'His first wife,' Dr Wills informed him, 'was a friend of mine. We shared similar interests.'

'I see.' He wondered at the extent of those interests, and whether spiritualism came into it. He rather thought he had heard a whisper from somewhere that the first Mrs Norton-Clive had held unusual beliefs. Something about holding seances at the Hall? He could not be sure, but made a mental note to ask Sally Armitage about it; and also to ask her whether she knew of the present whereabouts of the family papers. The Major might well have disposed of them.

When they reached the wood, Dr Wills surprised him further by suggesting they walk through it. Nick glanced at his watch, at the state of the undergrowth, and then at his companion; but she was perfectly serious.

'Why? I mean, as far as anyone knows, these things keep to footpaths and suchlike.'

'Well,' she said reasonably, 'the man Toby saw it in the margins of the wood, didn't he? And if that rotten old bridge doesn't lead to some sort of path, Dr Rhodes, then I'm a Dutchman!'

With that she grasped her walking-stick like a sword, and headed for the bridge. He tried to tell her about the elm stumps, where he had found the prints, but she merely said that they could study that area later, and carried on.

Feeling inadequate, Nick took a deep breath and followed her. He could not do otherwise, but he was less than happy amongst that tangle of branches. What surprised him, a little way into the wood, was that the path was reasonably defined. With the dying back of vegetation, it was possible to see the line of it, as though people still used it from time to time. People, or just one person on a regular basis: Toby, probably, on his hunting and poaching forays. In places the undergrowth was thick with bracken and brambles, the long, thorny arms reaching out to trap the unwary. Nick tried to protect Dr Wills by going first, but then he lost the path and she found it again, pressing on regardless, using her stick, striding over the obstacles with an agility that astounded him. If World's End had ever been a plantation, Nick thought, then it was difficult to discern; the trees grew now in haphazard fashion, many of the silver birches fallen or rotting where they stood, victims to the saturated earth. The air was dank, and deep within the wood were pools of stagnant brown water, surrounded by reeds and mossy stumps: not even winter sunlight penetrated here, while in summer the leafy screen would be complete.

Chilled, Nick wondered what they were doing here, and as if in answer to that unspoken question, Dr Wills said cheerfully: 'I'm determined to see where this path leads. It's obviously used – I'd like to know *why*.'

'I can tell you that,' he responded shortly. 'Pigeons nest in these trees, and there are rabbit warrens on the far side – I've seen them from the fields. Old Toby's partial to both.'

'You don't like woods, do you? You're a man who prefers to see the horizon.'

'You're quite right,' he said with feeling, imagining his ancestors as men of the plains, men who avoided forests and places where outlaws and footpads might lurk. Footpads. Padfoot. With his heart beating just that little bit faster, he caught himself listening for sounds that might herald the approach of something other than humankind: listening and looking. He almost wished that he was in possession of Toby's gun.

He was so uneasy, wondering how long it would take for

them to come out on the other side, that he did not immediately notice what Dr Wills had seen ahead.

'Well,' she suddenly exclaimed, 'I wonder how on earth they got that down here?'

Looking past her, he saw they had come to a small clearing, such as might have been used by charcoal burners in the last century, or gamekeepers in more recent times. To one side of the clearing stood an ancient railway wagon, of the type that had once been used to transport horses or other large animals. It had sunk well below the axles, and was even more decrepit than Toby's caravan, but someone had made a couple of windows, and the sliding door was partly open. Inside, Nick thought he could make out the line of a table, and beside it, an old chair. Curious now, he advanced to look in, with Dr Wills behind him.

'Don't,' she said sharply. 'Come away.'

He turned, and she was as white as a sheet. 'What's wrong?' He went to her straight away, afraid that she might be ill, that the exertion had been too much for her.

Gasping for breath, she plucked at his arm. 'Come away,' she said again, her breast heaving as they headed back towards the path. 'Something terrible – *terrible* – happened here.'

'What is it?' He was thoroughly alarmed now. 'Reynard?'

'No, no.' Retreating to the safety of the trees, she paused to get her breath. He could see that she was genuinely shaken, that this was no cheap trick employed to scare him. It was at least a minute before she was able to speak.

'Violence,' she said at last, 'a lot of blood – that's what I saw.' She looked up, her gaze boring into him while he stared back, uncomprehending. 'What happened here?'

'I don't know – I've no idea. I didn't even know this place existed.'

She sighed. 'No, no, of course not – you don't like the woods, do you? But somebody comes here regularly – this path . . .' She bowed her head, unable to go on.

Nonplussed, Nick said: 'What do you mean, you *saw* violence?'

For a moment she did not answer him; then, leaning back

against a tree, she said wearily: 'Oh, my dear, you're so *blind*. Can't you even guess?'

When he shook his head, she clicked her tongue irritably, and said: 'I'm clairvoyant – that's why I gave up medicine. Years ago now. Couldn't bear it – all I could see was death. Well, not all the time, but it got worse – I knew what was coming, you see – and couldn't do a damn thing about it. Well, not in the long term. I could stave it off, ease the pain, but –' She broke off, shook her head angrily. 'It was killing *me*, you see. I couldn't go on – had to give it up.'

This was not at all what he had suspected; her veracity shook him. 'I'm sorry,' he said inadequately, 'I'd no idea.' Mystified, yet in no way doubting her, he said: 'Have you always . . .?'

She shrugged. 'I suppose so. Sudden flashes of awareness in childhood – knowing when people were lying, that sort of thing. But I didn't understand it – I thought everybody had the same experiences. Then I found they didn't, so I was frightened and tried to suppress it. But it grew, you see, and wouldn't be suppressed. Now, of course, I've learned to control it – most of the time. But that –' she indicated the clearing ' – caught me unawares.'

'It certainly did,' he murmured. Glancing round, anxious to be gone himself, Nick said: 'If you feel up to it, I think we should go.'

It was impossible to walk two abreast, but this time Nick was willing for her to go ahead of him. That way he could keep her in view, keep the pace she was setting, which was much slower than on the outward journey. When they had cleared the wood, they were both relieved, happy to rest for a while by the elm stumps before retracing their steps to the house.

Lighting a cigarette, inhaling deeply, Nick raised his face to the sun. 'I'm glad,' he said with a dry smile, 'that we chose a sunny day. Nothing would have persuaded me in there if it'd been raining, or overcast.'

'Childhood,' she said keenly, glancing up at him. 'Something frightened you then.'

He laughed. 'Probably – that's where most fears start, isn't it?'

'Theatre – a Christmas pantomime. *Babes in the Wood*?'

It was his turn to stare. Suddenly, he was three or four years old, in a darkened place with other children; before him, barely lit, was a fearful scene, two sleeping children surrounded by huge, moving trees, all with eyes and mouths and waving arms . . .

Shaken, for he had never consciously recalled that incident before, he then remembered screaming for his mother, and being taken out in tears by some other woman.

With a sudden shiver, he said: 'Are you always so astute?'

'No, dear, but you have troubles hanging over you. I should get them sorted out before they ruin your life.'

'What do you mean?'

'I don't know – I'm tired,' she said irritably. 'This sort of thing is quite exhausting, you know – it drains me. And now,' she declared, taking his arm, 'I think I'm going to need your assistance . . .'

She looked pale and drawn, her former ebullience gone, her weight dragging on Nick's arm as they made their way slowly up the slight incline towards Toby's caravan. There was still no sign of life, for which he was thankful, and Dr Wills made no comment until they were well past.

'You say he's the one who walks that path?'

'Toby? I imagine so. I can't think of anyone else.'

'Then he's connected with it.'

'With what? The violence – the blood? You're sure it's not just killing birds, animals, that sort of thing – he is a poacher, you know.'

With a sharp dismissive gesture she said: 'Human violence – rape, murder – that's what I'm talking about.'

Away from the wood, it seemed incredible. Even more so to connect such unthinkable deeds with the old man he saw most mornings, the old man he had come to – well, be honest, he thought – had come to care about. 'For God's sake,' he said slowly, 'are you sure about this? I know the man, I – '

'I'm sure,' she said implacably. 'He may even be the one who's summoning Reynard.'

'Oh, come on, Dr Wills, surely – '

'You're a sceptic, I know that. Men usually are. But I'm telling you that someone in this area is attracting the beast. Whether they're aware of it or not, doesn't matter – he's around, and he's going to stay until he gets what he wants.'

'And what does he want?'

'I'm not sure,' she admitted as they reached the house.

Nick led the way inside and made coffee for them both. Dr Wills asked for a small restorative with hers, and Nick fetched the brandy. He poured a tot for himself too.

Taking up the conversation again, Dr Wills said: 'You see, he may still be a hunter, bringing down his own prey – or he may have degenerated into a scavenger, feeding off things that are already evil, already morally decayed.'

Although they had crossed the bounds of reasonable speculation about an hour ago, Nick was not prepared to take any more. Not yet, anyway. His mind was still trying to grasp what had happened down in the wood.

Bringing her back to that, he said: 'But what's the connection with the clearing? Is there one, or not?'

She thought for a moment, swallowed a little more brandy. 'No, I don't think so – it's too recent for that. Unless –' She broke off, shook her head. 'No. I was going to say, *unless he instigated it*, but that would be fanciful, I fear.'

That comment raised a smile from Nick, but it was a reluctant, rueful smile. He had never had dealings with a clairvoyant before, and would have said that most of them were quacks; but however extraordinary Dr Wills might be, she did not appear to be a fraud. She was possessed of some sort of extrasensory perception, that was clear enough; he was only in doubt as to her conclusions. If she was right, he reasoned later when he was alone, then this thing – this beast or whatever it was – had to be sentient, with a will of its own. Or subject to some other force, responsive at the very least. And such responsiveness implied some kind of life.

That was what he found hardest to accept. That the beast might be the ghost of Reynald de Briec, doomed to walk the earth as a hunting dog for all eternity, Nick was just about ready to believe; the rest seemed too fantastical for words. That this thing might be more than an earthbound spirit, that it might be tangible, sentient, and sucking on life, creating its own unfathomable evil as Dr Wills seemed to suggest, was to him beyond credibility. Like the old rector of Denton, he felt such beliefs were unworthy of enlightened minds.

Twenty Two

NICK'S THOUGHTS made him restless, uneasy. Desperate to talk things over with someone, he would have preferred Natasha. In the past she had always been such a good sounding-board for ideas, questions, even doubts. She understood an historian's brief, and her mind was sharp enough to grasp a problem, often before it was adequately phrased. Sometimes just the shaping of words was enough, and he would see what had previously been so hazy; at other times she would pull him up short, and tell him quite frankly that he was heading in the wrong direction. Particularly, he thought with a smile, when the problem was one of college politics or a matter of human psychology.

He missed that aspect of their relationship, and wondered whether she did too. Natasha had always been far more of a friend to him than Bernice. Bernice talked a lot but rarely listened; basically, she was not interested in anyone else's problems, except where they concerned her directly, and even then she was impatient, eager to be on with something else. Eventually, he had stopped trying to explain things, stopped looking for her assistance, even with regard to the problem of marriage. He stopped listening too. The wash of words passed over him and became part of the endless background noise of family life.

Natasha could not have been more different. She was quiet and self-contained, sensitive where Bernice was brash, and, unlike his first wife, willing to exchange ideas and opinions. Often, when she was working, she would break off to make a cup of tea, and suddenly present him with a scenario. 'If you were that man,' she would say, 'and in that situation – what would you do?' And he would tell her, and she would think about it, and off she would go, the problem apparently solved. He had enjoyed that; it made him feel that he was useful to her, that she needed him as a sounding-board as much as he needed her. Neither of them were party-goers; they enjoyed a mostly quiet life, listening to music, eating out, occasional trips to the theatre or a film. Even their silences were companionable; or they had been. But now the music was gone, the house was silent, and their lack of conversation had the atmosphere of an armed truce. Nick was aware, every time he came home, of a tension in the air like that preceding a summer storm; except that this was no passing squall, and summer was a long time gone.

He felt caged and frustrated by the empty house, desperate for a change of scene. Most of all he was in need of conversation, preferably with someone sane and sensible who could help him get these crazy ideas into perspective.

He poured himself a large whisky and lit a cigarette, pacing the room as he considered what to do. Giles came to mind, but it was Saturday and he would no doubt be going out somewhere with Fay; then he thought of phoning Sally.

There were things he needed to know, questions she could answer; nevertheless, for a moment he hesitated. He would have liked to ask her out to dinner, but the way he was feeling made the idea seem unworthy, even to himself. On his way to the telephone, Nick decided that it would be better to suggest meeting her tomorrow at the museum. She could show him round, and afterwards they could have tea together: nothing could be more innocuous than that.

But he had forgotten how well she knew him. They had not been speaking for more than a minute when she said: 'Do you know, you sound really strung up. What on earth did Dr Betty do to you?'

Laughing, he tried to side-step the question, but Sally was tenacious. A moment later, she tried again from a different angle. 'Why do I get the feeling that you're on your own and thoroughly pissed off?'

He laughed again, embarrassed by her perspicacity, but also grateful for it. 'Probably because I am,' he admitted, allowing her to make what she would of that.

There was a slight pause. 'Well, in that case,' she suggested lightly, 'why don't you come on over? I was going to ring you anyway – I've been rooting through the library this afternoon and found a couple of books that might be useful. If you come over, you can have a look at them, and then,' she added, 'you can take me out for something to eat as a thank-you for all my hard work. I sure as hell don't feel like cooking.'

At his end of the line, Nick grinned with relief. 'You're on,' he declared, 'I'll be over in about an hour.'

Armed with directions to her cottage in Ghylldale, he went upstairs to shower and change. Glancing at his watch, he saw that it was already past five. If he wanted to get out of the house before Natasha returned, he thought guiltily, then he would have to hurry.

He was in the bedroom, knotting his tie, when he heard a car coming up the lane. Slipping on his jacket, he looked down at the yard from the landing window, and saw Natasha climbing out of her car with several bulging carrier bags. Smothering a curse, he tried to marshal his thoughts, wondering how he could get out without telling her where he was going.

Expecting her to be tired and cross, which was how she generally returned from such expeditions, he relieved her of the shopping, and steeled himself to put everything away while Natasha moved her car into the barn.

When she came in, he was busy pushing biscuits and cereals into one cupboard, and cat-food into another. 'By the way,' he said without turning round, 'I'm going out in a minute.' Before she could ask where, he hurried on: 'Dr Wills gave me some interesting information today – I've got to follow it up. It won't wait, I'm afraid.'

'On a Saturday evening?' Natasha asked sardonically, glancing up at him.

In contrast to her tone, the glance was reproachful; her dark eyes seemed larger, the lashes longer, against the fragile pallor of her skin. For a moment his heart seemed to pause before rushing on and leaving him breathless; as he held her gaze he thought how much he loved her, and wondered what he was doing, taking Sally Armitage out to dinner.

Tearing his eyes away, pretending concern about the time, he reminded himself that Natasha didn't want him. 'Yes,' he said tersely, 'and I've got to drive to Newcastle, so I'd better get a move on.'

'Newcastle? Who do you know in Newcastle?'

'An old colleague,' he said, thinking of David, who lectured in Bristol, 'a medievalist – you don't know him.'

She paused to think about that. 'Will you be back tonight?'

'Yes, I imagine so – but it'll be late. Anyway,' he said, heading for the door, 'I've got my keys.'

'Nick!'

In the porch, he turned to see her standing rigidly in the hall, silhouetted by the kitchen light.

'Nick, tell me – what's going on?'

The irony of her question brought forth a sigh. 'That's what I'm trying to find out.'

'No, I – I don't mean . . .'

The catch in her voice tugged at him again; hardening his heart, he said, 'That's the trouble, Natasha – you don't want to know. But I do.'

Shivering, rubbing her arms, she turned away. 'Oh, never mind. It doesn't matter.'

But it did matter. It mattered very much.

By the time he reached Sally's cottage in Ghylldale, he was questioning his own wisdom. He accepted a drink gratefully, and was glad of Sally's ability to behave as though they had been in regular contact for the last five years instead of only sporadically. In fact he had not seen her at all for more than eighteen months, yet she chattered on about the museum, and showed him the tiny, four-roomed cottage with a friendly enthusiasm which both disarmed and relaxed him.

It was as fascinating as a Victorian doll's house, full of the period memorabilia that Sally had been collecting for years, but the low ceilings and doorways made Nick very aware that it had been built for a generation of people far smaller than himself. Smaller, and less demanding of space; people who had probably been servants to the owners of the Jacobean manor house which formed the nucleus of the Ghylldale Museum next door.

Looking out over Sally's tiny garden to the ancient buildings beyond, Nick suddenly shivered. It seemed strange to think that all those rescued habitations, the oldest dating from the fourteenth century, were empty. Wanting to ask whether she was ever frightened, he asked instead whether she was lonely, and caught a fleeting glimpse of pain, as though he had managed to touch a raw nerve.

She was, however, honest enough to admit it. 'Yes, I am sometimes.' She moved away from him and poured herself another whisky. Nick shook his head: come what may, he had to drive home tonight.

Seated again, nursing her glass, she laughed suddenly. 'It seems so ungrateful to admit it, though. I mean, I love the job – I've never been happier, more fulfilled – but it is remote, here. The locals are great – really friendly, keen to be helpful, all that sort of thing . . .' She laughed again. 'It's just that I'm not one of them. You know how it is.'

Yes, he did know how it was, he knew that brand of loneliness. In York, at the Castle Museum, she had been surrounded by people like herself, and however claustrophobic that could be – and he knew that too, from university life – at least they understood her, she was not unusual, not some kind of freak. Here, her position as curator, the fact that she was an attractive, unmarried woman with strong feminist and pacifist principles, would mark her out as being very odd indeed.

He wanted to comfort her, but was not sure that it was possible with words. Instead, with a quirky smile, he attempted to make light of it. 'I don't know, Sally, you'll have to get married – that's the only acceptable state for country life!'

'And is it working for you?' she asked dryly.

'Ouch!' He raised his glass to her. 'Touché, Miss Armitage!'

'*Ms*, if you don't mind!' But she was laughing. 'So – do you want to talk about it?'

'No.' He shook his head. 'Thanks, but no.'

She studied him for a long moment. 'God, Nick, you're such an idiot. Haven't you learned to talk things out yet? After all the work I put in five years ago, I'd have thought you'd learned a thing or two about communicating with people, particularly women. And don't give me that horrible scowl – it doesn't work on me, you should realise that by now!'

He started laughing, and the tension went away. 'All right – I concede defeat. It's good of you, Sally, but I really don't want to talk about it. I *need* to ask you something else. The thing is –' He glanced at his watch ' – I'm also starving. Can we go and eat, and talk over dinner?'

'Sure.' She drained her glass. 'We'll amble over to the pub – they've got a nice little restaurant and the food's great.'

He helped her into her sheepskin jacket, lifting the heavy braid of fair hair that reached halfway down her back. Beautiful hair, he remembered, which rippled into soft waves when it was brushed free. For such a busy and practical woman it was unexpectedly romantic, and, Nick reflected with a smile, almost her only vanity. On a sudden surge of tenderness, he hugged her briefly before they left the house.

'In case I forgot to say so before – it's wonderful to see you again.'

'That's funny,' she said, chuckling, 'I was just going to say the same thing!'

They stepped out into a cold night, full of stars and the heathery smell of the moors; taking a deep breath, Nick released it slowly, aware of a sense of peace, a lack of tension. Clinging to the steep sides of a valley, the scattered dwellings of Ghylldale showed clusters of lights here and there, but it was very quiet, with only the sighing of the wind and the chortling rush of a busy stream below the road. Rounded shapes like rocks turned out to be sheep, huddling together for warmth, while across the bridge, the village inn showed the welcoming lights of a Christmas tree beside the door. It was the sort of place that appealed to Nick, and he could understand why Sally loved it so much; but he could also understand the loneliness. Could he live here, do Sally's job? Somehow, he did not think so.

The short walk sharpened his already keen appetite. They went straight through to the restaurant, where Nick ordered the homemade celery soup and a large steak; Sally said she would have the pâté followed by chicken chasseur, and a red wine would suit her very well.

He laughed. 'You remembered . . .'

'Of course. I remember a lot about you, Nick Rhodes. We had a good time, and we parted friends – it doesn't happen all that often.'

'Doesn't it?'

'No. A lot of men get the wrong idea – they think because I'm a woman of a certain age, I must be itching to settle down. They decide they're in love, then can't understand when it's time to call it a day.' She smiled affectionately across the table, and briefly touched his hand. 'You weren't like that.'

'No, but I can understand why men fall in love with you . . .' He held her gaze for a long moment, and watched the suffusion of warmth in her cheeks and in her eyes. Light-blue eyes, reflecting every mood so clearly, as quick to sparkle with amusement as they were to freeze with disdain.

Unlike Natasha's eyes, he thought, which were as soft and dark as warm chocolate, and just as opaque. Natasha could hide her thoughts with no trouble at all, whereas Sally was as readable as an open book.

Watching her as they talked and ate and talked again, Nick was aware that Sally still found him attractive, and it was like balm to his wounded soul. He also suspected that she would like to go to bed with him, and that awareness added an edge of excitement and anticipation. All at once he was eager for the meal to be over, and hoping that she would suggest having coffee back at the cottage; but then the conversation turned to Bernice and his divorce, and Nick suddenly realised the gravity of the situation. He remembered a meal with Natasha, years ago, and a combination of innocence and blindness which had led to years of misery and emotional complications which were still not over. He was not sure he could go through that again.

She sensed the change in him, just as he had sensed her loneliness earlier, and that need of sexual release. 'What's wrong?' she asked as they walked back towards the cottage and his car.

He considered a light reply, then rejected it as unworthy. 'Everything,' he said heavily, 'apart from you.'

They walked on in silence until they came to Sally's door. 'Look, come on in, for heaven's sake. It's only just after ten, and I really do think you need to talk . . .'

In many respects she was a good person to talk to, since she knew the circumstances which had led to Nick's separation from his first wife, and seemed to understand how thoroughly confused he was now. She sympathised and made more coffee, asked the right sort of questions and shared her cigarettes with him; nevertheless, it was difficult to explain a situation which he did not understand himself. The fact that Sally had never met Natasha only served to complicate matters; she kept saying things like: 'Well, she was always a bit odd, wasn't she? At least, that's the impression I got when you used to talk about her before.'

He wanted to say, no, she wasn't odd, she was unique, a very special person who had brought great joy to his life; it was just that for the moment pain was outweighing it. He wanted to say that the lack of understanding was in himself, that if only he could find a way of getting through to her, then perhaps everything would be all right.

But it hurt too much. His sense of failure stopped his tongue, and when Sally, sensing his pain, came and took him into her arms, Nick did not draw away.

Twenty Three

AT A BREAK in the narrative, Natasha yawned and stretched and rubbed her eyes. Although the ashtray was full, she lit another cigarette and pushed the typewriter away. So tired, she thought, so bloody tired. For a moment she sat with her head in her hands, then, with an effort, stood up. Her legs felt weak as she crossed the room; she cannoned into the door-jamb and staggered across the sitting-room towards the kitchen. Only as she waited for the kettle to boil did she look at her watch: it was after one o'clock.

Galvanised by a jolt of panic, she hurried back to her office, gathering up half a dozen pages of typescript, shoving them hastily into a manila folder. Nick was bound to be back soon, and she did not want him to know what she was doing. Moving the ashtray, blowing ash off the desk, she opened a few packs of Christmas cards and jumbled them together, trying to make it look as though she had been busy writing letters to go with them. Tomorrow, she thought, it would be necessary to address a few envelopes as well.

Having stoked up the fire and set the thermostat to its overnight position, Natasha then went up to bed. She was too tired even to read. She fell asleep as soon as her head touched the pillow.

When she awoke it was to the smell of fresh coffee. As she pulled herself up into a sitting position, Natasha noticed that the curtains were drawn back, and low winter sunlight was streaming in across the foot of the bed. Bemused, she glanced at the clock, and was astonished to see that it was almost noon. Although she had slept for more than ten hours, she felt so weary and thick-headed that the effort of rising, talking, making decisions, seemed entirely beyond her.

She took a sip of the coffee, wondering about Nick and his trip to Newcastle. The only medievalist she knew was David, who, as far as she could recall, was still lecturing in Bristol. So it could not have been him. But Nick's contact might not have been a man at all; it might have been a woman, someone from his past that Natasha knew nothing about. It was possible, but her mind was still too befuddled to formulate any real suspicions. Anyway, whatever time it had been when he returned, she had not heard a thing.

Natasha reached for her dressing-gown. As she tied it, she caught sight of herself in the mirror and groaned. Her hair was lank and needed cutting, her face was streaked with yesterday's make-up, and the hollows around her collar-bones were as deep as salt-cellars. She looked dreadful. Loss of weight had never suited her, and it seemed the anxieties of the last few weeks had knocked off more pounds than a rigorous diet.

She went along to the bathroom and washed her face; but those marks around her eyes were not smudged make-up, they were shadows under the skin, purplish bruises that made her look more undernourished than ever. She swore at herself in the mirror, promising to give herself a break. That stupid story wasn't worth it; she needed to rest, to recover her health and strength.

At the top of the stairs there was the tantalising smell of bacon frying. Nick's voice called up to her from the kitchen: he was making bacon sandwiches, and would she like one? She was suddenly hungry, and the thought of being pampered, even just a little, was enough to send her back to bed. She brushed her hair first, though, making the best of a poor job, and touched her bloodless cheeks and lips with a soft coral blusher. Not too much, just enough to look natural: she did not want Nick thinking that she had made a special effort just for breakfast in bed.

He came upstairs a few minutes later, but while she thanked him for the sandwich and the fresh mug of coffee, Natasha's attention was on him. He was wearing black trousers and a dark Fair Isle sweater that made him look warm and solid and dependable. And very attractive: the subtle greens in the sweater matched his eyes. She wanted to hold him, have him hold her, bury her face against his broad chest and tell him how miserable she was, how sorry, what a stupid, idiotic fool she had been. And she wanted to confess about the story she was writing, because she was beginning to suspect that it was more than just a trivial romance. Certain aspects were worrying her, not least her own obsession with setting it down.

But Nick seemed sublimely unaware of her anxieties. In fact, he looked more relaxed than he had been for weeks. He smiled at the sunshine, asked whether he could fetch anything else, and told her to stay in bed as long as she liked.

It was too much. Her eyes narrowed. 'How did you get on in Newcastle?'

'Fine,' he said casually, turning to look out of the window. 'God, the front garden's a mess – I really will have to get to that in the spring.'

'Did you get what you wanted?'

'Oh, yes. Quite a bit about Brickhill and the guy who built the castle. And,' he went on, turning to face her, 'I now know where the Norton-Clive papers are. Would you believe they were deposited last year with the North Riding Historical Society? They kept that very quiet, I notice – I shall have words with Freddie Kirkpatrick when I see him.'

Frowning, wondering what the Norton-Clives had to do with the situation, Natasha was determined not to be sidetracked. 'What time did you get back? It must have been quite late.'

He paused by the door. 'Do you know, I'm not sure? It was gone midnight when I left there, so it must have been around two when I got back. I hope I didn't wake you?'

'No, no, you didn't. I just wondered, that was all.'

But as soon as she had finished her sandwich, Natasha scurried along the landing. She listened at the top of the stairs, but all she could hear from the kitchen was the faint, electronic buzz of the washing machine. For an instant, that struck her as odd, particularly since Nick was not in the habit of doing the laundry. He did sometimes, if he was in need of a clean tracksuit, but –

She went into the bathroom and looked into the linen-basket. Apart from several pairs of socks and some dark-coloured underwear, the basket was empty. In the main bedroom she looked for discarded clothes. There was none; all his shirts and shorts were clean, pressed, undisturbed.

Of what could she accuse him? Being unexpectedly helpful? He had made sure, however, that there was no evidence of perfume or lipstick or anything else to incriminate him, and yet that simple act only added to her suspicions. That old colleague might have answered a few outstanding questions for him last night, but Natasha was convinced that she had been accommodating in other respects too.

Her knees suddenly gave way. She dropped back on to the neatly made bed feeling as though she had fallen from a great height. After that moment of stunned shock, her mind started racing, adding all her old suspicions to these new ones. What was it people said about infidelity? A man who's betrayed one wife will go on to betray the next. Well, so they were right. It seemed they were also right about sins being paid back in kind. Natasha knew that she had hurt Bernice Rhodes all those years ago, and as a consequence, she had hurt the boys too.

With the feeling that her own pain was about to become unbearable, she dressed quickly and grabbed her car keys. Out, she must get out; get away from here before she fell apart.

Late that afternoon, when she came back, Nick wanted to know where she had been, why she had gone dashing off like that, without a word. Looking him straight in the eye, she said: 'I've been out. I needed a breath of fresh air.'

'Three hours of it?'

'*You* were gone for eight, last night!'

He turned away at that, looking slightly shamefaced, and went up to his study. After dinner, when he had returned to his work, Natasha lit a cigarette and tried to relax. It was no good. She was edgy again. Misery had given way to resentment, not just because of his actions, but because his presence in the house had driven her out that afternoon, and was now preventing her from seeking comfort in her own work. She wanted to get back to Sarah, to the world in which she lived. If life there was more precarious, it also seemed much simpler, with matters of honour and virtue being considerably more clear-cut.

Unable to sit still, she took refuge in her office and closed the door. Perhaps she would just read through the manuscript so far, and maybe add a little to it when Nick went to bed . . .

The winter that year was not particularly hard, but to me it seemed inordinately long. I chafed at the weather's restrictions as never before, cursing the rain and the cold. It was worse than snow, for with snow came frost, and then at least the air was dry. But that year we hugged the fires, while Mercy complained endlessly of her rheumatics, Polly of her chilblains, and old Samuel worried everyone about the horses. They were as miserable and ill-tempered as their masters, it seemed, and even the dogs moped round with hanging heads and heart-rending sighs.

During Lent, the Nidd broke its banks, turning the fields into lakes and making the roads impassable. We heard there were floods in York, people drowned and animals swept away. Fortunately, our Piper relatives were on higher ground, but they were as glad to see the spring as their country cousins, and just as eager to celebrate Easter.

It was late that year, and by the time we made our visit to the city all signs of the floods were gone, and spring was well under way. I felt happy and nervous as a young filly, ravenous for life, but equally unsure of my ability to match it. I thought about Richard Stalwell, as I'd been doing all winter, and wondered whether he would find time to visit the Pipers while I was there. It seemed unlikely, since spring was a busy time of year for any farmer, and my father could not stay to keep me company in town. But my visit was to last three weeks, in which I would endeavour to help my aunt in the house, go visiting with my cousins, and have some new clothes made. Whether I saw Richard or not, I told myself, I would have a most enjoyable time.

And I did. To my surprise I also saw Richard, and more than once, since it seemed he had various pressing reasons for being in town at that time.

Although he still wore black, he was much brighter than at Christmas, his spirits matched by a selection of embroidered vests which greatly took my fancy. He was attentive too, which pleased me even while I had difficulty overcoming my sense of awe. He was, after all, some ten years my senior, handsome, educated, and the owner of his own house and land. And he had been married, too, to the lovely Caroline with her dark hair and unblemished skin. I could not match her, not even at this time of year when my complexion was pale. The freckles across my nose were permanent, and while I had begun to fill out a little, by no means could I be described as soft and pleasing.

I wished so hard to be plump and pretty, to be older than I was, to be able to flirt with my eyes and fan as I had seen my cousins do; but all I had to recommend me was my robust health and future prospects. To me they were dampening attributes, to be found in plenty elsewhere. Richard Stalwell could have found a new wife in any one of a dozen parishes around the city, and no doubt would when he was ready. I could not imagine why Aunt Margaret bothered to parade me before him, even in my fine new clothes.

As before, my father came to collect me at the end of my stay, and as before we talked of this and that on the way home, but mainly of Richard Stalwell. It seemed that my father had found cause to do business at Sheriff Whenby while I was away, and had come home via Denton-on-the-Forest. He had called on his relative by marriage, and had been most impressed by the extent of his freehold, over seventy acres, including a sizeable proportion of good meadowland.

I was similarly impressed. 'Then he should have some good stock,' I said.

'Indeed he has, all fat and healthy after the winter. He feeds them turnips, too,' my father added wonderingly, 'and is experimenting, so he tells me, with different grasses on his pasture . . .'

Having heard something of such innovations elsewhere, the claims made for their success had always seemed somewhat outrageous to my father and myself; but if Richard was finding them successful, then he was obviously a man to watch. I began to understand my father's interest in him, and not just with regard to myself. It struck me, however, as it had no doubt occurred to my father, that to experiment in such a fashion required capital, and capital might be something he was short of.

Was that the root of his interest in me? Or was he not interested in me at all, but simply observing the conventions while he furthered his friendship with the Pipers and my father, to the extent of seeking a loan?

Those suspicions created a void beneath the shining brightness of Sarah's adoration. She had always been shy of discussing him with her father, but that sudden distrust made it impossible. As Natasha understood, reading on, the topic could not be avoided completely, since Richard Stalwell came to call on them three times that summer.

If those visits caused a flurry in the kitchen, Sarah discovered that her ambivalent feelings towards him had cured her shyness. In her father's house at least, she began to treat him with a certain condescension, which, far from offending him, seemed only to increase his interest. At fifteen years old, Natasha thought, Sarah was quick to learn, and that there was also a cool, calculating side to her nature began to be obvious. As soon as it was borne in upon her that she was being courted, she questioned Richard about his family, but not too much; she feigned lack of interest in his house and domestic arrangements, but then led him on about crops and stock, impressing him with some sharp, intelligent questions.

. . . Satisfied, I forced myself to refuse when asked to accompany them on a tour of my father's holdings. It near killed me to invent other, more pressing matters, since I longed to show how well we were doing, and I wanted to see Richard's reaction and hear his comments for myself. To be truthful, I wanted to be in his company, to savour the way he looked and spoke and laughed; but I would not let him think I was his for the taking. So I held back that first time, and the second, giving way on the third only when virtually ordered to by my father.

And on that third occasion, my father found reason to absent himself for a while, leaving us alone in the kitchen garden. That was clever of him, since the walled garden with its neat geometric beds of squares and triangles was my domain, a source of both pleasure and pride. It was then midsummer, and everything was lush and coming to fruition. High on their stakes the beans were in flower, flame red against their bright green leaves, with onions and chives in serried rows beneath. The potatoes were also doing well, and the peas were already in pod; two triangles of brilliant orange marigolds offset the beds of a dozen different herbs, while along the wall the dog-roses were in bloom. Come October, they would provide me with fruits for my rose-hip syrup, an excellent preventative for scurvy.

As we walked, my petticoats brushed a lavender hedge, releasing a sweet, heady scent that put me in mind of the linen-press with its stacks of neatly hemmed and embroidered sheets, half of which would come to me on my marriage. All in all I was pleased by what we surveyed, and pleased to be here with Richard Stalwell, who must surely realise that I was no idle fool.

Away from him, it was easy to tell myself that I cared not a jot for his opinion, but in his company I cared very much. I wanted to be as desirable to him as he was to me, and if that desire must turn on skill rather than beauty, then so be it. Nevertheless, although he was not slow to pay me compliments on my various abilities, I did wish that he might look on me more fondly, without that constant spark of amusement in his eye.

I thought of Robert Herrick, whose lines of poetry I often murmured aloud as I worked in the house and about the farm, and wished that my companion might be moved to murmur something equally romantic, but my hopes were in vain, even in that sweet spot.

He looked and smiled and admired; he even smiled upon me and took my arm as we paced the paths, making me painfully aware of his touch and hopelessly tongue-tied. His words, however, remained prosaic.

He mentioned his sister Agnes, who kept house for him, and said: 'Your father has visited us at Denton. It would please me to entertain you both, if you would care to undertake the journey. You might view the farm, and our kitchen garden too,' he added with a sidelong smile, 'although I must confess it cannot compare with this . . .'

Acknowledging the compliment with a smile and an inclination of my head, I tried to seem cool and calm despite the frantic pounding in my breast. Prosaic or not, there were serious implications behind that invitation, and for the moment I was too taken aback to deal with them.

When I did not reply, he turned and asked me again. 'I trust you will come. It would please me.'

'I – I must ask my father, sir,' I stammered with unaccustomed humility. Aware of his searching glance, I dared not look up.

'In this matter,' Richard said softy, 'he waits on you, I think.'

'Then, sir,' I whispered, swallowing hard, 'I shall be honoured to be your guest.'

Twenty Four

On Monday morning, Nick had to see Haydn Parker about the rugby match being organised for the end of term. Last week's meeting had been in committee, with neither time nor opportunity afterwards to discuss personal matters. Remembering Haydn's original offer to lend an ear should he need it, Nick felt apprehensive now as well as guilty.

If he had given himself time to think on Saturday afternoon, instead of being so thoroughly seduced by Dr Wills and her theories, he might have turned for advice in a completely different direction. The person he should have talked to was Haydn Parker, whose attributes included a fine mind as well as kindness and discretion. But, Nick reflected, it was too late now; and after all, as a cleric, he might well have expressed disapproval of Dr Wills and the entire investigation.

He would certainly have disapproved of what had happened between himself and Sally on Saturday night. And with regard to that, Nick was not even sure of his own opinion. In the most obvious and superficial way, he felt better for it, but under that lurked some very weighty regrets. He wished that Sally had been less sympathetic, and himself less susceptible; most of all he wished that he'd just stepped into his car and driven away. In spite of everything, Natasha was still the woman he loved; he had used Sally merely as a substitute, and the fact that she was more than willing did not alleviate his sense of guilt.

He wondered too whether Natasha suspected where he had been.

A little later, he found himself lying to Haydn Parker. 'No, really,' he said in answer to his friend's enquiry, 'things are fine. One or two problems, you know how it is, but nothing we can't handle. But thanks for asking . . .'

And after that, feeling guiltier than ever, he went to obliterate such thoughts by phoning Freddie Kirkpatrick, secretary of the North Riding Historical Society. Eventually, after a lengthy conversation in which various objections had to be surmounted, he was granted permission to search through the Norton-Clive papers for the handwritten journal of the rector of Denton.

Wednesday afternoon saw him ensconced in a tiny room in Northallerton, overlooking British Rail's east coast main line. Every so often the sudden *whooof* of Inter-City trains rattled the window-panes; drawn to the window for a moment, he worried about the distraction. Then the boxes arrived, brought in to him by an elderly woman who acted like an invigilator while he began his search for the manuscript he wanted. Her eyes never left those boxes or his searching hands; she did not speak and did not smile. Nick felt like a criminal under the watchful eye of a prison warder, so inhibited to begin with that he worked with painful slowness.

As time wore on and he ploughed through box after box, he wondered whether Dr Wills had been leading him a merry dance, inventing a pack of lies to give a spurious authenticity to her theories. By three o'clock his back was aching and his hands were filthy, the grime of centuries was under his nails and in his throat, and he would have given anything for a cup of coffee and a cigarette. The high-speed trains made no impression at all.

There seemed no logic to the order in which the papers had been filed and packed: personal correspondence and journals were interspersed with estate matters, business letters, designs for furniture and extensions to house and garden. Before his eyes and brain switched to a state of automation, Nick noticed a bill from Thomas Chippendale beneath a letter from William Pitt, and a notebook of cookery receipts belonging to Lady Amelia Norton-Clive on top of a poem addressed to her by Lord Byron. There was Civil War correspondence regarding the raising of troops for the support of the king, and official notices along similar lines from the period of the First World War. No wonder, he thought, that so many historians had pestered the Norton-Clives for a look at these papers.

They were as diverse as they were fascinating, and Nick would have loved nothing more than the time to go through every interesting little snippet. But time was something he did not have. He tried to ignore names and dates in favour of a bound book or chunk of manuscript pages, but none of those he came across was what he was seeking.

Eventually, he was left with just one box containing the estate accounts, a set of leather-bound ledgers from the year 1799. End of the road, he thought; a wild-goose chase; thanks a lot, Dr Wills.

It seemed impossible that the manuscript should be in there, but he looked anyway, lifting the books out one by one, and checking that they were what they purported to be. The next from last was smaller, scruffier, and of a not dissimilar binding. He thought it must be some earlier ledger, but when he opened it the book revealed page after page of cramped, spidery writing, long S's like f's, and a plethora of abbreviations.

'Oh, good God . . .' He turned to the front, saw the name, the date, the place in which it had been written, and groaned aloud with relief and frustration. It was ten minutes to four, and he had, at best, an hour in which to go through this journal, kept over a period of years by the Reverend James St John Everard Clive, of the parish of St Oswald, Denton-on-the-Forest.

He had hoped, of course, to digest details of the parish, perhaps even to establish names of landholders, with a view to checking the wills for Denton at a later date. He had hoped to find a reference to his own house, although the likelihood of it being mentioned by name was remote. But all that would have to wait until he could use up some more favours for another appointment to view. In the meantime all he could do was try to verify Dr

Wills's notes by searching for the name of the widow who had been at the centre of such controversy in 1723.

While he was still searching for the year, the name seemed to leap at him from the top of a page:

> *At last ys day buried Richd Stalwell & hs nephew, ye ground relenting after 12 dys snow and hd frost. Cght in ye blizzard rtrning frm York, found aft 4 dys ys side of Brickhill. Most untimely death, gt loss to ye parish, hs widow sore afflctd she being alone.*

Nick stared at the entry before him, aware that it was unfamiliar. This had definitely not appeared in Dr Wills's notes. He quickly made a note of the date, 4th February 1723, and copied the rector's comments. As he turned the page to scan the next, his elderly minder sighed and fidgeted and looked pointedly at her watch. Without raising his eyes, Nick said: 'I'm sorry, but now that I've found what I want, I'm not leaving until I've checked all the references. It shouldn't take long . . .'

He carried on reading, increased familiarity with the handwriting enabling him to scan fairly quickly for the name of Stalwell. He found a couple of references in March and April, recording visits the rector had made to the widow, and expressing his admiration for her decision to carry on farming alone. Between the lines it seemed to Nick that there was just a hint of disapproval for the dead man's family, who had evidently shown no support for their grieving sister-in-law.

The rector had next visited Mrs Stalwell in June, and again in July. There was some comment about the poor weather, and doubts as to the success of the coming harvest. In late August, he was expressing concern over Mrs Stalwell's reputed sins, while privately attributing them to loneliness and grief. A man ahead of his time, thought Nick in surprise, reading on. In October, the Reverend Clive was practically on his soap-box, denouncing his parishioners for a bunch of illiterate and superstitious peasants, all too eager to blame the poor harvest on some hound of ill-omen that was said to be haunting the locality, and the witch in their midst who did the hound's bidding.

By ten past five he had checked all the references to Sarah Stalwell, including those around Martinmas and at the beginning of the year 1724, in which the rector seemed mystified, and then anxious about the widow's disappearance. He had even gone so far as to make enquiries of the rector of All Saints, Hammerford, to see whether she had returned to her former home. But apparently the local cleric was recently appointed, and knew nothing of her. Very reluctantly, it seemed, the Reverend Clive concluded that Sarah Stalwell had taken herself off to the city. She had been, after all, a woman of wealth and independence, and in the city she could behave as she wished, without exciting the interest or animosity of her neighbours.

Nick would have liked to read on, to make sure that Dr Wills had missed nothing else, but it was late, his minder was ready to snatch the book from his hands, and he had a headache. As reluctantly as the old rector, he gave up on Mrs Stalwell, and went in search of something to slake his thirst. There was a coffee shop and a pub nearby; he chose the pub, still quiet at that hour, and ordered a pint of bitter. Sinking half of it in two swallows, he left the glass on the bar and looked around for the telephone. He rang home and told Natasha that he still had work to do and would be eating out; then he called Sally.

From Northallerton there were two routes to Ghylldale, both skirting the North York Moors. The southerly route was probably longer, but had the advantage of familiarity; from Pickering he allowed the car to pick up speed, half his mind contemplating the small, scattered pieces of evidence which spanned so many centuries. Not for the first time he thought how strange it was that he should be far more impressed by contact with an original document than by someone else's transcript; there was a *feel* to the originals that simply did not exist in a copy, as though the writer, like an artist painting on canvas, had managed to impress his own longings and beliefs, his doubts and suspicions, upon the paper.

Dr Wills had disturbed him profoundly, throwing rational thought out of kilter for a few days; and the notes she had left him with – tantalising but incomplete – had only added to the effect. But now that he had seen and touched the Reverend Clive's manuscript for himself, Nick felt that he could throw off the direst of his suspicions and embrace reassuring logic.

'You see,' he expounded later to Sally, 'what Dr Wills was implying was that this beast was some kind of familiar spirit, but without the witchery. Unless sexual promiscuity equates with witchcraft, and it seems the inhabitants of Denton, circa 1720, tried to pin that one on the Stalwell woman too.'

'You mean, they didn't like her anyway, so it was any stick to beat her with?'

'Precisely that. You'll appreciate this, Sally – it seems the woman Sarah Stalwell was not local, but from Hammerford on the River Nidd, which is a good eight miles to the west of York. And she was apparently wealthy in her own right. *Ergo*, she was not dependent upon her neighbours when her husband died, nor upon her husband's family – who don't seem to have been very kind to her, incidentally. I don't know how old she was, and I don't know what she looked like, but I think we can assume from the rector's comments about her husband – *most untimely death, great loss to the parish* – that she was youngish and probably attractive.' With a slightly cynical smile, he added: 'I can't see the rector being quite so forgiving towards a sex-mad old crone, can you?'

'Unfortunately not – but do spare a thought for the sex-mad old crones, won't you?'

'I'll try to,' he promised with a grin. 'But listen – how about this? If she was young, financially independent, sexually attractive *and* a stranger to the community, wouldn't that provoke a certain amount of envy and resentment among the other women?'

With great amusement Sally agreed. 'Oh, yes, I'd say so!' She started clearing away the remains of their meal from the coffee table; with a tray in her hands, she turned back and said: 'And don't forget she was recently widowed. . .'

'Meaning?'

'Well, she'd be missing a normal, fulfilling sexual relationship, wouldn't she?'

He thought about that. 'Yes, I suppose she would.'

'So she starts sleeping around . . .'

Following her into the kitchen, Nick said: 'You're right – she's sleeping around, but who with? Denton's a small place, and there wouldn't be many of her social standing, and they'd likely be married. So who does that leave, other than the local workforce?'

Squirting washing-up liquid into a bowl of hot water, Sally handed him a tea-towel. 'You're not seriously suggesting that a woman like that would have sex on her own doorstep with men who worked for her? She'd never get any work out them afterwards, now would she? That's always providing there was more than one attractive enough to cast a lustful eye over! I mean, just *think* of the living conditions in those days. We're talking poor people – disease, rickets, interbreeding, *ugliness*, Nick – not Hollywood's idea of an eighteenth-century farm labourer.'

'Yes, yes, I know – the well-fed and the well-bred stuck together, and the poor made do with what they could get. I know that.' He sighed with frustration as he stacked the dishes. 'The main point is, whoever she was having it away with, and wherever she was having it, she can't have been very discreet. Whatever she was doing, she was upsetting a lot of people – hence the rumours and the accusations. But, because of *who* she is – a leading landholder and employer of labour – she's virtually beyond the power of the community to reach.'

'So they link her behaviour with the devil – or the devil's familiar – '

'In this case, the beast of ill-omen – '

'And accuse her of witchcraft.'

'Precisely!'

They regarded each other for a moment, considering that conclusion. Then Sally grinned and turned away. 'And don't forget,' she said ironically over her shoulder, 'if she was tempting men away from their lawful wives – well, then, bound to be a witch!'

That point struck home unpleasantly. Nick felt his mouth move, but it was more of a grimace than a smile. 'Yes, quite . . .'

A moment later, she said: 'But the Stalwell woman disappeared? What do you think happened to her?'

'I don't know,' he murmured reflectively. 'It's possible the villagers made life unbearable for her, especially if they couldn't make the charges stick. She'd be shamed, anyway, and probably felt the need for anonymity – in which case she'd have been sensible to leave . . .'

'But?'

He shook his head. 'But it's odd that she just abandoned the farm . . .'

Twenty Five

TRAVELLING ANY distance could be a hazardous business, and on his various journeys my father generally took a servant for company and protection. Not old Samuel, who was past such discomforts, but one of the young men, armed with pistols behind the saddle and a knife at his knee.

Even avoiding York, we were on the road some hours, and it was mid-morning by the time my father reined in to point out a church tower peeking out from a nest of green. Denton lay in its fold of the hills, surrounded by trees. Woodsmoke from noonday fires added to the heat haze, but it was possible to see individual dwellings here and there, and the spread of open fields beyond.

From our vantage-point, which lay slightly to the north-west by virtue of the route we had taken, my father indicated Richard's fine brick house to the south of us, the fenced enclosure of his land, its crops and pastures and the lush meadowland below, watered by a good, broad stream.

I was hot and thirsty and ready for my dinner, but the sight of those neatly-fenced acres dispelled every last ounce of weariness. There lay the beauty of order and achievement; I saw the extent of Richard Stalwell's holding and I wanted it as much as I wanted its master. In that moment I was prepared to bargain everything I had, my youth, my strength, and whatever fortune might one day be mine, all for the privilege of being mistress there.

The glint of ambition must have shown in my eye. Catching that look, my father laughed and patted my knee in approval. 'I told you so,' he said with no small measure of satisfaction. 'I told you he was no fool.'

The house was long and low, but larger overall than our house at Hammerford. Built by Richard's grandfather before the Civil War, it was simple in design but most practical, with a through passage connecting front and back – a sensible arrangement, thought I, which must save mud being tramped through the main living-room – and with ample store-rooms and a dairy to one side. Beyond the main room, and warmed by its chimney, was a small private parlour, with an oak staircase which rose in a dog's leg to the bedchambers above . . .

Touched by a sudden chill, Natasha stood up and pulled the curtains shut. She gazed at the manuscript pages on her desk and was not sure that she wanted to write any more. That growing suspicion was now a certainty: Richard Stalwell's fine brick house was *this* house, and those seventy acres of well-tended land were the fields she saw every day, either side of the lane . . .

She glanced behind her, down the length of the room. The bookcases, her easy chair, were all in shadow, the only light that on her desk; for a moment she was afraid to move. Then, shaking off her fright, she leapt up and switched on the overhead lights. Everything came into focus: books, filing cabinet, the table with her photocopying machine; a perfectly ordinary twentieth-century room.

But just for a moment . . .

Biting her lip, Natasha strode through the sitting-room and across the stone-flagged hall – the through-passage connecting front and back: such a sensible arrangement for a farming family! – and into her kitchen. Store-rooms; a dairy. Of course that's what they were; Nick had said as much when they were renovating the place. That chimney, where the stove now stood against the solid inner wall, was a fairly recent innovation in the life of this house. It was not much more than a hundred years old. A hundred and fifty at most. Like the ninteenth-century extension attached to the outer, north-eastern wall, with its deep doorway into the pantry, and outside entrance into the fuel-store. All quite modern, to Nick.

Unlike the old chimney, in the sitting-room. The main room, the public room – what did Nick call it? – *relic of the medieval open hall.* That hearth probably dated back four hundred years or more, to the days when this house was no more than a single-storey, thatched-roof dwelling, the days when an entire household lived, cooked their food and ate together before the fire. For privacy, the women had probably retired to the little room beyond, where they worked at their spinning and weaving and sewing . . .

Feeling suddenly faint, she clutched at the door-jamb. Her office, the room she had chosen to be her own . . .

No staircase, though. The staircase, straight, steep and narrow, was in the hall, so that was different. As her breathing calmed, she went back into the kitchen and sat down with cup of coffee and a cigarette, telling herself that it was all in her subconscious mind. Evidently, she knew all these things, had absorbed the details of Sarah's life from various sources – books, Nick, a lifetime of interest in English history. The fact that she was churning them out now, in this easy, flowing, first-person narrative, did not mean that there was anything so strange about it. It did not prove that Sarah had actually existed, or that Richard Stalwell's family had rebuilt this house.

Anyway, according to Mrs Bickerstaff, the Whiteheads had always lived here, generations of them. They weren't particularly good farmers, they never seemed to have made much of themselves or the farm, but they'd hung on, as old families often did, to the bitter end.

Although Nick wasn't convinced they had been here for more than three or four generations, Natasha preferred to believe Mrs Bickerstaff. It was something to cling to, something which made her story into fiction, albeit of a kind she had never written before.

It was only as she went up to bed that Natasha remembered the dream she had had, that hideous nightmare in which something came scrabbling up the stairs and into the spare bedroom. In that dream, the door was in a different place. Instead of being on the south side of the chimney breast, and leading out on to the long landing, as it did now, the door had appeared to be on the north side, leading to –

The room that was now her office, that eighteenth-century private parlour, with the oak staircase which rose in a dog's leg to the bedchambers above . . .

On Friday morning, torn between a desire to keep on working and the realisation that she should shop for the weekend, Natasha examined the contents of the freezer and decided that she could make do with what was there. If Nick had any objections then she would tell him to shop for himself; either that, or eat out. He would probably find some excuse for being absent, anyway.

Determined not to think about that, she ran fingers through her hair and tried to assess whatever else might be needed. Cigarettes, certainly; she was almost out of those, but could buy some from the post office when she went to pay for the week's newspapers. She had a desire for sweet things too, a desire that went with pushing herself too hard. For a sedentary occupation, she thought, writing certainly burned up the calories.

She made a short list of things, including bread, that could be purchased in the village, and went out at lunchtime. It was a dull day and bitterly cold, with the possibility of snow. At one time she would have worried about being cut off, but now she merely counted the blessings of snow-ploughs and cars and modern conveniences. In the early eighteenth century, she thought, life must have been very different indeed, with everyone's existence so dependent upon the vagaries of English weather. Storms and droughts could wipe out the summer crops, while prolonged snow and frost could kill, directly or indirectly, in many different ways. In those days, only the toughest survived; and if life was hard for the farmers, it must have been tougher still for those they employed, those who made up the majority of Denton's inhabitants.

Today, the village's self-conscious prettiness was subdued by a louring grey sky which sucked the colour out of everything bar the Christmas lights outside the pub and in the post office window. Nevertheless, there was a reassuring solidity about the row of houses and cottages facing the Green, a well-cared-for neatness which spoke to Natasha of central heating, well-stocked freezers and deep-pile carpets. And, as Nick might have added, a Saab or a BMW in the garage at the back. All rather different from Sarah's first impressions in the eighteenth century: a huddle of low, thatched roofs clustered about the church, a muddy track descending to a ford across the shallow, brackish stream, and groups of curious onlookers gathering to watch them pass.

Remembering that description of Sarah's, Natasha could almost see it, could smell the pigs in their enclosures, hear the yelling of children playing some rough game in a nearby field. For a moment one reality intruded upon another, and she paused, feeling light-headed; but then the present reasserted itself and the rough surface of Dagger Lane again met the smooth grey road, the neatly defined Green, and the beck running between deep, man-made banks. The innocent faces of those houses above the road looked as solid and complacent as ever, but her steps towards them were suddenly tentative, as though what she saw might disappear at any moment.

There was a bench outside the post office, to which a little dog was tied by its leash, a shivering toy poodle with a coat on. As Natasha sat down to calm herself it whimpered and gazed at her appealingly, but she could find no sympathy to spare. Working too hard, she told herself, clenching her teeth against an inner trembling; too obsessed with that story, that's the trouble. But it was all so real, as she wrote she could see it in her mind's eye, like a film rolling inexorably on in the private cinema of her own head. She could see everything, from Aunt Margaret's half-timbered house on Goodramgate to Sarah's kitchen garden and the foldyard of Richard Stalwell's farm; old Mr Kirkham's embroidered vests and full-bottomed wig to Sarah's slender figure and square-jawed determination. So far, the images had stayed inside her own head; she must be careful not to let them escape, except on to paper which was where they belonged.

The door jangled as a woman came out. Embarrassed, Natasha stood up. It was hardly the weather for sitting outside. The woman smiled uncertainly and bent to release the little dog, cooing to it like a baby. Taking a deep breath, Natasha went into the post office which also served as a shop, made her purchases and escaped as quickly as possible. Once outside, the stretch from the village to Holly Tree Cottage seemed impossibly long. She felt weak and empty, chilled inside and in need of sustenance. She turned left, and walked the few yards to the Half Moon.

There were plenty of cars outside, and the staff were too busy serving meals to exchange more than a few words. Feeling that brandy was suitably medicinal, Natasha ordered a small one at the bar and looked round for a quiet corner in which to sit. She found one eventually, but not before she had bumped into the landlord, who paused long enough to tell her, *sotto voce*, that the Morrisons had got that dog, the Irish wolfhound which had been killing their sheep.

'Oh, right,' she said vaguely, not really taking it in. But once she had found her small, shadowed corner and taken several sips of that medicinal spirit, thought and feeling began to return. She lit a cigarette with trembling fingers and could have wept for the injustice of it all. Craig Morrison assumed the proportions of an ogre, brutal and insensitive, his blinkered vision incapable of seeing anything but the most obvious. That she had once found him so attractive, and had responded to him sexually, now disgusted her. 'That bastard,' she muttered under her breath, knowing that he had been determined to kill McCoy from the first.

Her stomach felt hollow, but the sight of businessmen and women tucking into Christmas lunches made her feel sick. They were looking at her too, darting, surreptitious glances that seemed to question what such a scruffy-looking woman was doing there, drinking spirits on her own.

Feeling like a bag lady, she picked up her plastic carrier, drained her glass, and made her way unsteadily towards the door.

The cold air outside was something of a shock. Huddling into her coat, Natasha put her head down and hurried across the Green, longing for home and privacy and a chance to think things through before Nick returned. She was halfway along Dagger Lane when, looking up, she saw Toby Bickerstaff ahead, lurking by the hedge. He was half-turned away from her, and she had instinctively slowed before the significance of his stance registered: he was busy relieving himself.

Fear and revulsion stopped her dead. She had not seen him since Craig Morrison's visit, and to come upon him like this, to catch him peeing into the hedge in broad daylight, was horrible. The brutal facts of the murder leapt to mind, sexual violence, severed genitals, and it was all centred on something she did not want to see: an old man's wrinkled penis.

She stood, rigid but indecisive, wanting to run away but afraid that he would notice the movement and see her. Perhaps if she stood quite still he would not realise she was there, and then he would carry on up the lane, quite oblivious, while she crept slowly and quietly towards home.

But as he finished, and shook himself, and covered himself up, the old man looked back over his shoulder. Meeting Natasha's appalled gaze, he turned and grinned shamefacedly, shoving his hands into his pockets as he waited for her to catch up.

He was waiting, she realised with horror, and grinning like a gargoyle. What did he want? What was he going to do? Where the hell was all that famous reticence, she thought in panic, that fear of strangers that led him to hide himself away and rarely speak? Well, she had two choices: she could turn now and hurry back to the village, or pretend nothing more than disapproval as she carried on towards home. At his age, she told herself firmly, the worst he was likely to do was say something disgusting; if he tried to assault her she would just have to run for it. She thought she could run faster than an old man.

Feeling in her pocket for the house keys, Natasha forced her wooden limbs to move.

'Sorry 'bout that, missus,' he said grovellingly as she approached. 'Got caught short, like . . .'

He continued to leer as she drew level with him, and, to her dismay, fell into step as she marched towards home. He seemed determined to speak to her, despite her hurried gait and frozen expression. She could smell the beer on his breath and the stale, decaying odour of his clothes.

'Morrison's lad,' he wheezed, struggling to keep up, 'Morrison's lad shot that dog – that there Irish thing – '

'I know,' she snapped, but he sounded so pleased, and she was so astonished that that was all he wanted to say, she slowed by the gateway and turned her head to look at him.

'Caught it, he did, havin' another go at 'is sheep. Caught it red-handed, like –' He broke off to indulge in a gasping, wheezing laugh, then said: 'Aye, it's grand news, I'm right glad, I don't mind tellin' thee.'

'Oh?' He really was revolting, she thought, sympathising with Mrs Bickerstaff. 'Why's that?'

His celebratory mood was not dented by her icy tone, but he did glance round, furtively, before answering her question in an undertone. 'Well, you see, Missus, I were afeard it were t'other thing – you know, black, shadowy thing –' He leaned closer. 'I thought it were after *me*.'

Natasha recoiled.

She remembered, afterwards, saying something inane and probably rather patronising before he shuffled away, muttering to himself, in the direction of his old caravan. There was no doubt that he had been sincere in that gruesome confession, and that he had managed to frighten her for a second time. But his fears were probably based on guilt, she thought, remembering the murder; and guilt could have strange effects on people.

Once again she wondered whether she should say something to Nick. She could, and probably should, tell him about the sheep and McCoy's violent end, although if what Toby Bickerstaff said was true, and the dog had been shot in the act of worrying those sheep, then that left her own arguments without much foundation. If McCoy really was the sheep-killer, and it now seemed he was, then what about the stray? Did it really exist, or had she imagined it? Nick had seen nothing that night, but then he had been half asleep when she ran into that dense black shape.

Yes, she had run into it, she had been sure at the time and was equally sure now; just as Toby Bickerstaff and Mrs McCoy were convinced of what they had seen. Are we all mad, she wondered, or just deluded by coincidence? Perhaps there was a stray dog that we each saw at different times and in a poor light, while fear and imagination distorted the image to frighten us further. But she could not forget Charlie Cramp and his story of Padfoot; nor could she forget the woman she had seen in the barn and by the wood.

Somehow, and she did not want to think how, that woman was telling her story, and she was using Natasha to do it. That was why she was getting no more than the barest outline of events, a sketch of her early life, of how she met Richard Stalwell and came to this house. She was leading up to something rather more important, and Natasha's desire to know what that was temporarily outweighed her fear of the means employed.

As the need to write tugged her towards the office, it seemed to Natasha that the possibility of life beyond the grave was no longer so ridiculous as once it seemed, and far less terrifying than the thought of going mad. And there was such comfort in writing, a complete world in which painful reality could not intrude.

Twenty Six

THE SILENCE which had existed between them, taut and fragile as ice across a black mill pond, broke that evening.

For Nick it had been a particularly stressful week, interspersed with anxiety and excitement and – if he was honest – not enough sleep. Trying to finalise paperwork before the end of term, issuing last-minute encouragement to certain students while others were suddenly infected by Christmas spirit and a riotous desire to break all the rules, had not been easy. That afternoon, outside his office, he had been ambushed by a group of giggling girls with mistletoe – but not Jane Bardy, thank God – and even Flora had pecked his cheek as she handed him a sheaf of papers to sign and wished him an ironic Merry Christmas.

Resisting the urge to down several large whiskies, he had drunk a single pint of bitter with Giles in their favourite local, and confirmed their usual arrangements for Boxing Day dinner at Nick's house, followed by a New Year's Eve party at Giles's. It was something they had done for years, and personal upheavals had never been allowed to interrupt the ritual; nevertheless, this year Giles hesitated, and even while Nick was busily reassuring him, part of his mind was questioning the sense of that annual celebration.

It was almost seven as he pulled into the yard. There was a light on in the office, but everywhere else seemed to be in darkness. As he climbed out of the car, one of the barn cats accosted him; the other one was sitting on the low garden wall, yowling.

Their dishes, he noticed as he opened the gate, were empty. Usually Natasha fed them about dusk, and they did not like to be forgotten, despite being perfectly competent at finding their own food. Irritated, Nick strode down the path, switched on the porch light, and then tripped over the house cat in the darkened hallway. Her indignant squawks punctuated his curses as he made his way into the kitchen.

Darkness, the fire almost out, and no tantalising smell of dinner.

He flung his heavy briefcase into the nearest chair, switched on all the lights and grabbed the coal scuttle, brushing past Natasha in the hall as he strode outside.

'Bloody hell, Natasha – what do you think you're playing at? If you can't do anything else, you might at least keep the fire going!'

She hovered uncertainly, getting in his way as he strode back inside and bent to the cast-iron stove with logs and kindling and small lumps of coal. He was so angry he could have knocked her out of the way, could barely trust himself to speak for fear the anger would take hold and drive him to something regrettable. She'd barely spoken to him all week, and seemed hardly to notice his comings and goings. It was like coming home to a prison.

Nurturing the fire, he steadfastly refused to look at her; nevertheless, he was aware of every indecisive movement – the fridge opening and closing, the sighs, the switching on of the kettle, the fridge again, the oven's fan starting up. She made the mistake of apologising.

'I'm sorry, I've been so . . . *busy* this afternoon . . .'

'Doing *what*, for Christ's sake?'

He heard the indrawn breath, the rustle of a fresh packet of cigarettes being opened. 'Well, I, er – well, there seemed a lot of letters to write – and – and *cards*. Such a list!' She gave a short, nervous laugh. 'I'd no idea we knew so many people – and I thought, if I don't get them all posted tomorrow, well, they won't get them for Christmas, will they?'

'Christmas!' Almost spitting the word, he turned and glared at her, and as quickly turned away. He did not want to see how dreadful she looked, it made him angrier still. 'What a damned farce – if it weren't for the boys, I'd go to a bloody hotel, do you know that? At least there'd be something to eat!'

'Oh, God . . .'

The fire was crackling, the flames licking around dry twigs and old, creosoted bits of timber; finding an affinity, Nick gave it his full attention.

'Look,' she said faintly, 'I'm sorry, but I – '

'Oh, for Christ's sake, stop apologising!' he said viciously, rising to face her. 'You're not sorry – why should you be? You've made it abundantly clear for some time that my needs aren't important, and all this just confirms it!'

His outflung arm was intended to encompass the entire kitchen and what it lacked – food, warmth, even a welcome – but she flinched away as though he had attempted to strike her. That made him angrier still. He had never in his life struck a woman, and did not intend to start now; but he wanted to hurt her, as deeply and profoundly as she had been hurting him all this time.

'Well,' he declared coldly, turning away, 'if you can't be bothered to speak to me, and you certainly don't want me in your bed, perhaps I'd better go elsewhere . . .'

On a choking sob, she cried: 'Oh, yes *do* – go to your girlfriend, whoever she is. And if she's so accommodating, you'd better bloody stay there, hadn't you?' She pushed past him on his way to the door, sobbing as she raced up the stairs.

Battered by waves of her distress, by his own shock at realising that she knew, for a moment Nick could not think. He stood, fists clenched, as furious with himself as with her, appalled by the inevitability of the situation. He did not want to leave, and yet he had unwittingly manoeuvred himself into a position from which it seemed he must. Unless he backed down, apologised; and he was not about to do that.

The muffled sounds from above suddenly became clearer. Natasha appeared on the landing, overnight bag in hand, and came careering down the stairs, a trail of Nick's clothes behind her. Trembling violently, her face distorted by rage and grief, she thrust the bag at him, her words a tumult of distress and vituperation as she tried to force him towards the door. The one word that registered was *bastard*, and at that he lost control.

Dropping the bag, he grabbed her shoulders and shook her hard. '*Don't*,' he said violently, 'don't you call me that – *not ever*. Do you hear me? *Not ever*!'

The shock silenced her. As he let go, she slumped against the wall, watching him with huge, frightened eyes as he picked up the bag, retrieved his briefcase, and opened the door. He had not, he realised, even had time to take off his coat.

'But I'd have thought,' he said later with bitter irony, 'that she'd have remembered to feed her precious cats.'

Less concerned about them than she was about him, Sally said: 'Nick, is this what you really want? Because if it isn't, you've got to go back.'

But he did not know what he wanted, and was in no state to make decisions. It was difficult for him to think clearly, and apart from telling her the cause of the row, Nick could not assess what lay behind it, and did not even want to answer questions. Once they had eaten – and it was after ten – he was exhausted, beyond thought or reason, and on the verge of falling asleep beside the fire.

They went to bed, but did not make love. He thought he would find oblivion as soon as his head touched the pillow, but, like the desire for sex, sleep eluded him. Sally lay curled behind him, her arm across his chest, her cheek against his back; it was comforting to begin with, but after a while he needed to move. Gently easing himself free, he waited for Sally to turn over before relaxing on to his back. But he was not really relaxed, and, with misery pressing down on his chest like a dead weight, could not sleep. Beset by images of Natasha and a jumble of memories, he could not see the errors which had led to this pass. All he could think was that it should not have ended this way, in such blind fury, and with him turning to someone else for solace.

Oh, Natasha, he cried silently into the darkness, we had so much that was good: what is it that's driven us apart?

The museum at Ghylldale closed for several weeks in the New Year, for repairs and refurbishment, but just before Christmas the weekends were busy. Staff and volunteers dressed up in period costume to conduct guided tours of the museum and children's farm, and to serve hot fruit punch and mince pies in the vast open hall of the Jacobean manor house around which the rest of the museum was built. As curator and chief co-ordinator, Sally had to be up and about and organised well before the opening at ten o'clock.

'Let me do breakfast,' Nick offered, 'while you get on with whatever else you have to do. Then I'll get out of your way, Sally – I've got some hard thinking ahead of me, and I don't have much time to play with.'

'True.' She glanced up at him and sighed. 'I wish we had time to talk, but – '

He hugged her briefly. 'We haven't – you haven't – and anyway, you've done enough for me already. I don't deserve it.'

As a mother might have done, she smoothed his rumpled hair and kissed his cheek. 'Nonsense – it was mutual, you know that.'

After breakfast, armed with a bunch of keys, Sally disappeared in the direction of the museum, while Nick repacked his bag and tried to be sure that he had left everything the way it was when he arrived. Even though she had said that he could stay as long as he needed to, he did not want Sally regretting her generosity. She was as understanding as she was good-natured, but he was not in love with her, nor she with him, despite the satisfaction they had found in each other's arms. At best this was a temporary haven, at worst an imposition upon her kindness.

There were practical problems too, even more immediate. The boys were to be collected from school on Tuesday; if he could not take them home to Denton, then where was he to take them? Not here: there was no room, and anyway, he was not up to explaining his relationship with Sally to a pair of twelve-year-old boys.

What was he to do? What *could* he do? Nick wondered as he left the house and walked across the road to where he had parked his car. A group of sheep lumbered to their feet and scattered at his approach, settling down again to nibble the frozen grass as he started the car and took the road for Whitby. It was a dazzling morning, the air clear and invigorating, the moors thick with a frost as white as snow. Despite the cold he drove with the window down, and with the little port in sight, pulled off the road for a while to smoke a cigarette and appreciate the view.

Today the North Sea was an almost cheerful grey-blue, which, because he was thinking of them, struck Nick as being the precise shade of his children's eyes. Grey-blue, *almost* cheerful, bearing up. A little wary, perhaps? Well, if they were, it was hardly to be wondered at, poor little beggars, shunted between himself and Bernice, and the tough regime of a boys' school. Christ, they deserved better than this: what was he to do with them? Should he go back home, insist on his rights, and take them with him? He tried to envisage the situation and winced: he could not impose that atmosphere on his sons, not at Christmas, when they were expecting fun and freedom, a good time after a hard term's work in school. Nor did he want to make his excuses and send them straight to their mother. Not only would Bernice kick up an almighty fuss, he *wanted* to see his boys, wanted to spend time with them, would have liked to share a little fun himself. They were growing up fast and he had missed so much of their childhood already.

He thought of booking a last-minute holiday, skiing perhaps; but then remembered that they were going to the Italian Alps in February with a party from school. And this really was last-minute, so much so that he was unsure of finding anything remotely suitable. A weekend trip to London might do the trick, to see the sights and do some of the things that appealed to boys of their age, a visit to the Tower and HMS *Belfast*, the London Dungeon and tickets for whatever stage musical was the latest rage.

That would take care of three days, but what of the rest? He thought of Giles, who at least had room for guests, but his mind refused even that temptation. Giles had work to do, he had been talking about it only yesterday, and anyway, it was hardly fair to burden their friendship like that. More to the point, what was he going to do in the long term?

No nearer a solution, Nick threw down the remains of his cigarette and ground it under his heel. Climbing back into his car, he closed the window and turned the heater up full; if the sharp air had cleared his head, it had also chilled him to the bone.

In Whitby it was noticeably less cold. He parked by the upper harbour and walked through the town, stopping for a cup of Viennese coffee at a little café he knew before continuing on his way to the seafront. The tide was going out, and below the West Cliff the sand was firm, just right for walking, as was evidenced by the number of people exercising their dogs along the shore. The sea, which from the height of the moors had seemed an undecided colour, was, at this level, almost turquoise as it rolled gently over the shallows; the waves curled rather than broke, a soothing lullaby of sound rather than the wild orchestration he had expected. Even in summer, he thought, it was rarely as calm as this.

There was, nevertheless, a tang of salt and seaweed in the air, and more than a hint of that bracing quality for which this stretch of the English coast was famous. Walking briskly, breathing deeply, leaving the town and people behind, Nick very quickly felt his depression begin to lift, and knew that he had been right to come. So far, and during some of the worst periods of his life, this place had never failed him. The air, the sea, the cliffs, even the mocking cries of the gulls, all conspired to banish negative thoughts, to make him feel that in spite of the metaphorical mantraps, life was still worth living, still worth the challenge.

He could enjoy this place alone, never felt the need of anyone else to share it. Perhaps that was the secret. In fact, he thought, another person would just as likely spoil it by reminding him that he was not alone, that there were always other people to answer to, other people for whom he was responsible, when what he truly wanted in moments like this was the illusion of freedom.

Freedom. It was an illusion, but no less necessary for all that. As a child, seeking escape from his younger brothers and sisters, he had thought it was real and that he had found it here . . .

Well, he had found it for an hour or so, until the tide started rushing in and he was almost stranded on the rocks. Just there, where the cliff jutted out and the water swirled so ferociously at high tide, he had almost been swept away; would have been, had it not been for the strong hands of his father – his stepfather – grabbing the young Nicholas and hauling him to safety on the other side. A hug and a good shaking had assured him that he was back, safe and well within the bosom of his family; but it had not prevented him from going off again . . . and again . . . After the first occasion, though, he had made sure that he was not caught out; indeed, he had become a pain-in-the-neck expert on local tide-times for the rest of the holiday. Nick was certain that he had not been a very likeable child.

How strange to think – and it could still bring that peculiar, almost physical, twist of the heart – that he had been conceived here, by the sea. He had not known that as a child, of course, just as he had known nothing about his father. Except that his father was dead, killed in a motorbike accident, Nick's mother had always been rather vague on the subject. Naturally, he had assumed that they were married, and that she was a young widow by the time she met and married Stanley Rhodes. But she was only nineteen when she married him and by that time little Nicholas was well over a year old. And of course Stan adopted the boy, so the truth did not come out for a long time. Not until after Nick's own sons were born, and by that time his mother was terminally ill with cancer, and knew she was dying.

Facing eternity seemed to cure her of the shame and embarrassment that had stopped her tongue all those years; and indeed, Nick had to admit that he was glad the fiction had held beyond his adolescence and early manhood. He could still recall the shock of realising his mother had lied – that everyone had lied, and so successfully – and he could still remember his sense of betrayal. The shock had gone a long way towards dampening his pride and arrogance; a good thing then, but it would have been unbearable during his teenage years.

It was a sorry little story, but, he imagined sadly, not untypical. His mother, Gloria, had been a pretty girl at the time just after the war when most people had very little money. Offered the chance of a holiday in Whitby with the parents of a girlfriend, she had accepted; she and the girlfriend had met a couple of young men who were camping on the cliffs, two attractive, fun-loving boys who were keen to join forces and have a good time. They were on leave from the army, but other than their names, Nick and Eddie, the girls knew very little about them. Nick was from London, and had a motorbike; Gloria remembered that his parents were divorced, simply because in her world divorce was practically unheard of. But she had never known his surname, or his address. For her, innocent as she then was, it had been love at first sight; in his case probably something more basic. Her parents swore that she had been taken advantage of, and tried to persuade her to have the child adopted. She refused, and embarrassed them severely by keeping her baby.

It had been a relief for everyone, his mother said, when she met Stan. Stan adored her, absolutely and unreservedly, and did not mind about the baby. His parents did, but Stan overruled them, and for that Gloria was prepared to love him in return. And she did, Nick knew that; theirs had been a most successful marriage, in spite of the cuckoo in the nest. Looking back, Nick realised that he had often underestimated Stan, his simplicity and his goodness, just as he had been stupidly envious of his brothers and sisters. He was older, of course, and always destined to be the clever one, but such cleverness was a two-edged sword, and in those days, not understanding that, he would have given almost anything to be like them. They were neat, attractive children, each one able, in his or her way, to be 'one of the crowd'; and at a time when such things were important, Nick had never been that.

Odd to think that he had never considered any of them clever or adventurous, and yet they had all done well in their chosen fields, which was, Nick supposed, a tribute to their upbringing. It was a pity, he thought, that the past filled him with so much pain, so many regrets. A pity, too, that he had cut himself off so irrevocably from the others, that he knew so little of them except from occasional letters. And such correspondence marked events, not thoughts or feelings; they provided no answers to the questions in his mind.

If only . . .

The saddest words in the English language brought a mocking half-smile to his lips. If only his mother could have been a little more honest; if only he had known the truth from the beginning, instead of being allowed to build up a series of fantasies, in all of which his natural father was some kind of superman, who – if only he had lived! – would have understood everything, conquered all problems, and provided enough money for clothes and sports equipment never to be a major issue. Beside Nick's wishful thinking, poor Stan had never stood a chance. And yet he worked hard all his life, treated Nick like his own, and displayed, generally, the most astonishing patience in the face of great provocation. His punishments were fair, it was just that they made not a great deal of difference to a child who should have been reasoned with, and to whom the error of his ways should have been explained by someone who understood how his mind worked.

Nick had known, instinctively, that he was not understood, and so had never bothered trying to explain why he behaved in the way he did. He was punished, but took his punishments without complaint, consoling himself with the thought of how different life would be if only his father were alive. There was a terrible irony in the realisation that his father had not been dead at all, that he had simply been tempted by a pretty girl on holiday, taken his pleasure and then gone on his way with no more than a few fond memories. Leaving her with a child.

Impulsive, arrogant, irresponsible: the epithets all applied. But they applied to youth in general, Nick thought, and were not his father's prerogative. He had shared them himself, at times with a vengeance, and had often regretted it. The real sadness lay in the wasted opportunities, the misunderstandings which had arisen out of deceit, and his sense of guilt following that deathbed confession, which had left him with no way of making reparation to those he had hurt.

For some reason he had never been able to tell Bernice. Distress and depression had followed his mother's death, to all outward purposes the manifestation of grief, and yet he had never been able to tell anyone the real cause. Not even his brothers and sisters, gathered so briefly together for the funeral. He had wanted to, but there had been no time, and they were too used to his aloofness to sense the measure of his need. And Stanley, who would surely have understood, had himself been dead for several years.

Looking back, Nick wondered whether that was the beginning of the end where he and Bernice were concerned. Certainly, that was when things had begun to go noticeably wrong. With both her parents still alive and doting on her and the boys, Bernice could not understand his grief, especially when – as she said so often – he had not seemed particularly close to his mother. She was impatient with him, dismissive; every time he came close to explaining, she would sigh in that slightly martyred way of hers, and suggest that he find something to do, something with which to divert his mind. So he did, he pushed it down, out of the way, told himself that he was being stupid, that nothing whatever could be done to rectify matters, and he must just learn to live with it.

He learned to ignore it. Work had always been a panacea, so he flung himself into that; but he was far from happy, and meanwhile his relationship with Bernice began to flounder. They made love rarely, and she became so scathing about that, Nick eventually found it impossible to respond to her. Because sex had always been so important to him, she then accused him of having other women, whereas in fact there was no one else, he was alone, locked inside himself with that ossifying burden from the past.

And it was at that point in his life, Nick thought as he reached the rocky end of the beach, when he first came into contact with Natasha.

Remembering opportunities lost, for a moment his vision blurred as he looked out to sea, over those unexpectedly calm winter waves, so temptingly blue. Slack water: the tide would soon be on the turn, coming in with surprising speed. Wiping the tears away, Nick told himself that they were prompted by the cold; he blew his nose, breathed deeply once more, and turned to climb the steps of the new sea-wall.

A recent innovation, this, of which he thoroughly approved. It was possible now to round the headland in safety, to explore the rock-pools with a safe retreat at hand; and possible to walk on for several hundred yards, enjoying that magnificent view of the far cliffs, with the pretty village of Sandsend nestling at the foot.

He had imagined that the sea-wall would lead on to the next stretch of beach, but, as he rounded another small headland, he saw that the wall came to an end. The cliff was there, the rocks below with a stretch of beach, and a path of sorts led upwards, presumably to meet the metalled road to Sandsend. Had he been the adventurous boy of thirty years ago, Nick would have made his way via one route or another – probably over the rocks – to the destination which had been in view all the time. But he was older now, and rather more careful of life and limb. He paused for a last, lingering look; then, with a sudden, grim half-smile, he reached his decision, and turned to go back the way he had come.

Twenty Seven

RETURNING TO Ghylldale with the intention of leaving a note for Sally, he saw her in the doorway of the museum. It was the costume that attracted his attention, the white cap and apron, the long, hooded cloak. At first he did not realise who she was, then she turned to speak to someone inside, and he recognised her hair, falling over her shoulders and the brown velvet cloak.

Spotting the car, she grinned and waved as he got out, and he smiled a little self-consciously as he crossed the road to greet her. They met on the pavement outside her cottage.

'You do look different!' he laughed, casting his eyes over her from head to foot, 'I hardly knew you. How's it going?'

'Very well. Lots of visitors this morning, the gift shop and the café are doing a great trade as well, so everybody's happy. How are you?'

'OK.' He smiled into her searching eyes. 'I'm doing OK. In fact – '

She grasped his arm and ushered him round the corner. 'Come on – let's go in and have some coffee. I could do with a break, and the rush has tailed off a bit.'

They drank their coffee sitting on the sunny windowseat in Sally's front parlour. She kept an occasional glance on what was happening outside while Nick outlined the plans he had made, but by her nods and murmurs of approval he could tell that he had 90 per cent of her attention at least, and that what he was proposing struck her as sensible and fair.

'But can you trust Natasha to play fair now?'

With a short, mirthless laugh, he shook his head. 'No, I can't. But I've got the boys to think about, and at the moment I'm more concerned about them than I am about her.' Nick drained his mug of coffee and stood up. 'I'd better go.'

For a moment she stayed where she was, looking up at him. The seriousness of her expression seemed incongruous against the frippery lace cap; looking down at her, it was impossible not to smile.

'Don't worry – everything's going to be all right.'

Without replying, Sally went straight through into the kitchen; as he came up behind her, she led him outside, to show him where her emergency keys were hidden in an outhouse. 'I'm going to be away,' she said, 'for Christmas, but if you should need somewhere . . .'

Moved by her generosity, Nick could only hug her close. 'Thanks,' he murmured against her cheek, 'I'll remember that. And as soon as I've got things sorted out, I'll let you know.'

'She wants her bottom kicking,' Sally said gruffly as he released her, 'and you can tell her that from me.'

He laughed, a little shakily. 'Maybe I will.'

Patting his shoulder, she said: 'You'd better go, Nick. But take care – and remember, this place is here if you need it.'

'Thanks.' He kissed her warmly and turned to the door. 'Enjoy your Christmas, Sally.'

'I will. And may yours be better than you expect.'

Local radio news bulletins warned of poor driving conditions across the Vale of York, and, as he came down off the moors, Nick discovered they were right. Fog patches thickened towards Malton, and along the A64, busy with the usual weekend traffic, visibility was down to a hundred yards. Nick slowed accordingly, but there were still cars willing to overtake on the two-way stretches, heedless of anything coming the other way. He was glad to turn off along the road to Sheriff Whenby, although the fog was thicker along the country roads, and white rime in the hedgerows testified to the freezing conditions. It seemed to take for ever to reach Denton-on-the Forest.

Natasha's car was in the barn, but the porch door was locked. Taking a deep breath to steady himself, Nick found his keys, opened both doors, and walked into a silent house.

Faintly alarmed, he stood quite still for a moment, listening. He opened the sitting-room door, but she was not in there, and no sound came from her office. The kitchen was also deserted, although the stove looked bright enough.

He took the stairs two at a time, and met the cat, slinking guiltily along the landing. Natasha was in bed and asleep.

Relief made him harsh. As she raised her head, startled by his presence, he said: 'Come on, get dressed, I want to talk to you.'

She subsided again, pulling the quilt over her ears. 'Well, I don't want to talk to you.'

Nick was in no mood for petulance. He swept the curtains apart and picked up a bundle of clothes from the chair. 'You don't have to talk – just listen. But you'll listen to me downstairs, and fully dressed.' Twitching the quilt away, he flung her clothes across the bed. 'And don't be long – I haven't got all day.'

Downstairs, he picked up a bundle of mail from the porch, discovering more, unopened, on the hall table. He scanned the envelopes, identifying several friends from postmarks and handwriting, together with a heavy airmail missive from his sister in Australia. The fact that he had been thinking about her only that morning brought a half-smile to his lips. Well, he thought, he would catch up with family news later.

In the kitchen, as he bent to add fuel to the stove, he noticed that one of the fireside chairs was piled with cushions, and that a paperback novel, marked by a Kit-Kat wrapper, was lying beside it on the floor. Somewhat mystified – why hadn't she gone to bed to read? – he also wondered why she had still been asleep when he came in. Above his head, he heard the sound of water running, and realised that Natasha was taking a shower. Ah well, at least she was up and making an effort.

Nick glanced at his watch: it was almost two o'clock and he was hungry. The fridge, however, contained little beyond eggs and cheese and the usual collection of proprietary sauces and pickles. The tomatoes looked sick, and the lettuce had gone to mush in its plastic container. Disgusted, he tipped it into the bin, and wondered what on earth Natasha had been doing with herself for the past week. She had not been to the supermarket, that much was certain.

He made himself a cheese and pickle sandwich, and washed it down with a can of beer. Waiting for Natasha, he opened a few of the Christmas cards, but his mood led him to think more of the cost of sending those expensive greetings than any genuine pleasure in receiving them.

She arrived at last, her hair wispy from the drier, wearing not the clothes that Nick had thrown at her, but a smart pair of dark-green ski-pants and a cheerful red and green sweater. But in spite of some cleverly applied make-up, she still looked pale and drawn.

With no more than a glance in his direction, she made herself some coffee and lit a cigarette. 'Is this just a visit, or have you come back to stay?'

'I'm staying,' he said. 'This is my home, Natasha, in case you'd forgotten.'

'*I* hadn't forgotten – but I thought you had.' She paused for a moment. 'And what about your *girlfriend* – didn't she want you for Christmas? I'm surprised – thought she'd have been delighted.'

He stood up. 'Let's get this clear. Her name's Sally, she's an historian, and I've known her for years. I'm not in love with her, and she's not in love with me – she's just a friend.'

'But you've *slept* with her,' she accused, unable to keep the loathing out of her voice.

That struck hard, but he shrugged and lit a cigarette. 'Have I? And what leads you to that conclusion – guilt?'

'Guilt?' Natasha shrieked. 'Why should *I* feel guilty? I haven't been out all hours of the night, seeing different men, lying to you about *bloody research*!'

'I've seen Dr Wills,' he said coldly, 'who's sixty if she's a day, and Sally, who's an old colleague. I haven't lied to you about the research – I can show you my notes, if you insist.'

'I don't want to see your bloody notes – what would they

prove? That you've been working as well as screwing somebody else!'

The force of her loathing, expressed with such vulgarity, roused angry, uncontrollable words. 'And what if I have? Why the hell should you care? You don't want me in your bed – you don't even seem to want me in your life! Yes, I slept with Sally – and if you must know, it was for all the wrong bloody reasons! Not out of love – not even out of lust – but just because she was there. I needed someone – and *she was there*.'

Natasha turned her back on him. He could see that she was trembling, but his anger had a life of its own. 'I needed you – I've always needed you – but all you could do was throw that need back in my face! If I'm guilty, then so are you – and don't you bloody forget that!'

He strode from the room and slammed the door behind him.

Without meaning to, Natasha gave voice to a string of obscenities. Rage, anger, guilt; a killing desire to do some damage, to pay him back for hurting her this way, made her seize the cup full of coffee and throw it at the kitchen door. The cup smashed and splintered, and coffee went everywhere, over walls, ceiling, window, floor; but it gave a measure of relief, a smaller, more manageable reason for bursting into tears.

She sat down and sobbed into a crumpled tissue until Colette crept out from under the table and on to her knee. As the cat rubbed her ginger and white head against Natasha's chin, the mixture of tears and cat-hairs became so unpleasant that the tears had to stop. Soothed by Colette's purring warmth, Natasha tried to think clearly, but could not get past the anger and resentment. It seemed typical of Nick that he should turn the argument round and place the blame on her; and yet no matter how great her contribution, she hadn't forced him into this. He'd known what he was doing that night he was supposed to be going to Newcastle – he couldn't wait to get out of the house.

Wondering what to do, where the road led from here, she seemed to be faced by a fogginess far greater than that outside. It was getting dark, too. Beset by fears and anxieties which had little to do with Nick or the state of their marriage, she stood up and switched on the lights. At sight of the coffee stains and that splintered mug, she could have wept again. Instead, she set about clearing up.

She was standing on a chair, washing the ceiling, when Nick came down. Surveying the remains of the mess, he sighed and took the cloth out of her hand. 'Get down – I can reach without the chair.'

Without protest, she let him carry on, turning her attention to the walls and woodwork. A few minutes later, when they were nearly done, he said: 'I'm not sure what you want to do about this situation, Natasha, but I think you'll agree we can't carry on like this. I'm thinking of the boys, of course, and the fact that it's nearly Christmas.'

'Oh, yes,' she said with weary sarcasm, 'we mustn't forget that it's Christmas.'

'No, indeed we mustn't.' Standing back, looking up at the beamed ceiling, he said: 'I have to think of the boys. It's not their fault this has happened – and it wouldn't be fair to spoil the holidays for them. I'm sure you agree.' When she did not reply, he said, rather more sharply: 'Well, I *hope* you agree with me?'

'Yes – yes, of course.' In that moment, she was so devoid of thought or personal desire that she was ready to agree to anything.

'So I propose we make no decisions until afterwards and that in the meantime we make every attempt to lead what passes for normal life in this household. In other words, we'll prepare for Christmas, we will be courteous to each other, and you will accompany me on the usual sort of jaunts when I take the boys out.

'With one exception,' he added, lighting a cigarette. 'I've decided to take them to London next weekend. Unless you really want to come, I thought it would be a good way of getting all three of us out of your hair for a few days. I'll bring them back Sunday evening, and they'll be going back to Bernice on Tuesday afternoon – Christmas Eve, in case you've forgotten. Then we've got Giles and Fay coming for dinner on Boxing Day. After that,' he added coolly, 'I dare say we can take some time out to consider our options.'

With a sniff of derision, Natasha said: 'You've thought it all out, haven't you? Cut and dried, as usual. I don't suppose it's occurred to you that I might have made a few decisions of my own?' She paused for effect, and, as the idea sprang to mind, added venomously: 'And one of them includes leaving this *bloody* house, to return to what I call civilisation!'

That shocked him. 'I see,' he said, less sure of himself now. 'And when are you planning to leave?'

'Well, nothing would please me better than to depart this instant – but I'm not quite ready to do so.' She rinsed cloths and poured water down the sink, taking her time about it while Nick paced the room uneasily. 'I've got things to do – things to organise. But when I do leave,' she stressed, 'I warn you, I shall want my share of this infernal money-pit, and I just hope you can afford to give it me!'

With that she pushed the bucket into its cupboard and turned towards the door.

'And in the meantime, will you do as I ask?'

She paused. 'In the meantime, yes, I'll do my best for your children's sake. I always have, haven't I?'

'Yes,' he agreed, 'you always have.'

'Well, then, we'll play house until Christmas is over. With one exception – I won't be sleeping with you. So work that one out!'

'I already have,' he said bitterly. 'Since I'm the early riser, I'll sleep on the sofa. The boys usually sleep late on holiday, so I doubt they'll notice.'

'Good. That's that, then. Can I go now?'

'Yes, of course.'

Over the next few days Nick kept up a relentless pressure, organising Natasha into activity. Previously, he had been concerned that she should take things easy after such a prolonged period of hard work, but with nothing to do but brood over imaginary wrongs, she seemed to have degenerated into sullenness. Keeping busy, he decided, would do her no harm at all, even though he had to bear the brunt of her temper as a consequence. He chivvied her along and tried to ignore the bitter remarks, the constant references to his 'girlfriend', and Christmas, and leaving. In spite of it all, by Tuesday morning there was food in the house, the Christmas tree was bought and decorated, and the bulk of the Christmas presents were purchased and wrapped.

At lunchtime, when Nick set off to collect his sons, he was not only relieved that the jobs were done, he was physically and mentally exhausted. And worried too. His mind flitted from one problem to another, but his chief anxiety was whether Natasha would keep to their original agreement, to a state of truce while the boys were in the house. If she did not, he would have to leave, take them somewhere else, to Sally's probably; but he did not want to do that. His one ace card was Natasha's pride, and he had played on that unashamedly, with subtle reminders of Bernice and how she would enjoy the situation if they parted. Particularly before Christmas.

He worried about the boys. Adam, particularly, could be difficult where Natasha was concerned, and Nick doubted her forbearance if he should wind her up too far.

As it happened, he was the one who almost lost his temper, and that within five minutes of meeting the twins. With the trunks and baggage stowed in the car, Adam immediately claimed the front seat, which prompted unusually vociferous comments from his brother. The matter was settled, but not before Nick had shouted at them both. It illustrated something that seemed to have been growing for some time. Previously, Adrian had been content to play second fiddle to his more assertive brother, but it was becoming clear that he wanted to be recognised for himself, and not just as the lesser one of an otherwise identical pair.

That widening gap between them was obvious as soon as they arrived at Holly Tree Cottage. Adam's greeting to Natasha was as perfunctory as ever, but whereas Adrian would once have imitated his brother's style, and either rushed off to explore the house or gone straight into the sitting-room to watch television, now he lingered in the kitchen to be favoured with tea and chocolate cake.

Watching them for a moment, seeing the growing warmth in his wife's eyes and smile, and the openness with which Adrian was regarding her, Nick was stabbed by the irony. After so much restrained effort in the past, the fact that she now seemed on the verge of cracking the carapace of that joint resentment was unfair in the extreme. And cruel; especially in Adrian's case. Just as he was gaining confidence with Natasha, she was about to walk out of their lives forever.

To Nick's astonishment, over the next few days it seemed Natasha could do no wrong. Having restocked fridge, freezer and larder on the Monday before the boys arrived, she happily cooked and baked for them, presenting all their old favourites and a few new dishes which were greeted with enthusiasm. She even volunteered to take them Christmas shopping on Wednesday afternoon, and accompanied them the next day on a visit to the Railway Museum. It quickly became clear that Adam, far from maintaining a cool front, was actually attempting to outdo Adrian in his efforts to impress. But while Natasha smiled and responded, and kept up the illusion that nothing had changed, Nick was constantly beset by that sense of irony, by his awareness that this was a stop-gap between a decision and its implementation.

With him, Natasha rarely made more than the briefest eye contact, yet in front of the twins she played her part exceedingly well. Only when they were alone, after Adam and Adrian had finally been despatched to bed, did the smile slip and her eyes reveal a weariness similar to his own. The effort of acting, Nick realised on the Thursday night, was far more wearing than he had ever imagined. Particularly when it covered a pit of misery at the core of his being.

Although he managed to sleep for six or seven hours each night on the sofa in the sitting-room, he did not sleep well, and his dreams were prolonged and unpleasant. Despite the ensuing sense of exhaustion, he was glad to wake, glad to be up and about and doing something. He went for his usual run each morning, came back, watched the early news on television over a cup of coffee, and then roused the rest of the household. As he had suspected, the boys did not notice that he was not sleeping upstairs.

'But Dad,' Adrian enquired in pained tones on Friday morning, '*why* isn't Natasha coming to London with us?'

The answer to that had been agreed before the boys arrived. Smoothly, Nick said: 'She's got a lot of work to do. She needs to concentrate, and three days on her own will just do the trick.'

'Does she have to work?' Adam demanded. 'It's supposed to be Christmas – can't she take some time off?'

In spite of himself, Nick was amused. In the summer, this very same son had been almost hugging himself with glee as the three of them took off with Giles on a canal-boat holiday. He had not wanted Natasha's company then, and had taken no trouble to hide it. Now he wanted her with them, but was equally unprepared to accept that it could not be so. Nick said: 'Listen, not everybody gets a month off for Christmas. Not even me. I still have work to do, even though it's supposed to be a holiday. And your mother only has ten days over Christmas and New Year.'

'But Natasha can please herself whether she works or not,' Adam persisted. 'Why can't she come to London with us?'

'Because she knows how much work she has to do, and doesn't want to be panicking at the last minute. It's called self-discipline,' Nick said weightily, 'and it's something you could do to learn.'

As Adam went off in a huff, his brother grinned, albeit without malice. 'He's funny, isn't he, Dad? He didn't use to like Natasha, but now he thinks she's great.'

Nick smiled. 'Thanks to you.'

Pleased by that unexpected compliment, Adrian blushed to the roots of his curly red hair. 'Me? But I haven't said anything . . .'

'You didn't need to,' Nick explained. 'You just decided to think and act for yourself. And *I* think,' he added, squeezing his son's shoulders, 'you made Adam realise that he was being a bit of an idiot.'

'Well, she *is* nice, isn't she? And he was carrying things on a bit. It got a bit boring, really . . .'

'It certainly did,' Nick agreed with a laugh. 'Anyway, thanks – I'm proud of you.'

Warm with embarrassment, Adrian grinned and followed his brother upstairs to collect his things. He seemed at least an inch taller, Nick thought.

Natasha was in the sitting-room, adding that morning's batch of cards to those already arranged on the deep windowledges. Others were strung in festoons across the chimney-breast. As he walked in, Nick thought how attractive the room looked, the dense, dark green of the Christmas tree, with its red bows and baubles, filling what had been an empty corner, and a great bowl of fir-cones and frosted twigs decorating the hearth. Sprigs of holly from the hedge were arranged above the picture-frames and pelmets. Even at this hour, and without a fire in the hearth, the room looked cosy and inviting; he was irrationally sorry to be leaving it.

'Will you be all right on your own?'

There was a short pause before she answered, and when she did, there was a slight edge to her voice. 'Is there any reason why I shouldn't be?'

It seemed to Nick that they had this conversation before. 'No, of course not, it's just – well, it's just that the boys are sorry you're not coming with us to London.' He hesitated for a moment, unsure of his own stance, then plunged in with: 'Would you like to come?'

She glanced across at him, and, with a rueful half-smile, slowly shook her head. 'No thanks, I don't think so. The last few days have been – oh, I don't know – enjoyable in one way, but all in all, a bit of a strain. I could do with a rest, and besides, I need some time to think.'

Relief and regret were mixed in equal measure. Responding to her smile, Nick said: 'Yes, I know what you mean. Well then, I suppose we ought to grab our things and go . . .'

'I'll get the car out.'

'Do you want to take mine?'

'No,' she said, 'I prefer to drive my own through town.'

Leaving the little red Peugeot in the short-stay section of the car park, Natasha accompanied them into the station to see them on to the train.

'Have a lovely time,' she said, suddenly realising, as she embraced first Adrian and then Adam, how tall they were, their square shoulders already on a level with her own. It was the first time that she had risked kissing either of them; the first time that it had seemed such an embrace might be welcome. They both coloured up, but with pleasure, judging by those identical smiles, rather than annoyance. Unexpectedly moved, she thought: I'm going to miss them, the little horrors. But they were no longer little horrors, they were growing up, and even Adam –

Nick hugged her, with such unexpected warmth that thought and breath were banished for a moment, and she was aware of nothing more than how wonderful he felt, how strong and safe and –

'I'm going to miss you,' he whispered against her ear.

'Yes, I – '

'*Dad* – come *on* – we'll miss the train!'

'Take care,' he said as he released her.

'You too,' she whispered, smiling through a haze, unable to see clearly for the tears in her eyes.

Doors were slamming, up and down the train; amidst the surge of bodies, two coppery heads bobbed anxiously until Nick joined them and ushered them safely aboard. All three waved; then the guard slammed the door and they were gone from sight. The train moved off, noisily gathering pace while Natasha waved blindly, as idiotically distraught as though they were going forever.

Not so idiotic, though, she thought as she regained the privacy of her car. Dabbing her streaming eyes with tissues from the glove compartment, she contemplated the forthcoming separation and knew that of the two evils facing her, it was by no means the lesser. A week ago it had seemed the only way out of an intolerable situation, but while she had resented Nick's high-handed attitude since, she had to admit that he had been right to insist on a truce.

The stupid thing was that on one level the last few days had contained more honest enjoyment than Natasha had experienced for a long time, and although Nick had virtually ordered her to be pleasant in front of the boys, it had not been difficult. For the first time their presence had proved a blessing rather than a trial, making it easier for her to talk to Nick. Without the boys, she would not have spoken to him at all; her pride was too deeply hurt by that admission of his, and her confidence undermined by his accusation that it was all her fault. The fact that he was basically right eased nothing, indeed it only made Natasha think less of herself.

Perhaps if he had said nothing . . .

But no; something needed to be said, they could not have gone on in that fashion. It was just ironic that things should have come to a head in such a way and at such a time. Thinking of the boys she felt dishonest, no better than a confidence trickster, and was only marginally comforted that Nick had seemed so genuinely sorry to be leaving.

But there was irony again, she thought, since it must be as clear to him as it was to her that in spite of sorrow and regret, the relationship was not working out. The differences were too deep; he was no longer young and malleable, and she had ceased to believe that he would change one day and become the man she wanted him to be. Nick was Nick: he saw no reason to explain himself, and evinced no particular desire to be understood. Nor did he realise how lonely she was, living in Denton; how much, just recently, that sense of isolation had come to remind her of the years she had spent as a girl, longing for escape.

There was an unpleasant side-effect too: when she did come into town nowadays, the busy streets and shops were something of a shock. In supermarkets, the crush of people could very quickly induce a sense of panic, a burning desire to get out, into cold fresh air, away from the lights and the buzz of voices, away from the oppressive warmth. But she would have to face the supermarket, however briefly, if she wanted a supply of convenience food to see her through the weekend. Cooking for the boys had been a pleasure, but with work on her mind Natasha was unwilling to waste time preparing food for herself.

The thought of work produced a leap of anticipation that was offset by a sudden fall of guilt. In deciding what they were going to tell the boys, Nick had not realised how much truth lay in that ready-made excuse.

The supermarket car park gave evidence of the fact that it was the Friday before Christmas, and inside the store was a heaving crush of humanity, all grabbing things off shelves and filling trolleys as though for a six-month siege. Overhead, fluorescent lights beamed, the piped music system played an incessant round of jolly carols, while at floor level the unyielding force of steel and rubber tyres jabbed and nudged at legs and ankles. Wound up almost to the point of violence, Natasha reached the chilled food, found herself unable to think, and grabbed a selection of English, Italian and Indian dinners before making a break for the in-store bakery and delicatessen. Sheer panic made her buy smoked trout as well as Scottish smoked salmon, a chunk of Ardennes pâté and far more slices of York ham than she could possibly eat. Ah well, she thought, joining the crocodile of trolleys waiting at the check-out, the boys will have to eat it up on Monday.

Her hands were shaking so much by the time she came to sign the charge-card chit, that her signature looked like a very poor forgery. The young man peered at it, compared it with her card, peered at Natasha over his glasses, and with a sigh accepted it. With relief she wheeled her goods outside, gulping at the air like a deprived alcoholic as she loaded things into the Peugeot. For a moment, the thought of being enclosed again was unbearable; pretending to be waiting for someone, Natasha lit a cigarette and smoked it while leaning against the boot. Once the sickly, jelly-like feeling was gone, she was able to get into the car and drive away.

As she drove through the village and up Dagger Lane, she found herself looking forward to ten minutes with her feet up before tackling the job of unloading the car. But as she walked into the house the telephone was ringing.

It was Fay, full of enthusiasm about a last-minute party she had decided to arrange for Sunday lunchtime. Did she and Nick want to come? They could bring the boys, some other friends were bringing their children too; it would be great fun, a buffet lunch with lots to drink – low-alcohol for the drivers, of course – and silly, old-fashioned party games.

'I – I don't think I can,' Natasha said uncertainly. 'I mean – the boys aren't here, for a start. Nick's taken them to London for the weekend, and I've just got in – I'm jiggered, Fay, desperate for a coffee and something to eat. Can I call you back in half an hour?'

But when she did call back, her attempts to inject some liveliness into her voice were not successful. Almost at once Fay was asking what was wrong, she had not seen Natasha for weeks, and was it something she had said? If so, she went on, could they get together soon and talk things over, because she, Fay, was anxious and concerned.

Natasha, listening with her head in her hands, wondered what to say. What *could* she say to that? Fay was kind and Natasha was fond of her; she could not fob her off with much less than the truth.

'No, no, Fay, really – I'm sorry – the fault's mine, not yours. I've been keeping out of everybody's way – I haven't wanted to see anybody. To be honest, I've been too miserable for words – hardly fit company for the cat.' She paused for a moment, and Fay's questions came pouring into the breach. 'Well, you must know it's all to do with Nick – Giles must know, anyway, even if nobody else does . . . but look, I can't talk about it on the phone . . . no, Fay, I just can't face another journey into town, not at the moment. I know you're busy, but if you want to come up this evening, or for lunch tomorrow . . .?'

But Giles had tickets for a concert that evening, and Saturday would be taken up catering for the party on Sunday. Once again, Fay tried to persuade Natasha to come along to that, but Natasha was thinking of the work she had to do, and Nick's return with the boys, which might be any time from four o'clock onwards.

'No, I won't, Fay, if you don't mind – I don't know what time they're coming back, and anyway you won't have time to *think*, with all those people in the house!' She laughed, making light of the situation, when in fact it was all she could do not to cry. She was desperate for someone to talk to, someone with time to listen, who was so trustworthy and non-judgmental that she could let it all come pouring out. All of it: the woman in the barn, the story she was writing, the sexual impasse between herself and Nick, and his affair with this woman, Sally. She would have liked to ask Fay whether she knew her. Instead she drew a somewhat ragged breath and reminded her friend lightly that they would all be together on Boxing Day.

'Are you sure you want to go through with that?'

'Oh, yes, it'll be all right – we won't embarrass you, I promise! And while they're busy knocking back the whisky, you can help me in the kitchen. We'll talk then.'

Fay seemed happy to settle for that, and Natasha put down the phone with a kind of tormented relief. The sound of Fay's voice made her realise just how much she needed to talk, and yet she was not at all sure how much she wanted to say. It would be so easy, the way things stood, to tell half a story and lay all the blame at Nick's door; to say, quite honestly, that he had confessed to an affair and was talking about a separation. Put like that, Natasha would seem the innocent, injured party, the rightful claimant of sympathy and support. But there was so much more to it than that, so much that lay beyond her own understanding. And anyway, she was far from sure that she was entitled to anyone's sympathy.

Twenty Eight

As darkness crept up on the winter's afternoon, Natasha filled the log basket, fuelled the stove, and made sure that both coal-scuttles and her two kitchen pails were full of coke. With the first stars showing in the clear, dark blue above, and the trees and the barn standing in silhouette against it, the view from the garden had all the perfect beauty of a stage-set; but Natasha was eager to be inside with the curtains drawn. She had no intention of stepping outside again until morning.

Having fed the outdoor cats and gathered Colette, protesting, under her arm, she locked the doors and then checked every window in the house before bringing her typewriter into the kitchen. With the table set for work, she piled up the cushions in her fireside chair in order to rest and doze in comfort when fatigue claimed her. What she did not want to do was go upstairs to bed before absolute exhaustion ensured that she would sleep without dreaming, or even caring if she was alone.

She did these things instinctively now, refusing to question why she felt so frightened after dark, or even why she felt the need to take refuge in the kitchen. She told herself that it was because of the number of lights in there, and the direct heat of the stove; but in fact it was the workaday normality which was so reassuring, and the fact that it was the newest part of the house.

Settled at last, Natasha took the first sheet from a fresh ream of paper, and inserted it into the typewriter. She worked for two hours without a break, then made a cup of coffee and continued for another hour. Just after seven she began to feel hungry, and popped a ready-made Indian meal into the oven. Half an hour later she stopped typing in order to eat, and, while she was doing so, watched a television documentary about wildlife in the Arctic. The sight of a cuddly polar bear having its own dinner, however, was not very edifying, so she switched it off and went back to work.

A little after eleven, when the level of her fatigue was showing in the number of typing errors, Natasha decided to call a halt, to read through what she had written so far.

She flicked through the early pages, reaching the point of Sarah's first visit to Holly Tree House. Judged by its outcome, the visit had gone well, although Sarah's critical eye had taken in the inadequate kitchen garden, a poor frontage to the house, and the shortcomings of Richard's sister, Agnes. She described Agnes as *a sour-visaged woman of perhaps two-and-twenty*, whose housekeeping – or so it seemed – was done out of necessity rather than love or pride. And she went on to remark that while the house was clean and the dinner wholesome enough, it might have been offered by a disgruntled servant rather than the mistress of the house. Obviously, Sarah was not impressed.

Agnes had kept house for her brother since the death of their mother some years before, and, according to custom, it should have remained her home until her marriage. Since women who did not marry tended to remain as subsidiary helpers to the head of the household's wife, it seemed Sarah was right to feel uneasy about any future relationship. She was not optimistic about her ability to make a friend of Agnes, and was afraid that any suggested improvements to the running of the house would be taken as criticism.

> That anxiety, however, was outfaced by a tour of Richard's enclosures. If fortune had placed him well, then hard work and stout judgement had bettered his position in recent years. With the rest of his life before him, there was no reason why that situation should not be improved upon.
>
> My father approved of Richard Stalwell and so did I.

Basking in that warm glow, we returned to the house for refreshment before saddling up to be on our way, via Brickhill and Towthorpe to York, where we planned to spend the night with our Piper relations.

The horses were brought round to the front of the house and, as I took my leave of Agnes, my eyes were taken by that slight slope, the way the house sat on its higher piece of ground, looking out over the church. At present, the approach was almost a casual one, off the lane and through a close-cropped enclosure of grazing sheep. There should be walls, I thought, or a goodly hedge, to hide stables and piggeries behind the humbler dwellings below; and a formal garden, perhaps with a terrace, would make an excellent approach to the house.

I was taken by the possibilities, while Agnes, seeing my attention was elsewhere, turned to my father, who encouraged her to walk a little way with him down the slope. Richard turned to me, his eyes alight with some secret pleasure. As before, I wondered what it was that so amused him whenever he chanced to look at me, and one day vowed to ask. The thought made my leave-taking rather more formal than it might have been, but as Richard bowed and I bobbed a curtsy, he raised my hand to his lips and kissed it warmly. The gesture took me so much by surprise that I froze for a second, then missed my footing and almost fell.

It was fortunate that my mare stood between us and the other two, for as he rescued me, Richard was laughing and I was furious.

'Forgive me, I – '

'Why do you laugh? I think it's cruel!'

'Nay, Sarah, you mistake me – '

'You do! All the time,' I hissed, dimly aware that he had used my Christian name. 'What is it about me that amuses you so? Am I a freak, or a child to be teased? Tell me!' I was in such a passion I stamped my foot, and with the mare dancing sideways Richard was hard put to answer me, shaking his head and uttering denials as he tried to regain control.

The mare tossed her head against his restraining hand, as much as I did when he turned to me. 'I'm happy to look at you,' he said with low intensity. 'Being with you lightens my heart, as simple as that.'

I searched his eyes, which were dark beneath a lowered brow, but my anger was not so easily dissipated. 'Why should I believe you?' I asked pettishly, gathering my skirts as I turned away.

'Because I do not lie,' he declared, placing a restraining hand on my arm. 'Sarah, look at me.'

Reluctantly, I did as I was bidden, and with that he leaned towards me, cupping my head in his free hand as he kissed me hard on the mouth. 'I don't lie,' he whispered earnestly against my lips, 'I want you for my wife.'

Stunned by his words, his actions, I could do nothing but stand and stare.

'Forgive me – I have spoken to your father, but –' He broke off, his eyes searching mine, concern and contrition written in his. 'I'm expected to call on you tomorrow,' he informed me with a rueful smile. 'I hope you'll receive me?'

As I slowly inclined my head, he touched my cheek and smiled, murmuring his thanks before we rejoined the others.

A few minutes later, as he waved us off down the lane, I noticed the dancing light was back again in Richard's eyes, but this time I did not mind it.

We were both quiet for some distance down the road, alert for footpads in the tree-shaded hollows, avoiding barking dogs and skinny children as we passed through various farmyards and along village streets. If my father was lost in private consideration, then so was I, taking stock of this new turn of events with Richard, and hardly able to credit it.

Did it truly make him happy to look at me? I wished I

had a looking-glass about me to see what pleased him so. But it warmed me to think that I lightened his heart and that he needs must kiss me in order to prove it. My lips and cheeks glowed again at the memory of that stolen kiss, and I longed for the chance to repeat it, to have the savour of his mouth on mine and not just the shock, to feel his arms about me in love and protection.

He wanted me for his wife! My heart leapt at the thought, even as I wondered when he had spoken to my father, and what had been said. My father could not have objected, that much I was sure of, but I did wonder why we continued to ride in silence. After a little while I gave voice to some of the day's impressions, but our conversation was desultory owing to the awkwardness of the road, and it was not until we reached the safety of the Piper house that we discussed what was foremost in both our minds, and even then, not until we were alone.

'Richard Stalwell has asked for your hand, sweetheart – what say you to that?'

I knew not what to say, so I took refuge in blushes and modesty. It was to no avail, however, my father knew me too well. Raising my chin, he looked into my eyes and I saw that he was smiling.

'He spoke of the matter to you, then?' Shamefaced, I nodded, and my father's grin became wider. 'So?'

'What should I have said? I was not prepared.' I raised my shoulders helplessly. 'But he said he had spoken to you.'

'And so he did, the last time we met.'

'Oh, Father! Why didn't you tell me?'

'He wanted you to see the house and the farm – he wanted you to know what he was offering you. We arranged that he would call on you, here, afterwards, to ask you himself.' My father laughed. 'I told him the answer must come from you. So – what is it to be?'

Delight and satisfaction coursed through my veins, but I was nervous, too. 'He pleases me,' I said slowly, 'and were we to wed, there's much I could do to help him. Only the distance grieves me, being so far from Hammerford . . . And,' I confessed, 'his sister, who looks so sour.'

'Aye, she needs a man to sweeten her,' my father said frankly, 'and a home and children. Richard must find her a husband, since I doubt she'll draw one for herself. I'll speak to him on that. Meantime, sweetheart, you must needs put up with her – 'tis her home, after all.'

We talked some more before he went to appraise Aunt Margaret of the morning's visit. She was all of a twitter at the news, and hurried off to the kitchen to discuss what might be served for dinner.

Next morning she was more concerned with my appearance, fussing over my hair, lacing me so severely into my bodice that I could scarcely breathe. The small curve of my breasts was forced up into two plump mounds that peeped unnaturally over the rounded neckline. I grabbed my kerchief to hide them while Aunt Margaret puffed out my sleeves and overskirt and stood back to survey me. She was glad, she said, that I had left the blue and cream gown with her, since it suited me so well and was perfect for the occasion. In truth, I had left it because I could see no use for it at home: country folks did not dress up in the same way as my city cousins.

Teasing the curls around my temples, she applied a spot of rouge to my lips and cheeks; when she turned her back, I rubbed the worst of it off, leaving just a trace of heightened colour that might be attributed to excitement.

In fact I was as nervous as a cat, my stomach churning beneath the tight lacing, my knees threatening to give way as we descended to the small parlour beyond the hall. I picked up some sewing and my aunt left me to it, since she had plenty to occupy her elsewhere; but having pricked my finger several times I gave it up in favour of staring from the window at the profusion of herbs in the kitchen garden.

When Richard arrived it was my father who showed him in. Hastily I rose to my feet and bobbed a curtsy, aware of my father's voice but not taking in what was said.

Then, with a hearty squeeze for Richard's shoulder and a huge wink for me, he turned and left us together. The wink brought a nervous giggle to my lips, quickly suppressed, but as I bit my fingers and glanced at Richard, I saw that he was smiling too, some colour returning to his cheeks as he crossed the room towards me.

As he moved from shadows into the light, I saw that the coat he wore was not black, but a rich dark blue which suited him exceedingly well. Suddenly I was glad that I had been chivvied and bullied into my fine gown, and lifted my chin as he approached, quite forgetting modesty in my eagerness to read what was in his eyes. He seemed of the same mind, since his glance never left mine, and we stood a little apart in smiling silence, examining each other until some subtle change in his expression made me blush and look away.

Richard reached for me then, taking first one hand and then the other, and raising both to his lips. His warmth travelled through me, the look in his eyes lighting such a flame in my heart that I could not speak nor hardly breathe.

'Yes or No?' he murmured huskily, his breath soft against my fingers. 'Sweet Sarah, what is it to be?'

I think I nodded; I might also have whispered the affirmative, but then my limbs betrayed me. Like a feeble woman attacked by the vapours I sank down on to the windowseat. I must have turned pale, for Richard looked anxious as he knelt beside me.

'Forgive me,' I breathed, hands pressed to my stomach, 'but I fear Aunt Margaret laced me exceeding tight . . .'

He was halfway to his feet. 'Should I call her?'

'Nay,' I protested, 'I shall recover by and by. It was the excitement and the lacing – and I must confess I'm unused to both!'

I was babbling, I could hear it, and as I struggled to take shallower breaths, I was suddenly afraid I was over-frank. But as Richard took my hand and sat beside me, his relief broadened first into a smile, and then into soft laughter.

'Is this how you take your revenge? I feared you were sick – That I made you so!'

Laughing weakly, I shook my head.

He squeezed my hand, and then, with a wicked, sidelong glance, said: 'Were we married already, I'd offer to release you . . .'

'But alas, we are not,' I answered pertly, sitting up straight and remembering my kerchief, which had become disarranged, 'so I fear I must suffer.'

'But not too much,' he softly replied, 'nor too long, I trust . . .' He leaned closer, his hand at my waist, and as I turned towards him his lips met mine in as sweet and tender a kiss as any maid could wish for. I sighed with pleasure; at that he kissed me again, and, regardless of propriety or the severity of my bodice, I kissed him back, winding my arms about his neck and allowing myself to be lifted until we were standing, pressed together in the fondest embrace.

I know not how long we stood there, only that Richard's lips were fervent and mine willing; if I was breathless when we parted, then so was he, and somewhat shaken by the meeting.

Looking down at me, his blue eyes alight with something other than amusement, he murmured: 'I think, sweet Sarah, that we shall do very well together . . .'

Once it was decided, I should have liked to be married quickly and simply, but so many things had to be considered. Both my father and Richard would shortly be involved with harvest, neither of them free until the end of September, after which there came the date of Caroline's death and that of the poor little baby, so October was also unsuitable. November was often a wicked month with its low-lying fogs and incessant rain, but December was held to be generally dry and frosty.

General opinion favoured my sixteenth birthday, at the beginning of the month, but my heart sank at the thought of beginning married life in winter, with another woman's store-cupboard to draw on, and the festival of Christmas almost upon us. To give Aunt Margaret her due, she did understand my objection, but could see no way round it other than to suggest what had already crossed my mind, working harder in the fall to take my own supplies with me.

One thing did lighten my heart, however, and that was Richard's adamant declaration that I should be mistress at Holly Tree House.

'I have discussed things with Agnes, and it has been decided that as soon as we marry, she will go to my other sister, Hester, who lives up the hill beyond the village. Hester and her husband have three children, with another on the way, so Agnes's help will be appreciated there.'

'Oh, but she must not go for my sake,' I protested, envisaging trouble, 'I would hate her to be put out on my behalf – '

'Nay, Sarah, you've been mistress in your father's house, and played second fiddle to no other woman. I'd not have you start now. Besides,' he added more gently, 'it's high time Agnes was married, I've leaned on her too much. As soon as we are settled, I shall make it my business to find her a husband.'

He sounded firm and confident, as though all had been settled amicably within the family and to Agnes's satisfaction, but still I had my doubts. My father and I visited Denton again in September, for their harvest-home, and found Agnes surlier than ever, almost a match for Tom Whitehead, her brother-in-law, who, it seemed to me, looked on Richard's plenty with envious eyes. Other than the farm servants, who were smiling and deferential, of Richard's family only Hester seemed pleased to greet us. She was a large, warm, untidy woman, not at all what I expected, but immensely good-humoured. Hester had married for love, Richard informed me later, although it had been against his advice and their mother's wishes, since Tom Whitehead had more ambition than background. Still, as Richard said, he rented his land and was doing well within its limits, and Hester seemed happy enough.

I was glad somebody in the Stalwell family was happy about Richard's forthcoming marriage, although I sighed when I realised that Hester's confinement would probably exclude her from travelling to Hammerford for the wedding.

Our relations outnumbered Richard's by more than two to one, but amongst his Stalwell and Ellerby cousins, Tom Whitehead and Agnes were reasonably disguised. I did notice them once or twice afterwards, however, and wondered why it was that they should make me feel so cold. I sensed something about them, a similarity that made them seem like partners. It was disturbing, but I did not wish to dwell on such a puzzle on my wedding day.

Everything went well, and I shed only a few tears before leaving the house on my father's arm. We hugged each other, and he wished me all the happiness in the world, but there was a suspicious huskiness in his voice as he said it. I knew, despite his previous protestations, that he was going to miss me very much. That was when I wept. But he wiped my tears away, told me I looked beautiful in my rose velvet, and that Richard Stalwell was a lucky man.

We walked to the church – it was not very far, and the villagers were out in force to wish me well. It was cold and frosty, but the sun was shining, and I felt nothing could have been better. Richard was waiting with his best man, and the rector was standing there, looking suitably solemn. That walk to the chancel steps seemed to take forever, but the ceremony was over so quickly, I could scarcely believe I was married. But the ring was on my finger, and at the rector's bidding I lifted my veil of ivory lace so that Richard could kiss my lips . . .

I swear I floated from the church, borne up on a sea of happiness and good wishes from everyone around us. From everyone, that is, except Tom Whitehead and Agnes. Their congratulations seemed forced, for separate reasons, no doubt, but still they chilled me, those two, and I had no wish to linger in their company. Nor was there any need, since everyone sought my attention, and Richard's, and in the jollity of the wedding breakfast there was no time for mawkishness. Too soon, it seemed, we had to leave. Richard had hired a carriage to take us to Denton, and the journey via York would take several hours; with the short December afternoon ahead of us, we had no time to waste.

Although I had a moment's sadness leaving my childhood home, there was so much to look forward to that I waved a cheerful goodbye. And it was good to be alone with Richard, to settle down and look at my new husband, so handsome with his black hair and strong teeth, and the blue brocade coat that matched his eyes. We held hands and gazed at each other, we laughed and talked, and on the lonely stretches of the road, we did quite of lot of kissing and cuddling. Not too much, though, because the road was rough and the carriage, I swear, had no springs at all. My behind was numb well before we reached our destination, and when we arrived, after dark, we were both weary from the journey.

The servants, fortunately, had been well primed, and there was a good fire roaring up the chimney, a meal waiting, and on the table a flask of sweet red wine. Our coachman was directed to the men's quarters above the stables, where he would have his meal and spend the night, and our luggage was brought in by a middle-aged manservant and a boy of about twelve. Father and son, Richard explained; the boy's mother was the cook, and they lived in the village. There were no servants living in the house, he said, but if I wanted to employ a girl to do my hair and help me dress, it would be simple to arrange.

Never having had a personal maid – only Mercy, who

had been more like a mother to me – I found the idea both novel and appealing. But the idea made me think of Caroline, whose former existence I had managed to forget for a while, and then all my childish fears came back. Did Richard really love me? How could I compare with his first wife? Here we were, alone in Richard's house on our wedding night, and I did not know what to do. I knew what was supposed to happen – I was not a farmer's daughter for nothing – and Mercy had dropped enough broad hints to indicate that the coupling should be pleasurable after the first time; but what if I did something stupid, and spoiled it? And I was so bony and shapeless: what if he didn't like me with my clothes off?

Something of that rising panic must have shown in my face, for a moment later Richard was handling me a beaker of hot wine, and suggesting that we help ourselves to portions of cold pie and hot rabbit stew.

'After the rigours of the journey,' he said gently, 'I thought we might dispense with formality. No point in sitting for hours over several courses, when we're both too tired to eat much.'

I glanced up gratefully and saw him smiling at me, a pewter plate in his hand. 'Shall I serve you? Just a little?' As I nodded, he cut a small portion of ham and egg pie, then went to the fireplace to ladle some stew from the pot. It smelled delicious, and suddenly I was hungry, and thankful, and a little restored in faith.

There was a fire burning in the main chamber above, a small fire, but enough to take away the chill and ensure that the bed was aired. In one corner stood a screen, behind which I assumed were the usual offices of ewer, towels and chamber-pots; under the window stood my trunks and baggage. As I tried to recall which one held my hairbrushes and night attire, Richard laid gentle hands upon my shoulders. 'Tomorrow,' he whispered, touching his lips to my neck, 'you can unpack and find places for everything. Tonight, we'll manage.'

With that, he began to unlace my bodice.

Although his hands and lips were warm, I shivered every time he touched my skin; wanting to turn and press my mouth to his, I forced myself to stand quite still until I was free of bodice, stomacher and overskirts. With a chuckle of amusement, he confessed my petticoats were beyond him; I unfastened those myself, letting them fall until I was standing there, trembling like an aspen, in nothing more than my shift. As I turned, he clasped me in his arms, while I, for shame, buried my face against the front of his shirt and wished that he would snuff those flickering candles.

Instead he caressed my back, pressing my trembling body against his, murmuring soft little words of reassurance as he felt for the pins in my hair and finally removed them. As the weight of it fell I heard him sigh, and, as he buried his hands in the length of it, I heard him whisper that it was soft, and beautiful, the most beautiful hair that he had ever seen.

Those words, unbidden, heartfelt, moved me more, I think, than anything else Richard could have said. He appealed to me in such a strongly physical way that I wanted to be physically desirable to him, and it was the fear that I had nothing much to offer that made me so shy to begin with. But a moment later, when he touched his mouth to mine and parted my lips with his tongue, I found myself responding, opening to him, caught up in such a sudden, giddy whirl of sensation that had he not held me, I would have collapsed.

Weak with desire, we sank down on to the bed; Richard kicked off his boots and pulled back the covers while I slipped in between the cold sheets. Removing his breeches, Richard climbed in beside me, and, discarding his shirt, clasped me tight along the length of him. He was trembling as much as I, with cold and passion and, I suspect, not a small amount of nerves. We teased each other with kisses, laughing a little as we shivered and shook, sighing softer and deeper as warmth blossomed between us, as the kisses became longer and the caresses more intimate. He stroked my breasts, and the place between my legs where I sometimes touched myself and then worried afterwards about impure thoughts; but his touch was different, more demanding, and when he slipped a finger inside me, I gasped, more in longing than fear, but still he murmured reassuringly, kissing me gently as he told me to relax.

I did, but it was still a painful experience, if much shorter than I had imagined. Not understanding then, I did wonder why, when it had been so painful, I should still feel that I wanted more of it. I was sore and tense, and ready to devour Richard with my hugs and kisses. Fortunately, being older and wiser and somewhat more experienced in these things, he hugged me in return and laughingly explained that if I wanted more, I should have to wait a little while.

And then something seemed to occur to him. He drew away to look at me, to search my face and eyes, while I wondered what was wrong, what I had said to inspire that look of amazement. Very slowly, his mouth curved into a smile. 'You do want more, don't you? You want me to love you again?'

I managed to nod while biting my lips. At that he laughed and hugged me, rolling over so that I was above and looking down on him. 'Kiss me,' he said, 'and tell your husband that you love him.'

'But I do love you,' I said.

The laughter faded, and suddenly he was serious, stroking my cheek and tracing the line of my lips with his finger. 'Sweet Sarah, I'm beginning to think you do . . .'

The next time, as Richard had promised, there was a little soreness, but no real pain, and a great deal of enjoyment. I found I liked what he was doing to me, I liked the feel of him inside me, and I loved the pleasure it gave him, that final burst of ecstasy before he collapsed, limp with satisfaction, into my arms.

Over the next few days we indulged ourselves as often as we could, retiring early, rising late – the winter was a wonderful excuse for that! – and often creeping upstairs immediately after dinner, while the servants were clearing away below us, and the men were still out in the yard.

I think it was towards the end of the first week that I suddenly discovered the magic of release. I don't know what caused it to happen, whether it was the caresses beforehand, a change of position, or simply that I forgot to think about him. Whatever the cause, I know that I was suddenly borne up on a rising wave of sensation, a wave that rose and broke and dashed me into the unknown. It was like flying, and dying, and then being born again. That day I became a woman. And it was that day, I think, that Richard began to fall in love with me.

We were happy together, not just in bed, but on almost every level of our relationship. Richard could talk to me about the farm, about his ambitions and his difficulties, and I mostly knew what he was talking about. What I didn't know, I found out by asking, reading, seeking people out and writing letters for him to those who might provide the answers.

We were neither of us socially ambitious, but we did visit our grander neighbours, the Clives at Sheriff Whenby, the Paulls at North Gilling, the Forsyths at Paxton, largely because of their contact with other landowners, and the exchange of ideas that generally came about when the men grouped together. I was less enamoured of the female company, but I had to put up with it in the cause of progress. We visited our smaller neighbours too, but that was often frustrating, since so many of them were too cautious, or had not the capital to experiment with these new ideas.

Not all of them were good ideas, I hasten to add: many ended poorly, and one experiment cost us a great deal of money, money we could ill afford to lose. But we struggled on, it taught us a lesson, and Father made us another loan until we were back on our feet again.

Although we did not make as many visits to Hammerford as I would have liked, we generally made a point of meeting up with my father on market days, often over dinner at the Pipers', and occasionally my father came to us and stayed overnight. But he was getting old, and after Aunt Margaret's death he suddenly seemed older still, and less inclined to travel.

I worried about him, just as I worried about the other sadness in my life, the lack of children. I began to fear that I was like my mother, destined to have one child late in life, and perhaps, like her, to die of it. Although we rarely spoke of the matter, I knew that Richard was grieved, that he would have loved a son to carry on his work and inherit the land. It saddened him more, I think, because his sister Hester was so fertile, continuing to produce babies year after year, and as easily as shelling peas. But as the years passed she grew increasingly fat, to the extent that she hardly moved from her sofa, and left all the work to Agnes and the servants.

Whenever I called, which was infrequently, the house was like a pigsty, and it was difficult to move without falling over children. I found it strange that Agnes seemed to mind so little. She scowled as much as ever, and at me particularly, but still she stayed with her sister and Tom Whitehead.

Richard had tried to interest her in various suitors, but she found fault with all of them. She was about thirty years old, I think, when he finally washed his hands of the matter and said she must find her own husband or die an old maid.

But I had begun to wonder whether she was a maid still, or whether in fact that strange relationship with her brother-in-law was closer than anyone else suspected. They never seemed to speak to each other, and yet they were always in accord, the two of them as watchful as a pair of stoats. And yet, if they had indeed been lovers for years – and I dared not voice that suspicion to anyone, least of all Richard – how could Hester not know about it? And how had Agnes managed to steer clear of pregnancies? It seemed too much of a coincidence that there should be two of us barren in the same family.

Then, miraculously, it seemed, Hester went more than a year without having a child. It was a matter of God be thanked, since there were ten of them living, the eldest at that time being a boy of fifteen, the youngest still a babe in arms. Richard made a few coarse comments to me in private about Tom Whitehead, but we neither of us guessed that Hester was ill.

Because of her weight, it was a long time before the growth became apparent, and then she simply looked pregnant although she swore to me she was not. Then she began to lose weight, and to complain of pains in her stomach and back. As she became weaker and thinner, the pains grew worse. Doctors were summoned, but nothing could be done. Hester was dying, and she knew it.

The strangest thing of all was that she begged to come home, to Holly Tree House, to peace and quiet, away from the noise of the children, away from her husband and sister . . .

It was a year of deaths, Hester's followed by that of Sarah's father in Hammerford, and, shortly afterwards, Uncle Piper, Aunt Margaret's husband, died in York. Sarah had nursed Hester for months, up to and through the most agonising death, and it seemed she had gone straight from one sickbed to another, although in her father's case his illness was brief, and his end mercifully peaceful. She grieved most deeply for him, but it was at her Uncle Piper's burial that she wept the most. It was as though, she explained, a dam had burst somewhere inside her, and all the emotions she had not been able to express for Hester and her father were suddenly released in that little churchyard in York.

Richard took her home, and she was ill for several months, afflicted by a desperate weariness that was not lifted by the spring, and continued through most of that long, hot summer. She could not bear to set eyes on Tom Whitehead, and would not have Agnes near her, although they often called at the house and asked after her health. Richard thought she was being unreasonable, but she could not explain, bound as she was by the secrecy of Hester's deathbed confession. According to Hester, Tom Whitehead had been enjoying Agnes for several years, probably since the early days of her arrival in the house. He took his conjugal pleasure with his wife, often enough to ensure her constant pregnancies, but that cold, unemotional man was truly bewitched by Agnes, who satisfied him in ways that Hester could not.

That wretched, sobbing confession cut deep into Sarah's soul. In some ways it was no more than she suspected, since she had always seen those two as curiously in accord, but she was disgusted by Hester's weak-willed compliance. Sarah could not imagine why she had done nothing about the situation, and fear of Tom and of the attendant scandal, should the truth come out, seemed no excuse. There was, too, the fact that she did not want to believe it, so she challenged Hester with Agnes's childlessness. Afterwards, she wished she had kept those doubts to herself, since Hester fought back with such a tale of sexual perversion – oh, yes, she said, she'd caught them out more than once! – that Sarah was revolted. But, like Hester, once the first shock had passed she reasoned that if Richard knew he would surely kill Tom Whitehead, and where would that leave them? Richard hanging on the Knavesmire, most like, and herself a widow.

There were times when she wanted to kill Tom Whitehead herself. To public view he was so righteous, such a hard-working pillar of the community, and a churchwarden to boot! And there was an irony, since for all his self-seeking ways, his secret envy of his brother-in-law, Richard, Tom Whitehead was popular in the village, he was the elected People's Warden, while Richard was the rector's man. As a consequence, vestry meetings did not always go smoothly.

Agnes she loathed and despised, since she could not imagine how a woman could betray her sister in such a way; as it was hard to keep those feelings to herself, Sarah avoided the other woman's company whenever possible. Fortunately, Agnes had plenty to keep her busy at home, and as time went by, she called at Holly Tree House less often.

For most of the Whitehead children, the girls especially, Sarah had a kind of affectionate pity, and she tried to concentrate on the fact that they were also Richard's kin. Two of the older girls had come to the house to help nurse their mother, and after her death had simply asked to stay. Sarah was glad of them when she herself became ill, and later, when she was once more up and about, she realised how much they had changed. Alice, the older of the two, had always been sweet and biddable, though somehow cowed, whereas Bess was sullen and dirty in her ways. After almost a year with Sarah, however, they were both taking pride in their work as well as their appearance, and exhibiting bright eyes and a ready sense of humour.

Their brother John, who at thirteen years old was between them in age, had been helping Richard on the farm for some time, and after Hester's death, he too came to live at the house. He was a quiet, good-looking boy, very much like his uncle in temperament and appearance, and Sarah had always been fond of him. With John and the two girls, it seemed they had become a ready-made family, and, when Richard asked her to take the boy aside and teach him his letters, Sarah began to wonder what was on his mind. They had been married for ten years, and she was only in her mid-twenties, but she began to think her husband had given up hope of children, and was thinking of making young John his heir.

Twenty Nine

NATASHA READ for some time, absorbing and assessing even while she was fascinated by the progress of the story. Nevertheless, the critical faculty, hovering like a devil's advocate at her shoulder, would insist on presenting questions and observations.

There were parallels here, the voice insisted, between Sarah Stalwell and Natasha Crayke. Both were young and unsure of themselves when they met and fell in love with the men they were ultimately to marry. The age differences were similar, both men had been married before, and in each case there had been a strong sexual attraction between the older man and the younger woman. And as for the location of the story, it was not merely similar, it was the same – same house, same village – different time, that was all. Even the Whitehead family were now involved.

The critical voice said: *Are you sure you're not involved, here? In some subtle working out of your own problems with Nick? Are you certain this is not the product of your subconscious mind, just as the woman in the blue dress was mere hallucination?*

But I'd have to be sick to imagine that scene by the wood.

They say all women fantasise about rape, in some form or another, at some stage in their lives.

This was no fantasy.

Are you sure?

And the answer to that was, *not entirely*.

She would have liked to consign the devil's advocate to perdition, but he refused to be silenced completely; and those questions, having been raised, forced her to look at certain aspects again. Was there a similarity in the sexual relationships? Sarah Stalwell seemed to have taken to sexual pleasure with enthusiasm and in her case the satisfaction had apparently held good for many years. Not until the dreadful times of 1721 and 1722, when she had been beset on all sides by illness and death, did she complain that her relationship with Richard had suffered.

And that was hardly surprising, Natasha thought. After all that Sarah had endured, no wonder it culminated in illness and depression, and, with her attention and energies focused on the sick and dying, of course Richard had felt neglected.

Sarah's debility had lasted several months, and it was not until the end of August that she began to improve, and to take notice of what was going on around her. Almost at once she was concerned about Richard; she noticed that his liveliness and optimism had gone, that he had developed a tendency to complain at every small irritation as at a major disaster. Although the harvest had been good, it might have been better if only the rain had held off that last day; and if Jack had paid more attention instead of mooning after that girl in the village, then the cattle would not have broken out and been halfway to Brickhill before they were rounded up . . .

The complaints seemed endless. Then, at average-time, between harvest and Michaelmas, when enclosures had to be taken down to allow the village livestock to wander at will, Richard's usual sense of frustration threatened to get out of hand. The ancient laws were all very well, he declared, but it was hardly just that the majority of livestock ended up on his land, simply because it was better tended and provided better grazing. He said it every year, but mostly confined his grumbling to Sarah. That year, however, he had had an altercation with Tom Whitehead that almost came to blows.

As he was a freeholder, most of Richard's land was hedged and sacrosanct, and it was on his own land that he had conducted his first experiments with rotation crops. Wheat, turnip, barley and clover followed each other in annual succession, and had proved so well that he would have liked to extend the system to certain fields that he held in tenancy. But, like many others around the village, those fields were protected only by wattle fences, which had to be taken down at average-time. And he'd be damned, he declared to Sarah, if somebody else's animals were going to get the benefit of his rich lucernes and carefully hoed turnips. Nevertheless, earlier that year, he had spent time and money improving one of those rented fields, and as a consequence had taken from it a decent hay crop which promised to be even better the following summer. He did not want it grubbed-up by pigs or grazed to nothing by sheep, and was even prepared to offer an alternative in exchange for leaving it protected.

But Tom Whitehead was having none of that. He wanted the fences taken down, and his demand was backed by half a dozen of the more aggressive village inhabitants. Richard refused to back down, so, that night, his fences were removed, and in the morning pigs, sheep and cattle were feasting on all that rich meadow-grass.

There was so little that could be done about it that Richard's frustration almost choked him. He was particularly incensed because he had always treated Tom Whitehead fairly, and without Tom, the other men would have been more amenable. As far as Sarah was concerned, it was one more nail in their brother-in-law's coffin, and she did not try to alleviate her husband's sense of grievance. But more than one good thing came out of it: Richard finally saw Tom Whitehead for what he was, and the anger jerked him out of his apathy. It also made Sarah realise that she had devoted more than enough time to misery and grief, and that she must take her place once more as Richard's partner, both on the farm and in his bed.

He responded so wholeheartedly that only then did she realise how much he still loved and needed her, how much he had missed her participation in his everyday life. For the first time in months they shared the same bed every night, and with the shortening of the days enjoyed a prolonged and passionate reunion that reminded Sarah of their first winter together. Nothing was said about a child, but, with hope renewed, the idea drew them together again and again. Sarah began to pray, with a fervency that was unlike her, that this time Richard would not be disappointed.

The autumn was mild and clear, with an abundance of fruit for making wine and preserves. With the aid of Alice and Bess, Sarah worked hard to ensure that nothing was wasted, not an apple from the orchard, not a berry from the hedgerows. They packed and pressed and simmered, made rose-hip syrup and damson wine, apple cider and October ale. And when the fruit harvest was over, and the first frosts came, they slaughtered a pig, hanging the hams to cure in the chimney, salting the bacon, making black pudding from the blood, and sausages from the chitterlings. Preparing for the onset of winter, they were busy for weeks, but in an atmosphere of good fellowship which made the work seem light. With thrift as part of her nature, Sarah enjoyed seeing the results of hard work: full store cupboards, good food on the table, and a row of bright and shiny faces in the firelight.

The children whom she'd tried to love for her sister-in-law's sake had become, under Sarah's roof, lovable in their own right. They had learned to smile, to show their good points, and, following her example, to keep themselves clean and tidy, particularly in the house. She had taught the girls to sew, and helped them to make their own clothes; she was teaching them about the growing of herbs and their use in the kitchen, and for an hour each evening after supper, she gave all three children some elementary lessons in reading and writing.

At the end of the day she was tired, but pleasurably so; and that was the time she loved best, when she and Richard could escape up the stairs to their own chamber, to the intimacy of a few hours alone. As the days grew shorter and the work, of necessity, became less, they enjoyed each other more, revelling in rediscovered knowledge and the confidence that comes of long association. Although his dark hair was beginning to grey at the temples, he seemed little changed from the man she had married more than a decade before. He was as lean and firm as ever, and she enjoyed the look and touch and smell of him as much as she had done in the very beginning. When his glance fell on her, Sarah knew that he felt the same way, even though she was no longer the slip of a thing he had married. In the last few years she had matured, her figure had become fuller, rounder, more pleasing to the eye; and with experience she knew how to use it, to tease and tantalise as much as to satisfy.

Looking back on that time, those few months between September and Christmas, Sarah regarded it as being one of the happiest of her life. Everything seemed set fair, and they needed only the promise of a child to make their fulfilment complete.

After Christmas, however, the winter began to make itself felt. Richard made his usual trips to market, generally about twice a month, but instead of staying in town overnight, which he had often done the previous winter, he aimed to return within the day. As the weather became colder and more unpredictable, Sarah begged him to take care and not to linger too long in York. After dark, the roads were not safe, and in the depths of winter poverty and desperation often drove otherwise peaceful men to acts of violence. But Richard travelled armed with a pistol, and anyway, he worried more about the weather.

When he set off with young John, just after dawn on that January morning, the sky was clear and the fields and fences were white with frost. He kissed Sarah briefly and said he could remember well all that she needed, and that they would be sure to be home again by nightfall.

> The sky began to darken in the mid-afternoon, great clouds building rapidly to the north-west, while the sun was still shining to the south. It did not shine for long. The wind came up with a crack like thunder, rattling all the windows in the house, and suddenly it was snowing, thick and fast, like a plague of white moths settling at once on the frozen ground.
>
> Within minutes, everything visible was covered, and the sky was a whirling mass of white. I think I knew then that it was too late, that Richard and the boy would be on the road already, and caught in that dreadful blizzard. I watched and waited and fought the knowledge, telling myself that no, Richard would have delayed setting off as usual, and seeing those clouds would have stayed on in town. Or perhaps he had set off earlier, and found shelter

in one of the villages along the way, Strensall perhaps, or Brickhill.

But as we dragged logs in and built up the fire, as day became night and the blizzard continued, my heart felt like lead with fear and apprehension. Old Jacob had stayed with us, and I had the girls, but none of us slept, myself least of all. The storm eased towards morning and finally stopped. Reflected by that mass of white, dawn came early, but it was dark inside the house. On the northern side, the windows were covered completely, and to the south we could barely see across the foldyard. I ran up the stairs to the chamber above and looked out. The lane had disappeared, and of the village I could see only trees and one or two chimneys, and the square mass of the church tower. Across the foldyard the drifts had all but covered the barn and byre.

Seized by panic, I could do nothing. Richard, Richard, Richard, was all I could think or say. I wanted to rouse the village, get the men out and searching, but we could not get out of the house. Old Jacob tried to calm us, telling me the master would be all right, sheltering in some farmhouse, or comfortable in one of York's many inns. He had been telling me that all night, but I was not convinced.

Snow was packed halfway up the door. We had to climb over it and through it to cross the yard. The two men who slept above the stables threw out shovels and we started to dig a way to the door. It took all of us most of the morning to clear a path to the byre, so we could get in and out to feed the animals.

From the upper windows I could see similar activity in the village, and that helped, like the physical work, to cure my panic. In between digging at snow, I set the girls to cook the dinner. We needed food to carry on.

Jack, old Jacob's son, struggled up from the village to see we were all right. I told him about Richard and young John Whitehead, that they had not returned from York and I feared for their safety, but he knew, as well as I did by then, that nothing could be done. Even as we talked, it began to snow again, steadily this time, but at sight of it I could have wept.

It was three days before we could get out, before the risk of more snow abated and anyone dared to leave the village on foot. Tom Whitehead and his eldest son Matt – a surly youth just like his father – set out with Jack and another of our labourers to walk to Brickhill for news. They continued as far as Strensall, and returned the next day, but of Richard and young John, nothing had been heard.

The day after that, just as everyone else was saying they *must* have stayed in York, a young shepherd staggered into our yard. He had found them while searching for his sheep. Just over the ridge, no more than a mile from Brickhill and less than two from the house, their bodies were together in a hollow only a few yards off the track. Of the horses, there was no sign.

I had known all along that the blizzard had caught them, but at the shepherd's words, I lost my senses. I refused to believe that Richard was dead. I refused to believe it until they brought the bodies home on hurdles, and when I saw my husband, my strong, upright, handsome Richard, curled and frozen like a stillborn child, my heart and mind tore themselves apart.

I cursed God. I cursed Him long and loud, I cursed Him until those gathered round fell back in horror, and I challenged Him – if He had power – to strike me dead. Without my husband, my beloved Richard, I did not want to live.

God, the Father of us all, should have taken me then, and saved me from what was to come. But I cursed God and turned away from Him, and I have lived in His absence ever since.

And if Hell was the absence of God, as certain theologians had been heard to claim . . .

Shivering suddenly, Natasha pushed the typewriter away and went to stand before the fire. It was after five and she was chilled with exhaustion, beyond the desire to speculate on anything but sleep.

Tucking Colette beneath her arm, she went upstairs to bed.

When Natasha awoke, it was with a sense of loss. Sarah Stalwell was so clear in her mind that it seemed she had just left the room, unavoidably called away in the middle of a conversation. Words and context eluded her, but in Natasha there remained a depth of sadness, as though a dearly loved friend had just confessed some personal tragedy to which there was no answer, no comfort, and no alleviation.

Of course, Richard. Richard was dead, and, beside herself with grief, Sarah did not want to live. She was twenty-seven years old and her life was over; she was alone and childless in a community which could hardly be said to have taken her to their hearts. Richard had been everything to her, friend and business partner, husband and lover; she had been his wife, and he had been a remarkable man, the most forward-thinking farmer for miles around. Not aristocracy, not even minor gentry, just a small landowner who utilised everything at his command to increase yields and improve the land. The intelligence and foresight were his own, the capital and encouragement largely Sarah's; but they had worked together with a common aim. Richard was liked by some and envied by others, and if he was respected in the village it was largely for his thoroughness and decency. His ideas, in a largely entrenched society, were regarded with suspicion, and, since it took so long to prove a point in agricultural terms, only at the time of his death were the locals beginning to see the method in his madness.

Sarah was as much a foreigner to them as she had been on the day she arrived. She was young and fair-minded, but she favoured no one, could not be cheated, and never failed to make it clear that she would not suffer fools gladly. The women respected her, but they did not like her, and made it their excuse that she did not *belong*. It was also said throughout the village that she was the one with the money, that Richard Stalwell was in thrall to her and could deny her nothing. It was said that she gave the orders, while he obeyed.

Other slanders circulated too, stories that were part truth and more exaggeration, things taken out of context and elaborated upon, so that as time passed the gap between Sarah and the village grew wider, not smaller. The ignorant were prepared to believe that she had turned Agnes Stalwell out of her home all those years ago, and that she had subsequently enticed three of Tom Whitehead's children away, turning them against their father in the process. And now, as a result, one of them was dead. The only ones consistently to refute these claims were those who worked at Holly Tree Farm, but, since they were mostly men, it was said that they had fallen under the same spell as Richard Stalwell.

When Sarah, in her rage and grief at Richard's death, cursed God, the story went round the village like wildfire. Agnes Stalwell said her sister-in-law was a witch whose evil had long been hidden behind a fair face and golden hair. Agnes Stalwell said it was not right that Tom's daughters should be alone in that great house with such a woman and her dead husband: God alone knew what corruption they might be witnessing. And, while they all waited for the weather to abate so that graves could be dug, she persuaded Tom Whitehead and two of his cronies to rescue Alice and Bess from Holly Tree House.

> It was the third day, I think, that they came to take the girls from me. It was early in the morning, I know that. The sun was barely up when they came hammering on the door, and Alice, bless her, went to answer and to tell them please be quiet, the mistress was ill and had passed a poor night.
>
> They dragged her out with such force that she screamed, and Bess, having warning, put up such a fight that I needs must struggle downstairs to her aid. But it was too late, they had both girls, and I could do nothing. Young

Jack and his father, old Jacob, had come in from the yard, but they were warned with sticks to keep to themselves.

I asked why they would deprive me so, and Tom Whitehead told me, his eyes burning with such hatred as he listed all my supposed misdemeanours, that I fell back before him. It was a mistake. I should have faced him down and quoted a few home truths for his cronies to hear. They might have been less inclined to restore those girls to their father's care. But I was ill, and weak, and my wits were not about me. It must have seemed that I did not deny his accusations, that his righteousness was greater than my capacity for evil, and that I was vanquished.

Vanquished I was, and more utterly than they realised. I could not fight them, I had nothing to fight them with, not even a woman's traditional weapon, words. So I let them take sweet Alice and brave Bess, and I was left only with the memory of their affection, and the echo of their promises to return.

Old Jacob tried to comfort me, to see me back up the stairs to bed, but I trailed, distraught, into the chill of my parlour, to sit by Richard's bier. He was not there, only his body laid out by Widow Megginson, but I talked to him just the same. In truth, I was glad of the snow, though it was thawing day by day. I did not want them to bury him in the cold earth. While ever he was with me, I could pretend he was only sleeping.

Two days later, Bess escaped from home and came back to see me, her face white and pinched, and showing the marks of more than one heavy blow. Much as I grieved for her, I had to tell her to go away. If she stayed with me, they would say I held her by witchcraft or some such nonsense, and she would suffer the more because of it. She wept, but she went in the end.

When the rector called again to see me, I told him what was afoot. He, good man that he was, had let me rail and rant the first time, showing none of the horror I might have expected at such blaspheming. Since I seemed to be calmer, he tried to offer words of comfort, but nothing could comfort me, and I did not want to hear about God and the sacrifices made by Jesus Christ our Saviour. I was numb, not concerned about my own soul, but rather for the temporal care of Tom Whitehead's children.

For the first time I gave voice to Hester's deathbed confessions. With Richard gone, there was no one left to protect, and I wanted the Reverend Clive to know that accusations would be made against me, and why.

He did not seem to be shocked by what I had to say. Perhaps he knew, or perhaps his years of caring for so many ignorant souls had left him inured to shock. I do not know. He said he would remember, and do what he could. He also asked whether I wanted Richard's body removed to the church, where it was colder than in the house. I said not.

Three of my Piper cousins were still alive, but I sent no word to them. I had not seen them for some years, and could not imagine that they would feel the need to stand beside Richard's grave, even if they were able to travel, the roads being near impassable, first with snow and then with mud.

When the thaw came, it came quickly. The stream, in flood, swept away a flimsy cottage at the foot of the lane, and made the village street a river for a day and a night. Then, as quick as it rose, it fell again, and the pallbearers came to me for Richard's body, and to the Whiteheads' for young John.

I remember nothing of that joint service, only that the church was full, and that I stood beside the single grave, facing Tom and Agnes, with as much hate in my heart as grief. With me a widow, and the farm entailed, who, I wondered, would inherit when I was gone? I should not have minded John, who was a Stalwell of Richard's cast, hardly his father's son at all; but I could not bear that the sum of our efforts should fall to the hypocrite who faced me across that open grave.

Old Jacob, who had served the family well, took my arm to see me home; bravely, it seemed, since most of the others drew away as soon as the interment was over. They were ranged behind Tom and Agnes, who forced herself, briefly, to offer me help. I turned away in disgust, of course, and thus placed myself, in front of witnesses, entirely in the wrong. But I had old Jacob, and his son Jack, to see me home through the mud and the gathering gloom.

For a moment, by the gate, I paused to look along Dagger Lane, towards the ridge where my beloved Richard and his nephew had perished in the storm. I could not help seeing it: it would be there whenever I turned my face to the south, the sight as painful to my eyes as the eternal question in my heart. Why? Why them?

As I turned away, to follow the two men into the house, I saw, very briefly, a black hound lurking in the shadows, its great eyes upon me. But as I looked back, it seemed I had imagined it. The thing was gone.

Since his wife's death, old Jacob had taken over much of the work about the house and the kitchen, assisted by the two girls. With them gone, he did his best for me in a fatherly way, although he would not sleep in the house. That night, he heated food for me that I did not want, and said, with regret, that he must go. It mattered not to me, but after a low, heated exchange, his son came back, and insisted that I must not be alone.

So young Jack, who had worked about the house and yard since boyhood, became my servant and bodyguard, bringing me wine when I asked for it, and doing his best to supervise the working of the farm.

I seem to recall that I ate little or nothing for a long time after Richard's death, but drank instead, ale during the day and wine at night. With wine I could sleep.

Weeks passed, and winter began to give way to spring. Work was done about the farm, but half-heartedly. I did nothing, issued no orders, and let Jack oversee all. He did his best, but he was not Richard, and the men would not obey him. They came to me to ask about the ploughing, and which fields were to be planted with what. In truth I could not have cared less, but I had to go out with them and make a pretence of my decisions, and, having gone out reluctantly several times, it then became a habit. Gradually, I took over Richard's role about the farm, while Jack and his father did the usual chores. We managed.

But with spring and growth and the return of new life, I missed Richard more than ever. My bed was empty and I ached with longing, for Richard, for the love we had shared and the child we never had. I could not sleep, so I drank the damson wine we made together, and when I still could not sleep, I wandered, light-headed, along Dagger Lane and over the fields. I talked to the cows in the moonlight, and I lay down in the grass to embrace the land that Richard had loved.

So much love, so much faith, had gone into making that land what it was. Good, rich, productive land, that would continue to produce as long as it was cared for. But Richard had gone, and to me it meant little without him. I had seen the lawyers, and probate had at last been granted: the farm was mine for my lifetime. But after I was dead, what then? That question returned, again and again, to torment me. I could not bear the thought of Tom Whitehead's eldest son, he was so much like his father.

I was angry and despairing, and in all my wanderings I found nothing to bring me comfort, nothing to say, *for this you must live*. The world, to me, was a godless place, my existence without meaning. Until the night that I was followed, and when I lay down in the damp grass to look for Richard's face in the stars, another lay down beside me, to stroke my hair and kiss my lips, to respond with passion when I turned to him.

Afterwards, to my surprise, I realised that it was not Richard at all, but young Jack, who had made himself my protector. By then, he must have been about twenty-two or three, and not dissimilar to Richard in height and build, though nowhere near so handsome. In the darkness he had fooled me. Or was it in my drunkenness that I fooled myself? Either way, I gave myself willingly, and for a while the pleasure was so intense it took all my pain away.

He loved me, he said, and could not bear to see me so distressed. His love meant little to me, I am sorry to say – it was Richard I loved, Richard I wanted – but for the time being, Jack's virile young body was satisfaction enough. In the weeks that followed, if I had wine to drink and closed my eyes while he made love to me, I could pretend that it was Richard I held in my arms, Richard who made me cry out with pleasure.

I had to teach him things, of course; it would have been no good unless he had known what I wanted and when. But he was an apt pupil, so besotted that he could not leave me alone for long. For a while that was exciting, but then it became tedious, especially when his new-found position as the mistress's lover went to his head. He became too familiar in the presence of others, even to the extent of giving his own father orders, as though he, Jack, were the master in *my* house.

Something had to be done about it, especially when old Jacob threatened to give notice. I did not think I could do without Jacob, whereas Jack had begun to lose his appeal. I decided to show him his place in the order of things. I took another lover.

It was about the time, I think, that people had begun to talk, not just about me – they had been doing that for months – but about an old myth, a creature of the devil which was supposed to haunt these parts, a spectral hound they called Reynard . . .

Drawing back from the typewriter, Natasha stared at the page, her thoughts confused by alarm and apprehension. Uncertain where Sarah was leading her, she sat quite still, contemplating the last few words. After a while, deepening shadows within the house made it impossible to distinguish them clearly, but that hardly mattered, since they were imprinted like a banner at the forefront of her mind.

It was mid-afternoon on the shortest day of the year, and already it was growing dark. That sudden awareness jerked her back from the table. Switching on lights, twitching at curtains, she hurried outside with her collection of containers for fuel, going through the same ritual as before. Colette had been out since Natasha came downstairs at noon, so she called her in and fed the others, made sure the windows were shut and the outer doors locked, and settled herself in for the hours of darkness.

Only when all was secure did she ask herself why she felt so threatened. As a child she had never been particularly afraid of the dark, although it was not the dark, as such, that frightened her now. It was what might be out there, a dense black shadow, darker than the night, Charlie Cramp's Padfoot, Sarah's spectral hound . . .

Thirty

THAT SENSE of menace increased throughout the evening, intensified by the irregular but prolonged calling of an owl. Colette seemed uneasy too, pacing about the kitchen, leaping up to the windowledge facing the yard, scratching and sniffing at the door.

Natasha told herself that Colette was simply restless, that she could hear the owl and was eager to be after it. The little cat loved being out in the dark and often did not come in until nearly midnight, whereas today her freedom to hunt had been severely restricted. While telling herself that, Natasha also looked for practical explanations of her own unease. She was alone and feeling vulnerable; she was tired, her mind was overstretched at the moment; most of all, the present context of the story was enough to instil alarm into the most hard hearted sceptic. If this tale was no more than a product of her own subconscious mind, then she was surely in need of a good psychiatrist; but if Sarah Stalwell really was telling her life story from beyond the grave, then Natasha had reason to lock herself in and to stay alert during the hours of darkness.

In the spring and early summer of 1723, while Sarah Stalwell smothered her grief for Richard in the arms of other men, it was being whispered throughout the village that *Reynard* was on the prowl again. Old women, hugging the warmth of their fires, repeated the tale of his last proven appearance as though it were yesterday: the entire congregation of All Saints, Brickhill, had witnessed the hound of Satan disappearing through the south wall of their church, going back, some claimed, to his lair in the old castle. It was said by others that he was the devil's familiar, sent into the world to hunt for human souls, that he was called up by witches and warlocks, and could change his size and shape at will.

Sarah heard the stories, laughing at the ignorance of those who told them. She turned her back when the women of the village made their signs against the evil eye, and shrugged her shoulders when young children scattered at her approach. Fortified by wine and the attentions of her latest lover, Sarah cared nothing for anyone, least of all herself.

She heard most of it through Jack, and even laughed at him as he begged her to repent, and to consider her immortal soul. To her, such pleas seemed ridiculous, particularly since he had a tendency to beg for other things too, things which had little to do with the immortality of the soul. Just occasionally, to pacify him, she would let him have his way with her, rather as she might have tossed a few scraps to the animals. He called her a bitch, a term she found curiously apposite, for that was precisely how she felt, like a bitch on heat with a constant stream of rampant hounds at the door.

It seemed that all she had to do was look at a man, and he was hers for the taking; age, looks and marital status were no barrier. Few were as pleasing to the eye as Jack, and certainly none were as tender; none of them cared for her the way he did, they were simply driven by a lust which had to be satisfied. But their coarseness and crudity, even in some cases their bestiality, excited her. She wanted to be used and debased, and felt neither shame nor regret; and she took pleasure afterwards in denying the men what they were so anxious to repeat.

By the end of May, old Jacob was long gone, since he could not tolerate the shame of witnessing his mistress behaving like a whore. Jack stayed on, partly from desperation, but mostly because his family had disowned him and he had nowhere else to go. He fed the domestic animals and prepared food for himself and the two remaining labourers, while Sarah haunted the fields or took men to the stables, or sat drinking alone in her little parlour.

The Reverend Clive called and tried to remonstrate with her. Fornication was a mortal sin, he reminded her wearily, and if she had no thought for herself, then she should have a care for the tribulation she was bringing to others. Her behaviour was becoming known beyond the village, and people – he managed to imply that by *people* he meant the local gentry – were liable to be scandalised. She should have a care for the consequences.

Throughout the interview Sarah kept her eyes closed. The old man was becoming weak and frail and she had no wish to alarm him. He only wanted to protect her, and it was not his fault that she did not wish to be protected.

Towards the end of June, which had been so cold and wet that a poor harvest threatened everyone's livelihood, the mutterings became worse. The rector called again, seeming sadder and wearier than ever. There had been a deputation, he said, led by the churchwarden, Tom Whitehead. Unless Sarah Stalwell agreed to sell up and leave the area, complaints would be sent to the bishop. She would be accused of fornication and, if found guilty, was liable to be excommunicated by the church courts. Some – and here the rector hesitated – were even suggesting that the charge should be witchcraft, but the Reverend Clive was confident that he had managed to talk them out of that certain folly.

That, I knew, would be Agnes. I was not afraid of the power of the church courts, but I was incensed at the threat issued by Tom Whitehead. That he and Agnes Stalwell should accuse *me* of fornication, after all they had done – and that they should use such a threat to blackmail me into selling the farm – provoked in me such a rage that I think the rector was alarmed. He poured wine for me and made me drink it, which calmed my mind and eased his concern a little. Once he had gone, I began to search for ways in which I might punish them.

Answering their accusations with charges of my own would do no good: it was too late and, other than the rector, no one would believe me. The children were too frightened to tell the truth. I thought and thought for half the night, to no avail, but in the morning, as I peered into my looking-glass for the first time in weeks, the answer came to me.

If Agnes thought I was possessed by the evil eye, well then, she would soon discover the truth of it. I had noticed long since that if I wanted a man all I had to do was look at him in a certain way, while thinking certain thoughts. My trouble was that I wanted a man – just about any man would do – most of the time, so I had to be careful where my gaze rested. I had never wanted Tom Whitehead, or his sons, although I had probably lain with most of the working men in Denton and Brickhill, not to mention the Clives' two sons from Sheriff Whenby, and Kit Forsyth from Paxton Manor.

I decided then that I would have Tom Whitehead, and young Matthew – a sullen, boorish youth exactly like his father – and I would have them both in front of witnesses.

The best place would be in the open fields, or along the lane, where we could be seen. And the best time would be harvest – if the harvest was ever ready – when every able-bodied man and woman would be working out of doors.

The only drawback to this plan was the matter of timing. By the look of things, harvest would not be for another month, which meant that I ran the risk of those accusations reaching the bishop before I could stay Tom Whitehead's blackmail. For I had no intentions of moving out, nor of selling the farm. Not when I knew that it was Agnes and Tom Whitehead who wanted it. They would get it only over my dead body.

So Sarah waited, and in the meantime Tom Whitehead circumvented the rector of Denton with his doubts and procrastinations, and enlisted the help of another member of the Clive family, someone with a harder heart and more influcnce. The formidable Lady Clive was wife to the rector's nephew, Sir

James, and although her husband and Richard Stalwell had shared a common interest in advanced farming methods, she had never cared for Sarah. Too interested in the men, she had always thought, and was not surprised – although she was severely affronted – by the woman's recent behaviour. So she took the matter to the bishop, and while that august gentleman might be able to ignore the common herd if he so wished, he could not dismiss such a distinguished patroness.

At the end of August, just as harvest was beginning, Sarah had another visit from the Reverend Clive, this time to inform her that she would shortly be summoned before the Archdeacon's Court in York.

It was time to put the plan into action.

Tom Whitehead was a big man, taller and more heavily built than Richard had been. He was older too, in his middle forties, and far more cunning than any man I ever knew. It was also true that he hated me. When it came to it, I was not at all sure that my tricks would work on him. I wondered whether to aim first for his son, Matt, whose youth made him far more vulnerable; but if I succeeded with him I might still fail with the father. In the end it seemed better to try for the more difficult prize.

I watched and waited for a few days, until they were reaping close to the village, and on the morning that I could be sure of a goodly number being in view, I decided to act. When a watery sun was reaching its zenith, I called to Jack to follow me and be my witness. As I strolled down the lane, the women were coming out with food and drink for their menfolk. Most hung back when they saw me, or looked the other way as they hurried on. One woman, restrained by another, screamed insults as I passed, and a moment later I felt the thud of a stone in the middle of my back. I turned and glared for a moment, but carried on into the field. Poor Jack caught the rest of their fury, but followed me, nevertheless.

My heart was pounding with the fear of failure. There

was no room to be afraid of anything else. I barely heard the hisses and jeers behind me, I was looking for Tom Whitehead. The moment seemed endless – perhaps fear blinded me – I could see him nowhere, and in my panic I turned to one of the men nearby.

'Tom Whitehead – where is he?'

Fear and lust battled for supremacy in his eyes. He was one I had lain with several times, and he would have begged me now but for his wife yelling at him from the group behind us.

His ugly mouth twisted into a grin as he indicated across the field. I turned to look and, along the line of corn-stooks, I saw the burly figure of Tom Whitehead coming towards me.

Suddenly my vision cleared and I was calm. I took his measure and then glanced back to see whether Agnes was present. She was not. So much the better. I could do without her stirring the ill-feeling behind me. Thrusting my hatred aside, I watched Tom Whitehead through narrowed eyes as he warily approached. He's afraid of me, I thought, and the knowledge brought forth a surge of power so strong I almost laughed.

'What're you doing down here?' he demanded belligerently. 'This is my land – what do you want?'

I gazed into his flinty grey eyes and smiled, all the while thinking of his physical strength and his talent for sexual abuse. I had tasted enough of it from other men, there was no need to be revolted now. Nor was I – it was enough to imagine the power I would have over him once he was mine. Agnes would have cause to complain after that!

'Why, Tom,' I whispered, 'it's *you* I want. Just you.'

There was conflict in his eyes. He dragged his gaze away, looked out across the field and then towards the group of women, as quiet now as an audience at a mystery play.

'Well I don't want you,' he declared, but his voice cracked, and when I touched his bare forearm he jerked as though stung. 'Get yourself gone, woman – off my land *now*, before I throw you off!'

I stood my ground, smiling up at him all the time. He was so enraged by that, he made the mistake of laying hands on me, dragging me forcefully towards the gate and past that silent, goggle-eyed crowd.

I protested for effect, even indulged in a scream or two as he manhandled me into the lane. My resistance infuriated him, and when I bit his arm, drawing blood, he smacked me so hard that I fell to the ground. For a moment, I saw stars, but only for a moment. As my head cleared, I forced a smile and drew up my skirts, which were already above my knees.

He was bending over me, his face livid and distorted. 'What are you so scared of?' I challenged him under my breath. 'Has your manhood deserted you?'

That did it. With a roar like an angry bull he ripped at the flap of his breeches and fell upon me in full view of half the village. The men yelled their encouragement, while the women stood like statues, unsure whether I was getting what I deserved, or what I had specifically asked for. I, while seeming to thrash about in the most terrible anguish, was actually giving Tom Whitehead just what he wanted. Like all the rest, he would soon be begging for more.

Unfortunately, the excitement proved too much for some. While wives dragged their menfolk away, when Tom Whitehead had finished, I had two more to contend with. And when they were done, I was badly bruised and bleeding. Not so much from where they had used me, although I was sore and grazed there too, but from the stony lane. My back was cut and bleeding, my bodice in tatters where they had pulled at it to get at my breasts.

Jack was throwing up into the ditch, his face red and puffy from weeping. I slowly dragged myself upright, and went to his aid. He, poor fool, had tried to help me, but the others had held him down, punching and kicking him for good measure. He could not understand my air of triumph, why I was laughing weakly despite the pain. But I told him I had Tom Whitehead now, I had shown him up for what he was, and he could not bear witness against me.

In early September the case was presented to the Archdeacon's Court in York. Sarah attended, wearing her finest clothes and the proud, though injured, expression of a woman who has suffered much at the hands of envious neighbours. Depositions had been taken, and these were consulted, but Tom Whitehead's stance as People's Warden of the parish of St Oswald, and chief complainant, was severely undermined by Sarah's evidence.

She stood accused of harlotry, of giving offence to her neighbours by persistent fornication with single men, and of enticing husbands away from their lawful wives. Since she did not deny the charges, the usual form would have been to reprimand her, impose a monetary fine, and order a public confession; and in most cases that pressure to conform would have been enough. But Sarah was determined not to bow to any pressure. She opposed the ruling of the court with charges of her own, charges against Tom Whitehead, the chief complainant, that he had raped and assaulted her in full view of a score of witnesses. If she must confess her sins, Sarah declared to the astonished company, then so must he. And if she must pay a fine, then his should be greater, since she had suffered much under his hands.

'And I beg leave to say, my lord, that the men I have known, far from issuing complaints against me, have a tendency to come back for more.'

There was muffled laughter at that, but the ecclesiastical lawyer who sat in judgment was not so amused. After a stern reprimand to me, and some consultation with his learned colleagues, he ordered the case to be referred to the next sitting.

I was satisfied by that. With no immediate conclusion, the matter might drag on indefinitely. I had managed to thwart Tom Whitehead nicely, and his patroness, Lady

Clive. I wondered whether she would be so keen to support him in the next round.

Tom Whitehead, having had his guns spiked, hated Sarah more than ever, but it seemed he could not leave her alone, nor could she keep him away. He enjoyed abusing her, and employed his son to keep Jack from the room while he did so. As a reward, he held Jack down while Matt took his pleasure with Sarah, and laughed at the young man's impotence.

One night, a group of labourers from Brickhill, whom she had employed on a casual basis at harvest time, came late to the house, bursting in as soon as the door was opened, their intentions very clear. They were drunk, but not incapable. Three of them had her, one after the other, while a fourth, whose inclinations were more to men than women, sodomised Jack.

That shocked her, to a greater extent than she would have believed possible. Jack, whom she had treated so badly, about whom she cared so little, had become important to her. To see him raped, like an innocent girl, was more than she could tolerate. For the first time she saw the evil that was spreading from her own actions, and in an attempt to master her own waywardness, Sarah cut down the amount she was drinking. She tried to make do with ale, which was far less potent than wine, but then she did not sleep very well, and in the long, wakeful hours she began to be frightened, to feel that she was being watched.

At first she thought it was something to do with Agnes, who had berated, threatened, and one day attacked her as she walked through the village. Sarah had managed to escape, but at night she imagined Agnes watching in the darkness, her face set in that malevolent scowl, just awaiting the opportunity to strike . . .

And then Jack disappeared. It was not entirely without warning, since he had been in a state of abject misery ever since the visit of the Brickhill labourers. Nothing could cheer him after that. His wretchedness became so absolute that he no longer came to Sarah's bed, and when she went to him, he merely clung to her and wept.

He must have gone before dawn. Sarah was up with first light, and the house was empty. She searched, went outside, looked in the outbuildings, sent one of the men to enquire at old Jacob's house; but he was nowhere to be found. She had a fearful sensation about his disappearance, akin to the dread she had experienced in the blizzard. Without further ado she set off on horseback towards Brickhill, and ordered the two men to search the fields and nearby woods.

He had not been seen in Brickhill, and, thinking perhaps he might have passed that way in darkness, she continued to Strensall. But there was neither sign nor word. With a sick sense of loss she began the return journey, hoping against hope that he would be at the farm when she returned.

On the way home she noticed apples ripening in orchards, and damsons hanging in fat purple bunches; and where there were hedgerows there were also brambles, with juicy black fruit just begging to be picked. Trivial though it was, the sight of all that fruit unsettled her further, because she had done nothing so far towards stocking her shelves for winter, and, with no one to help in the preparation, it was likely to be a lean and hungry season. She thought about the previous autumn, with all its hopes and abundance and cheerful activity, and could have wept.

It was almost noon when she reached home, to find the men relaxing in the sunny yard, supping ale and eating bread and cheese. It was the final straw. They were slack and idle and she had let them become so; it was also obvious that any search they had conducted had been cursory in the extreme. They did not care for Jack, he had lorded it too much when he was the favourite, but Sarah berated them anyway. Yelling at them to get up and do some work, she stalked into the house and gave way to the burning tears of self-recrimination.

When she had recovered a little, Sarah told herself that it would soon be Michaelmas. She could get rid of those two idlers then, and at the hirings fair pick up the half-dozen men she needed to run the farm properly, and a couple of sturdy girls for the house. This year she had neglected both most shamefully, and would have to dip into savings to survive the winter and get things going again in the spring.

That decided, she felt better, stronger, and went to find something to eat. Afterwards, she went out searching again for Jack. Somewhere in her mind, not fully acknowledged, was the thought that he had done away with himself, so she scoured the hedgerows and followed the course of the stream, still running strongly after all the summer's rain. She found nothing in that direction, which was hardly surprising, since it would have taken a singular determination to drown in less than a foot of water, but nevertheless she looked. She walked for miles, calling his name, shouting enquiries to men clearing ditches, women and children picking fruit, but no one had seen poor Jack.

Eventually she turned back towards home, cutting across the fields and using World's End Wood as a marker. She realised that it was the one place she had not looked, the place where perhaps she should have started; but it was too late, the nights were drawing in fast and already it was dusk. She skirted the perimeter, glancing in amongst the trees, aware as she did so of a strange uneasiness, that sensation of being watched which had so disturbed her just recently.

It was a relief to reach the lane.

I paused for a moment to catch my breath, peering anxiously around for any sign of footpads before turning to hurry up the hill towards home. In that moment I saw it, a movement in the shadows, a black shape against the dark stillness of the trees.

My heart leapt. I was petrified with fear, thinking of wolves and wild boar, wild creatures native to foreign parts which might somehow be loose, here, threatening me. It was massive, like a huge hound, yet it did not move like a dog, it moved like something unused to its four legs, with an ugly, lurching gait. Then it raised its great head and looked at me, into me, as though it knew the very depths of my soul . . .

Thirty One

When Nick returned with the boys, late on Sunday evening, he was shocked by Natasha's appearance. Make-up could not disguise the hollows beneath her cheekbones, nor the shadows around her brilliant eyes; and that over-bright smile did not distract his eye from the number of cigarettes she smoked, nor the slight trembling of the fingers that held them.

She looked ill, he thought; in fact consumptive was the adjective that sprang to mind, since it suggested a burning-up of the flesh, some kind of physical sacrifice to the consuming power of a hungry spirit. It frightened him. As she darted about the kitchen, putting finishing touches to the meal she had prepared, listening to the boys, laughing with them, and looking suitably impressed in all the right places, Nick wondered how she could have lost so much weight in two and a half days. But, he reminded himself, she had looked dreadful a week ago, and although he had ascribed that to the stress and misery of their situation, she did not seem miserable now. Tense, taut in the extreme, but certainly not depressed.

His sons were not pleased when he packed them off to bed before ten o'clock, protesting that they'd not yet told Natasha half of what they'd done in London, and tomorrow she might be too busy to listen. But she promised not to be busy, and eventually they went.

Nick poured himself a large measure of single malt, and sank down into his chair beside the fire. It was a cold, still night, and the logs were crackling nicely, the Christmas lights were twinkling, and the presents Natasha had wrapped were piled beneath the tree. Having finally obeyed his instructions to sit down, Natasha was lying on the sofa, ostensibly watching television, with a glass of wine in one hand and a cigarette in the other. The scene, Nick thought, was reminiscent of a Christmas TV commercial for some luxury product: it had that quality of visual perfection so beloved of advertising directors.

And yet, like all commercials, it was unreal, top-show, a lot of glossy paint covering fragile chipboard and the mechanics of illusion. Last week the illusion had worked quite well, so well, in fact, that he had been almost convinced of its reality by the time he was leaving for London. By then, of course, he had not wanted to go, and had spent the entire weekend missing Natasha and longing for the moment of return.

Now, he was so bemused by the latest changes that he hardly knew what to say: they had become so distanced from each other that it was impossible to be frank. Instead, he opened the conversation with something comfortably neutral, something he might have used with a stranger.

'So, what sort of weekend did you have?'

'Oh, you know – quiet.' She paused and listened for a moment to what was being said on the television: a sycophantic interviewer was asking an ageing film star about his autobiography, which was currently receiving much media attention. But Nick, who had heard it all before, could not have been less impressed.

He waited for her to go on, and when she did not, asked again what she had been doing while he was away. Getting answers, he felt, was rather like drawing teeth.

'What did I do?' She shrugged and pulled a face, but did not look at him. 'I don't know – the usual things, I suppose. Nothing very exciting.'

He looked at her, long and hard, but Natasha gave every indication of being far more interested in the televised interview.

With frustration rising like bile, Nick made one last attempt to gain her attention. 'So how come,' he said slowly and clearly, 'if you've had such a boring and deadly-dull weekend, you look as though you're hopped-up on something?' Until he said it, the idea of drugs – either prescribed or illegal – hadn't consciously crossed his mind, but with that phrase hanging between them, he recognised its accuracy. And, a split-second later, that he should have been more tactful.

Natasha turned, her mouth agape. 'And just what do you mean by that?'

'I'm sorry – I shouldn't have said that, I – '

'Then why did you? What do mean, *hopped-up on something*? Are you suggesting – '

'I'm suggesting *nothing*.' As she stood up, so did he. 'Look, Natasha, I'm sorry, I shouldn't have used a phrase like that. What I should have said is that you don't look very well, and you seem very tense and strung-up. I was trying to get around to asking you what's wrong.'

'What's wrong? You have to ask me a question like that, when just a week ago you came home to tell me about your little bit on the side, and how you thought we should separate, but let's just keep up appearances for the sake of the boys? Christ, Nick, you've got a nerve!

'I've kept my part of the agreement, and it hasn't been easy – I think I'm entitled to look a bit strained and pale about the gills! For your information, I'm taking *nothing*, not even a bloody aspirin – and, in case you were wondering, this is the first alcoholic drink I've had all weekend.' Swigging down the remains of it, she handed him the glass. 'There you are – and now I'm off to bed. Goodnight!'

At breakfast the next morning she was very quiet, and gave the impression of not having slept well. Nick, after a night spent tossing and turning on the sofa, felt similarly wrung out, and found the effort of speaking naturally and casually in front of the boys much greater than it had been the week before.

There was food shopping to do for their special Christmas Eve lunch, and for the dinner party they were giving on Boxing Day. Eager to get out of the house, Nick went off to do it, while the boys disappeared to watch cartoons on television, and Mrs Bickerstaff went upstairs to do the bedrooms.

After lunch, Nick insisted on taking the boys for a walk while Mrs B cleaned up in the sitting-room. The sun was already sinking in the south-west, but he thought a brisk walk in the fresh air would do them all good. Natasha, however, was reluctant to join them.

'I wouldn't mind, but I don't want to go down the lane – it's bound to be muddy, and the boys will come back filthy.'

'Muddy? How can it be muddy?' he asked. 'It's hardly been above freezing point for the last week. Come on, get your coat on.'

'Why does it have to be the lane? We always go down the lane – I should think the boys are sick of it. Let's take them to Sheriff Whenby, instead, and have a look round the castle.'

'I don't want to get the car out, Natasha, and it's too far to walk there and back before it gets dark. Anyway, they've seen the castle before.'

'They've seen the lane before.'

'Oh, for God's sake,' he muttered between clenched teeth, 'I've had enough. I'm going – if I stand here much longer, it will be too late to go anywhere.'

Clad in warm jackets and boots, they were already out in the yard when Natasha hurried after them. 'Wait – I'm coming with you.'

Nick turned and gave her a smile that was compounded of pleasure and exasperation, but, as she struggled with the zip on her dark-green jacket, she pretended not to notice. Full of high spirits, the twins ran on in front, ducking and diving in and out of the hedgerows, their curly hair brilliant against the frosty, colourless landscape. There was no sign of Toby as they passed his caravan, and, as he remarked on that, Nick's mind skipped to the shooting of the Irish wolfhound. He had not seen Mrs McCoy to speak to since the day he had called at the house to warn her of the Morrisons' threats, and he could not help but wonder how she had reacted to the dog's death. Of course, there was hardly any doubt that McCoy had been the culprit and had simply got what he deserved, but that connection with – what? he asked himself; Reynard? Padfoot? – still left a question mark in his mind. *Why* had the dog suddenly turned sheep-killer?

And as for old Toby, who had deemed it necessary, a few days later, to give him all the gory details of McCoy's death, Nick could not help wondering at his evident sense of relief. Natasha had told him about the old man's confession, when, under the influence of several pints, he had told her that he thought *the black, shadowy thing* was after him. It seemed strange that he should imagine that, unless he associated it with tales heard in childhood, rather like the woman in the post office at Brickhill. Such foreknowledge might, Nick considered, explain the old man's air of secretive triumph that first morning, as he challenged the learned doctor to put a name to something that could not be explained.

And if the grim childhood folk tale, not entirely disbelieved, had suddenly sprung to life before him, and if he also had a bad conscience about certain things in the past –

Just at that moment, he saw the ramshackle figure appear from the trees ahead of them. 'Well, there's Toby, the sly old bugger. What's he got, can you see? He's nabbed something, that's for sure . . .'

Natasha hesitated as she peered through the bluish haze of a shortening afternoon. 'I'm not sure – could be pheasants. But listen – do call the boys and let's go back, I don't want to run into him.'

'We can't do that, he's already seen us. Anyway,' he added with a grin, 'if it's gamebirds he's got, he'll be worth running into. He'll be wanting to flog 'em, not eat 'em – a pretty prize at this time of year.'

'We don't need them,' Natasha said repressively, her full mouth compressing itself into a thin line. 'I know you regard him as one of a dying species,' she added with distaste, 'but I happen to think he's rather horrible. And as I really *don't* want to meet him, I think I'll just head back home.'

'Oh, for God's sake, don't be such a kill-joy,' he said, 'just because you caught the poor old bugger having a quick pee in the hedge – '

'Yes I did,' she reiterated sharply, 'and don't you dare patronise me, Nick Rhodes, I won't stand for it. If you were a woman, instead of – instead of a mere *man* – you'd understand *exactly* how I felt about catching him peeing in the lane. I was frightened, it's as simple as that.'

'But – '

He hesitated, torn between the need to go after her, and his concern for Adam and Adrian, who might end up in Brickhill unless he called a halt to their heedless enthusiasm.

In the end, he continued downhill, calling the boys, their progress slowed by the sight of Toby with his pheasants. The old man had broken the shotgun, Nick noted with relief, and was now showing his booty to the curious youngsters. The gleaming red and gold plumage of the male bird formed a third point of brilliance as he held it up, and Nick suddenly wished that he had a camera with him. The colours, the fresh-faced, identical boys, the life-battered old man, would have made a wonderful photograph.

On that thought he caught himself. A picture like that was the stuff of sentiment and propaganda, so easily digestible that it slid down virtually unnoticed. Had he, Nick wondered as he made his way towards them, been a victim of his own sentiment where Toby was concerned, judging him not as an equal, but as a relic of the past – *one of a dying species*, as Natasha had said – and as such, worthy of some respect. Far more, certainly, than was generally accorded to Toby Bickerstaff. With that came the awareness that he prided himself on being the only person in the village to recognise the old man's worth and his traditional position in local society, and for the first time Nick questioned the validity of that.

Although he was annoyed with Natasha for marching off, he was not really surprised by her over-reaction. Indeed, he was half grateful to her, since those sharp words of hers illumined certain doubts which had been lurking for a while. Nick generally said that he liked the old boy, but now he asked himself whether it was Toby Bickerstaff he liked, or the image he had created in his own mind. He had always regarded Toby as a harmless eccentric, but ever since that walk through the wood with Dr Wills he had been wondering about the old man's past, and why he lived like a hermit, uncared-for and alone. Could it be true that in his case there was less of the true eccentric, and more of the outcast?

The only way to find out would be to start asking questions, and he had to admit that he had not made much progress in the past. The locals might talk about each other amongst themselves, but Nick had long ago discovered that they did not often do so to outsiders.

'Dad, Dad – have you seen these pheasants?'

'Afternoon, Toby – it's coming in cold again.'

'Aye, it is that. I'm on me way 'ome now, I've 'ad a good innings.' He grinned, showing an uneven row of rotten teeth, and held up the day's prizes, a cock pheasant and three hens.

Adam nudged his father. 'He wants to sell them, Dad.'

Nick laughed. 'I expect he does, but we've done our shopping.'

'Nice, plump birds – be lovely when they've hung for a bit.'

'You have to hang them, you see,' Adrian chimed in, 'to make them more tender when they're cooked.'

'Well, I can see we've got an expert here!' Nick shook his head, laughing. 'We won't be able to eat them tomorrow – they won't be ready.'

Adam pulled a face, but could not resist stroking the brilliant feathers. Adrian said: 'Never mind, you can tell us what they were like.'

'Seems you've got a couple of good salesmen on your side, Toby! You'd better let me have the cock and one of the hens – what do you want for them?'

'A fiver to you, Doctor,' Toby said promptly, and Nick realised that he had been intending to call at the house anyway.

He felt in his pocket for money, extracted a five-pound note, and handed it over. The boys took a bird each – inevitably Adam took the gaudy one – and set off, gleefully, up the hill. Nick, left with Toby, made his apologies. 'I'd better go after them and keep an eye on my dinner – I don't want them mangled!'

'Aye, you do that, Doctor. Good lads, though.'

'Yes, they're not bad.' He smiled, then said awkwardly: 'Look, if I don't see you before, have a good Christmas.'

The old man grimaced. 'Aye, well, it's not what it used to be. But a merry Christmas to you and yours, Doctor – and tell the missus to pepper the feathers, it'll keep any flies off.'

'Right, I will.' He raised his hand and strode away to catch up with the boys, torn between old feelings and new suspicions. That the old boy liked *him*, and seemed to appreciate their snatches of conversation, was in no doubt. It made him feel as though he were betraying something.

Thirty Two

EVERYTHING FELT unreal, including herself. She had a sense of operating within a bubble, very carefully, with ordinary life going on at one remove. Nick spoke to her and she answered him, but defensively, as though to ward him off. If he came too close the bubble might burst, and her existence seemed so fragile, there was a danger that she too might disappear with the iridescent haze.

She was anxious about the story, desperate to finish it now that the ending seemed close, and so obsessed that it was difficult to think of anything else. Something was waiting to happen, and whatever it was had to be important, a key, not just to Sarah Stalwell's fate in the eighteenth century, but to what was happening now. Nick could not possibly understand that, so she had to keep him at bay, at least until the story was finished. Then, there might be something to talk about.

As the twins went up to bed, still laying bets as to the contents of the parcels they would be opening in the morning, Natasha was beset by a sense of time running out. Tomorrow would be Christmas Eve, with an early celebration for the benefit of the boys, who were due to return home to their mother in the afternoon. While Nick drove them back to town, she would have, at best, an hour and a half to herself. Not long enough to make any worthwhile progress, and with no hope of using her typewriter tonight, she began to think that the only way of complcting things was to take a pencil and notepad to bed, so that she might work on undisturbed. Physically, she was aware that she must be very tired, but a relentless mental energy continued to drive her on.

'Shall I pour you a drink?'

She came out of her abstraction with a start. 'No – no, thanks.' Alcohol would make her sleepy: that would not do at all.

'I was thinking,' he said casually, 'about old Toby, and what he said when he found out that McCoy had killed the sheep.'

Natasha eyed her husband warily. Although he was not looking at her, his face bore that deceptively pensive expression which made him look abstracted when in fact he was at his most alert.

'You mean when he said he was relieved?'

'Mmm. When he said he thought the thing, whatever it was, might have been after *him*. I thought it an odd thing to say.'

She waited for Nick to go on, wondering whether to end the conversation with some suitably abrupt remark, or to sit it out and discover what was on his mind. She opted for neutrality. 'Well, he's not quite right in the head, is he?'

'I don't know, I wouldn't like to be the judge of that. The point is – and this applies no matter what our separate opinions are – Toby was talking about two different creatures. McCoy who killed the sheep, and the other thing that he saw at the beginning of November. At the time he described it to me, I thought he didn't know what it was, and that he was asking *me* for an opinion. But this afternoon – and I don't know why I didn't make the connection earlier – it came to me that he wasn't after an opinion at all. He *knew* what he'd seen, and was just laying down a challenge. As though he was saying: *There, if you're such a clever bugger, put a name to that*!'

Surprised, not quite following his reasoning, Natasha said: 'How do you figure that out?'

'Because he's local, do you see? He's lived in this area all his life. Just like the woman in the post office at Brickhill. I don't think I ever told you this, but when we went to look at the church that day, I got into conversation with the old dear who looks after the keys, and she knew all about the black hound that's supposed to haunt this area. She even put a name to it.'

'A name?'

'Yes. She said it was called *Reynard.*'

If she had not been sitting down, Natasha thought later, she might have fainted. With an effort, she raised a hand to her face: her forehead was hot, the hand icy cold. As the moment passed and her circulation returned to normal, she felt the prickling pain of pins and needles. She rubbed at her arms and legs, but Nick was still talking, and staring into the fire.

'. . . although why he should think it was after *him*, I don't know. Makes you wonder about his past, doesn't it?' he observed ruminatively. 'What he might have done to make him think that Reynard was some sort of retribution . . .'

The murder sprang to mind, a vision of gory detail based on Craig Morrison's words, and fleshed out, as it were, by her own imagination. She shuddered, as appalled by Nick's connection of names and suspicions as she was by the knowledge she could not reveal. 'Could be anything,' she said distantly. 'He's had time to do a lot of things.'

'True.' For a while, Nick seemed lost in contemplation; then, as he stirred to pour himself another drink, he said: 'Dr Wills thought it might be some kind of violence.'

'Dr Wills?'

'Yes, you know, Betty Wills, the folklorist who came here the other week.'

'Oh, yes, *Betty* Wills.' For a moment, Natasha wondered at the connection. 'Anyway, what would she know about Toby Bickerstaff?'

'Not a thing, that's the point. But she insisted on going into the wood, and we got as far as the clearing – there's a clearing over towards the far right-hand side, I don't know if you realised that – and she suddenly came over all peculiar and said there'd been violence done there.'

Natasha paused in the act of lighting a cigarette. Suddenly, her hands were trembling. 'Oh, how ridiculous,' she said with as much disapproval as she could muster. 'Was she was pretending to be some kind of medium, or what?'

'She wasn't pretending *anything*,' Nick murmured as he turned to look at her. 'And if you'd been there, Natasha, you'd have seen how upset she was by what she sensed in that place.'

'What did she say?'

He looked away, running fingers through his hair. 'Not a great deal, really. Just that there had been violence, and a lot of blood, and that it was connected with the person who used the path. Obviously, I thought of Toby – I don't know anyone else who goes regularly through those woods – and I said he was a poacher, but she said no, it wasn't the killing of animals, but violence towards a human being that she could sense.'

'Murder?' The word came out in a whisper.

As he nodded, a great chill passed through her; she dropped the cigarette she was holding, yet could not co-ordinate her limbs to retrieve it. As Nick bent to rescue it from the rug, he saw her white face and felt her icy hands, and then he was kneeling beside her.

'No, don't fuss – I'm all right,' she insisted weakly, but he knew she was not, and said so. He made her lie flat on the sofa while feeling for the pulse at her wrist, and as he touched her clammy forehead, his eyes were dark with anxiety. It was the unexpected tenderness that made her cry, great welling tears that spilled of their own volition, since she had neither the will nor the energy to sob.

'Oh, *darling*,' he breathed as he gathered her into his arms, 'I'm sorry, I didn't mean to frighten you like that – I didn't think, I just wanted to –' He broke off, cradling her gently while she lay for a moment, limp and unprotesting, against him. That unexpected closeness overwhelmed her. His warmth and strength, the faint scent of his body, so dear to her in the past, made her blood race as though she had been running.

It was the first time they had touched – really touched – in so long. The magnetism which had been between them before was suddenly revitalised in a great charge of sexual energy, so urgent and demanding that she felt the crackle of it under her skin. He felt it too, it was there in the way he held her, in the rapid beating of his heart and the whisper of his breath at her throat.

Concern held him back; she knew it and was impatient. That momentary weakness was gone, forgotten, like all the stupid and hurtful things which had conspired to keep them apart. She wanted him so much; he felt so good, so right, so absolutely hers, and she wanted him now before anything else got in the way. As his lips grazed her cheek she turned his head towards her, kissing him with deliberate passion.

'Natasha . . .' Her name was a sigh as he drew back to look at her, and for a moment there was conflict in his eyes. But as his mouth closed on hers all hesitation vanished. It was a hungry, demanding kiss which set her senses reeling, releasing a sudden glitter of stars as his tongue invaded her mouth and his hand found her naked breast. He pulled at the buttons of her blouse while she slid her hands beneath his sweater; she slipped off her underwear while he undid the buckle of his belt. They did not even bother to undress. Seconds later he was inside her, hurting as much as pleasing, but it was the most pleasurable kind of pain and she climaxed almost immediately, and then again as he reached a harsh, gasping conclusion.

For several seconds everything was echoing in the aftermath, with lights dancing behind her eyelids and her body raw as though every nerve was exposed. While Nick lay with his face buried against her neck, shoulders heaving like a marathon runner, she came down off that emotional pinnacle with a jolt. For a moment she could hardly breathe, and then, swamped by confusion and regret, she was suddenly racked by uncontrollable sobs.

He held her and kissed her, trying to comfort and reassure with soft words and gentle hands, but the emotional pain would not be eased. The intensity of that consummation, the bitterness of his recent betrayal, and a sudden recognition of the fear which had surrounded her for weeks, made Natasha weep and cling like a child. It was several minutes before she was able to calm down, and even when she did, she could not bear him to leave her. When the worst was over, he picked her up and carried her to bed.

As though he understood that need, Nick stayed with her. He said nothing as he helped her to undress, but she could tell that he was shocked by the weight she had lost. By contrast, she watched him peel off sweater, shirt and trousers with almost voyeuristic pleasure. Wanting him to come to bed, wanting him to hold her close and make love to her again, she was irrationally disappointed when he reached for his towelling robe.

'I'll be back in a minute – I just want to check the boys really are asleep.'

In the soft light from the bedside lamp, his eyes were gentle but questioning. With a sinking feeling Natasha realised that he wanted to talk, and that she was going to have to find some satisfactory answers. Defensively, she pulled the quilt up around her shoulders.

He returned a few moments later, seating himself beside her on the edge of the bed. As he leaned across to kiss her forehead, she slipped her hand inside his robe and caressed his neck and shoulders. She wanted to pull him down beside her, but he drew away slightly and captured her hand instead, pressing it to his lips. She was surprised by the intensity.

After a moment, with a quirky little smile, he said: 'You know, I had begun to think – well, that we'd never get it together again . . .' Very gently, he stroked the side of her face, and then it was Natasha's turn to feel something of his doubts and regrets.

'I'm sorry,' she whispered, dreading the inevitable questions.

They came, as she had known they would. With the expression of his concern, his need to know what was wrong and what on earth she had been keeping from him, Natasha found herself regretting what had taken place between them. That momentary union, so thrilling, so ecstatic, should have been followed by more of the same. Words were useless, they simply cluttered the issue, gave rise to further misunderstandings. She did not want to talk, either about her health or why things had gone so badly awry; she certainly could not talk about the work she was engaged upon. It was not yet complete, and, until it was, explanations were impossible.

Lying sleepless beside her, Nick wished that he had let things be, asked no questions, voiced no opinions, and made no attempts to discover what was going on inside her head. Above all, he regretted that moment of sudden and ungovernable passion, which he had longed for and believed in as a solution to all their problems.

That belief had lasted all of half an hour.

What was it, he thought, that made the combination of love and lust so powerful, and yet so utterly unpredictable? It was like a cargo of high explosive, capable of shifting mountains yet just as likely to destroy the people handling it.

It would have been better, he decided, not to light that optimistic beacon. He had been learning to live with the dull misery of existence as it was, and his brief sojourn with Sally had at least provided balm for his damaged ego. Although he had felt guilty, now he was just grateful for her undemanding affection. By comparison with Natasha, Sally struck him as being kind and uncomplicated, and he had a moment of wishing that he could have fallen in love with her instead.

From the distant viewpoint of Ghylldale, all had seemed so clear: why go on in such pain, when the simpler answer was to part? Had it not been for the boys and Christmas, that decision would probably have been effected by now, thus saving this further episode of grief.

His sigh was almost a groan. He turned, carefully, on to his back, staring into the darkness, very much aware of Natasha's body, warm and relaxed, beside him. Asleep. How could she *sleep*, for God's sake? That ability was like a slap in the face, so infuriating that he had to conquer the urge to shake her, to take her slender body in his hands and rattle the truth out of her. Lies and evasions, the merest smattering of direct answers, and nothing that made any sense. 'I'm tired,' she kept saying, 'let's talk about it in the morning . . . I don't know . . . I can't think, I'm tired . . . hold me, just hold me . . .'

So he had complied, holding her despite that inner torment, and letting her have the rest she craved. He reminded himself again that she was not well, and recognised – yet again – that anxiety about her physical and mental state was part of his current anguish. He did not know how to help her, when she steadfastly refused to explain what was wrong. Something was desperately amiss, that much was obvious; but while he could see the effects, he could not identify the cause. The worst frustration of all lay in knowing the sheer impossibility of helping those who do not wish to be helped.

And so, on the heels of his frustration came anger that she should refuse his assistance, reject his concern, and thus allow what he had believed to be a good marriage to crumble, irrevocably, to dust.

Thirty Three

ALTHOUGH HE slept eventually, it was not for more than a few hours. When he awoke, just after seven, it was still dark. Snuggled deep beneath the quilt, Natasha was curled on her side with her back to him.

For a little while he lay there, aware of her warmth, thinking of other mornings, bright summer mornings, when, waking early, he had turned with care, just for the pleasure of watching her sleep. He remembered her face, innocent and unmarked, the long black lashes soft as butterflies against her cheek. Sometimes, especially when they had made love the night before, he would find the resurgence of love and desire so intense that he had to wake her, to make love to her again. But she always said she enjoyed that.

Or at least, she *had* said that, when things were right between them, in those far-off days when it had taken no more than a certain look to bring her into his arms.

But such memories were achingly physical, goading him with the tension of unsatisfied need. Lying there in the darkness of a chill winter's morning, Nick knew he should put such thoughts behind him, get up and do something strenuous, stoke the fire, go for a run, worry about his research or the essays waiting in his study, anything but dwell on the past.

And then he remembered that it was Christmas Eve, their day for celebrating with Adam and Adrian, opening presents, overeating at lunchtime . . . and later, of course, returning his sons to their mother's care.

He swung his legs out of bed, picked up his robe and a pile of clothes from the chair, and made his way quietly to the bathroom. The water was barely warm, so he took a very quick shower and ran the electric shaver over a stubborn growth of beard. Dressing quickly, he went downstairs.

Using one of Natasha's cookery books as a guide, Nick stuffed the chicken – rather large to be so described, but chicken it was – smeared it with butter, laid bacon rashers across the breast, and placed it in the oven on the requisite setting. He found the plum pudding and set it to one side; then he prepared the vegetables, carrots, sprouts and broccoli, and peeled what he hoped were enough potatoes. At ten o'clock, he finally heard creaking floorboards and voices in the bathroom. The boys, at least, were awake.

One wanted bacon sandwiches, the other demanded scrambled eggs; Nick told them they could have cereal and toast. 'And Natasha is staying in bed – she's not very well. So when you've finished eating, one of you can take her a cup of coffee, and ask what she'd like for breakfast.'

'Bet *she* can have bacon sandwiches if she wants – '

'Don't be such a pig, Adam,' his brother said, 'it's supposed to be Christmas.'

'That's what I mean – I thought we could have what we liked at *Christmas*.'

Nick could have throttled him. Instead he told the boy, sharply, to leave the table. He did so, but there was a suspicious quiver to his lip as he dashed out of the kitchen.

Adrian broke the silence. 'Actually, Dad, I think he's a bit upset. We never get to be with you for *real* Christmas – I mean, like *tomorrow* – and, well, you know . . .'

Looking into his other son's eyes, which were anxious and apologetic, Nick felt the iniquity of the situation. Abandoning his own pretence at breakfast, he stood up, squeezed Adrian's shoulder, and went upstairs to have a talk with Adam.

Some time later he looked in on Natasha, who was not asleep, but sitting up in bed, reading. She looked bright but frail, he thought, her dark eyes enormous in a face that seemed pared to the bone.

'Sorry,' he said awkwardly, 'minor crisis – didn't mean to wake you.'

'You didn't. I've been awake for a while. I'll get up in a minute.'

'You will not. You'll stay in bed until lunch is ready. I'm managing just fine, so don't worry. But I did think,' he added with a smile, 'that we might bring the presents up here? The boys are getting anxious to open them.'

'Yes, do. That's an excellent idea. I was feeling a bit guilty about holding up the proceedings.'

But although she looked contrite, Nick had the distinct impression that she had forgotten what day it was.

Everything went well. Adam cheered up, both boys were thrilled with their Christmas presents and, with a few added instructions from Natasha, Nick managed to serve an enjoyable meal. Afterwards, he felt entitled to take a rest on the sofa, and woke up a couple of hours later feeling hot and crumpled and horribly thick-headed.

Sitting cross-legged on the rug, Adam regarded him with a slightly sardonic expression. 'I don't want to rush you, Dad, but we have to be going soon.'

'Yes, yes, I know – just give me a minute . . .'

He drank the weak cup of tea one of them had made, and ten minutes later was checking their room for forgotten items, discovering a pair of socks under one bed, a comic book under the other. Apart from those few things, the room was reasonably tidy, the beds roughly made, both trunks packed. His first thought was that their expensive school taught them *something*; the next brought an unexpected lump to his throat. It would be some time before he saw them again, and, with his life in a state of flux, it was impossible to say what the circumstances would be. He moved their trunks out on to the landing, then hurried into the bathroom to wash his face.

Natasha appeared as he started to carry the luggage downstairs. She looked pinched and cold, in spite of the warm dressing-gown she was wearing.

'You should be in bed – '

'No, I'm all right. I just wanted to come down and say goodbye . . .'

Nick looked at her and sighed. 'You know, as soon as the surgery opens again after Christmas, you're going to see a doctor – in fact I should have insisted on it this morning.'

'Oh, don't fuss – I'm just *tired*, that's all.'

'You're young – you *shouldn't* be tired. Not like this, anyway.'

'He'll probably give me a prescription for iron tablets,' she said irritably, 'and I can get those from the chemist.'

Biting back a sharp reply, Nick said it might be better to let the doctor decide.

Urging her not to linger downstairs, he took the car keys and crossed the dark and frozen yard. The barn doors were open, as always, and he felt just inside for the electric light switch. There was a dank, fetid smell about the place, a sharp contrast to the air outside, which halted him for a second. Damned cats, he thought, but in the shadows cast by two bare, 60 watt bulbs, he could see no sign of them. That struck him as odd, because they were usually hanging around at this time, waiting to be fed. And then he sniffed the air again, and wondered whether that smell really was feline; it reeked less of tom-cats than of unwashed urinals, and it occurred to him that they might have been unwitting hosts to a drunken tramp, one who had slept overnight in the barn and relieved himself against the wall.

Disgusted, Nick climbed into the car and backed it out. No point in attempting to close the barn doors now, the runners would be frozen. Anyway, the deed was done.

He parked by the garden gate and opened the boot. With assistance from each of his sons the trunks and various paraphernalia were stowed; with hugs and thanks and best wishes for Christmas, the farewells were said to Natasha, who waved them off from inside the porch. Not wishing to worry her, he said nothing of his suspicions about the barn.

The gritters had been out, but still he drove carefully along the frosty country roads; aware of tension in himself and silence from the twins, he asked if they would like some music. Almost in unison, they asked for Radio 1, which enabled Nick to indulge in his usual protests, and the twins to insult his age and sensibilities. It was an old formula, but it worked; and, in truth, he quite enjoyed the selection of Christmas pop songs. Most of them were so old, he was able to sing along with them himself, which provoked groans and insults from the boys.

Almost before they were aware of it they were in York, the traffic rather less than usual for a normal weekday, although still surprisingly busy for half-past six on Christmas Eve. Passing the massive barbican of Walmgate Bar, Nick followed the one-way system towards Fulford and his old family home, where the boys still lived with their mother.

The street was not a through road; it ended in steps leading down to the river. Nevertheless, cars were parked almost solidly down both sides, making it difficult to park sensibly. Nick stopped as close as he could to the house, and let the twins carry the smaller stuff between them while he hoisted the first trunk. As he returned with the second one, Bernice was standing there in the hall, hugging her sons like prodigals returned.

It was impossible not to feel the pangs of jealousy and resentment, old familiars, but no less painful for all that. She was their mother, and they needed her, but he could not help but feel that she needed them in rather less measure. She made her career the excuse for their boarding, but the number of times that he had taken the twins at the last minute, because she was going on holiday 'with a friend', made him wonder whether she found them more of an encumbrance than a blessing.

But still, he asked himself, in her place, would he have coped any better? He thought not; and besides, he was the one who had walked out on them.

She asked him in, less as a gesture of hospitality than because she wanted him to carry the trunks upstairs.

'But for goodness' sake, Nick, do mind the wallpaper – I've just had the staircase done, and it cost me a small fortune!'

He bit his tongue, while Adam, ahead of him with an armful of parcels, muttered, 'Oh, *Mum*,' under his breath, and turned to give his father a sympathetic look. 'She just doesn't realise how heavy they are,' he said as they reached the first landing.

'No, I'm sure she doesn't,' he responded through gritted teeth, steeling himself for the next flight of stairs.

The room the boys shared was massive, covering almost all of the top floor. They had their own bathroom and plenty of space for all their possessions, which were numerous. Things had changed in the last few years, and the house which used to have an air of warmth and comfort was now as perfect as a picture in a glossy magazine. So was Bernice. The soft Indian silks and cottons she had favoured had given way to tailored suits and crisp shirts, and her hair, which had been long, was now cropped shorter than Natasha's. On Bernice, however, the style was too harsh.

'Do you want to stay for a Christmas drink?' The invitation was more polite than sincere, but Nick had grown used to the feeling that they were strangers now. He smiled, with equal politeness, and explained that he was driving, that his car was double-parked, and he really must be getting home. He hugged the boys, rumpled their already rumpled curls, and made a swift retreat. It was easier that way.

Waving from the car, forcing a smile, he felt drained, and wished he could have accepted that drink. At the end of the street it dawned on him that from here onwards there could be no more procrastination; he no longer had the twins as a buffer, and he must face up to some hard decisions. It was not going to be easy, he knew that, and he longed for some good advice.

He thought of Giles, who lived no more than a few hundred yards away, but was not sure whether Giles was a good idea. Really, he should get home. Nevertheless, he hesitated, and as he did so, a figure crossed in front of him: Giles, with an armful of carrier bags.

'Taxi, sir?' he called out, watching his friend's bemusement turn to laughter as he recognised both car and driver. 'You're late,' he said as Giles dumped his parcels on the back seat, 'I thought the shops shut *hours* ago.'

'Well, not *that* long ago, I do promise you – I just stopped off for a rest, really, but of course, being in the pub, I had to have a drink . . .'

Nick laughed. 'Well fasten your seat-belt, and I'll run you home.'

They talked of inconsequential things, but Giles's inevitable good humour was infectious. By the time Nick left, he was feeling considerably restored. He mentioned the fact that Natasha was not well, but made light of it, saying that she was looking forward to their dinner on Boxing Day, even though he, Nick, might be cooking it.

It was a quarter to eight when he left Giles, and twenty minutes later, turning down the lane into Denton village, he was suddenly very much aware that it was Christmas Eve, and that his present concerns seemed worse because of it. This time last year they'd been happy in spite of chaos in the house. After taking the boys home, they'd gone for a drink in the Half Moon, and later on he had persuaded Natasha to come with him to the midnight service at the parish church. He would have liked to be there tonight, but thought it a vain hope.

His chances of an hour or so in the Half Moon were just as slim, and he envied the revellers whose cars lined either side of the Green. With regret he turned across the street and into Dagger Lane, the Rover's engine growling softly up the slight rise to the house. Frosty twigs and grasses sparkled like decorations in the headlights; noticing them, he felt sadder still. Then, ahead of him in the gateway to the yard, he saw what he thought was a car parked with its lights on. Wondering who their visitor could be, he dipped his own as he automatically braked and changed down.

As he looked, the lights moved and seemed to flicker. The shape behind them moved too, and with a horrible sensation of fear Nick realised that it was not a car but something black and amorphous, and that it was coming towards him. In a split-second of panic, he stalled the engine. He fumbled with the key and depressed the clutch, but his head was askew, his eyes riveted to the density moving in on him. It drew nearer, growing bigger with its approach, until its blackness filled the whole side window of the car.

He found himself looking into a face, or what some unknown part of his brain identified as a face. It was massive, contorted, a changing series of shapes with no apparent cohesion; only the eyes, huge, vivid, red, made a terrifying kind of sense. He had an impression of jaws, a mouth of some kind; but the ferocity was real enough: the unbearable horror of the thing was beyond any ghoulish imagining.

The car started suddenly, still in second gear; and the engine, although it complained, impelled the machine forward with a spasm of power that jerked Nick back to life. Somehow he made the turn and shot into the yard on a screech of tyres and brakes. Feverishly he locked all doors and doused all lights; grabbing what remained of his courage, he turned to look back.

He could see nothing, only the hedge and a bit of the lane, the house walls and the garden. Darkness remained, but none of it as black as that into which he had looked.

Natasha had heard his noisy arrival. The porch light went on, and she opened the kitchen door. As she stepped into the porch, her hand outstretched, he opened the nearside window, yelling at her before she could open the door.

'Get back inside and lock the doors!'

There was such power in his voice, she obeyed at once.

Almost five minutes passed before he could bring himself to unlock and climb out of the car, to cross the yard and let himself into the house with his keys.

He bolted the doors behind him, went down the hall to the front door and checked that too, even though it had not been opened since the summer. He went into every downstairs room, switching on lights, pulling curtains, while Natasha stood at the top of the stairs, demanding, in a high and unnatural voice, to know what was wrong.

He went up to her, and she fell back at the expression on his face. 'For God's sake, Nick – what *is* it?'

Swallowing hard, he grasped her wrist, frightening her so much in his effort to speak that she instantly broke free. 'I've seen it,' he said at last, his voice so drained and flat that he heard, rather than felt, his own exhaustion.

'Seen it? Seen what? Not . . .'

'I've seen the beast, as close to me as you are – I've seen it,' he explained again, pushing past her into his study and collapsing into the chair. As she followed him, dumbly horrified, he said: '*Reynard, Padfoot*, or whatever the fucking hell it's called.'

She sank to her knees beside him, raising a trembling hand to his brow, cold and clammy with sweat. 'Are you all right?'

'Yes – no. Oh, for God's sake, *no*, I'm not all right. It came up to me – I stalled the bloody car and the thing walked right up and *looked* at me. I tell you, I've never seen anything like it in my life – it would have made the devil himself turn and run, believe me!'

She slowly shook her head, then laid her face against his hand. He stroked her hair, finding comfort in her trembling humanity.

'I slowed right down, you see – just for a moment, to see what it was – and then it was right beside me.' He thought how quickly it had moved, yet without apparent effort. It was as though it had been drawn towards him.

He tried to describe what he had seen, but his vocabulary was inadequate. How to interpret impressions, when those impressions were almost hallucinatory? All that he vividly recalled, all that would fit into words, were the red and human eyes of the thing, deep and hollow and brilliant, all at the same time.

'Why?' Natasha whispered against his knee. 'Oh, for God's sake, *why you*?'

The relevance of that question escaped him; because it seemed no more than rhetorical, he said: 'Who knows? But I've seen it now, haven't I? It came to me this time, not Toby or Mrs McCoy, but to *me*. God knows why.'

And then, as fear and panic subsided and rational thought took over, Nick realised something else. 'The strange thing is,' he began, and then broke off, struggling for words. The ones he found were so banal he almost rejected them. 'I mean,' he went on in a rush, 'if I hadn't been so bloody frightened, I might almost have felt sorry for the thing. It was so – so – I don't know, *agonised*, like a thing in torment . . .'

Thirty Four

'DON'T TELL me you feel sorry for it!' Natasha exclaimed, digging her nails into his hand. 'It's *evil*, can't you see that? It creates evil and feeds off it!'

He had been staring into the corner, blindly, but at those words he looked down, as though registering her presence for the first time.

'How do you know that?' he demanded. His fingers curled around the back of her neck, forcing her to look at him. '*Tell me*. Christ Almighty, Natasha, tell me – I *have* to know!'

She nodded vigorously, so tense with cold and shock that she could hardly speak. 'Yes. All right. But let's go down, where it's warm.'

Inside his coat, Nick was shivering too, and a nerve was jumping beneath his eye. He looked at her for a long moment, and then strode into the boys' room and whipped the quilts off the bed. 'Come on,' he said, wrapping one around her shoulders, 'let's get those fires banked up.'

Terrified to let him out of her sight, she stood in the porch while he brought in fuel from outside. It struck her that Nick was doing precisely what she had done, those nights that she had spent alone; the instinct to make a fire against the powers of darkness, and cling to it, was basic and primitive, but evidently common to all.

He piled up fresh logs on the hearth, feeding the fire in the grate until it was crackling up the chimney. A few minutes later, having stoked the kitchen stove, he returned with a bottle of good red wine and a couple of glasses.

'This is definitely medicinal,' he declared, pouring for them both. 'Drink this one down and you can have another to sip.'

Raising his glass in a small salute, he watched her drink. He was right to insist, she thought, feeling warmth and strength returning, and also a measure of calm. She had been agitated before he arrived, high on the adrenalin which had been coursing all day, excited and apprehensive and in a fever of anxiety to get to the end of Sarah's story; and she'd done it. Reached the end – my God, the end! – less than an hour ago. She'd been reading through the last twenty pages of handwritten scrawl when she heard his car coming up the lane. And then, after a moment of silence, that sudden roar and dreadful squeal of brakes –

Shaken by what she had written, and even more by the look on Nick's face as he came lurching up the stairs, Natasha was glad to drink the wine and feel the warmth of the fire. She would answer his questions – Sarah had told her story, it was over, finished, and now Natasha could tell it to Nick. But he must believe her, he must understand that it was not just a piece of historical fiction, it was relevant to them, today, and to that hideous creature lurking outside.

He refreshed their glasses and took a seat beside her, gripping her hand. 'I've worried about you,' he confessed in a fierce undertone, 'and I've worried more because I didn't know what the hell was going on. I still don't.' Regarding her intently, he took another mouthful of the wine. A moment later, he said: 'I don't really care where you start, my love, as long as you tell me everything. If it's bizarre, then it's bizarre – I just want you to tell me.'

'I will,' she promised, 'but you must have patience – I'll have to start at the beginning.'

She went back to the afternoon when she had first seen the woman standing in the barn, and first of all apologised to Nick for the accusations she'd levelled at him. Then, somewhat shamefacedly, Natasha confessed that she had seen the woman again, the next day, but this time down by the wood. Describing the rape scene was easy enough, but she found it difficult to put into words that simultaneous feeling she'd had of being touched and invaded.

'For heaven's sake, why didn't you tell me?' he exclaimed, his anger and distaste so apparent that she found it hard to go on. 'I mean, you told me about the sheep and the fracas with young Morrison, why couldn't you tell me the rest? You were acting so strangely, I thought –' He broke off, shaking his head. 'Christ, I thought it was *me* . . .'

'Nick, I'm sorry, but if you keep wanting to know *why*, every five minutes, I'm not going to get this story told. And *I don't know why*, that's the truth. Except,' she added in an undertone, 'I thought I was going crazy.'

He hugged her then, and said he was sorry; his tension, she felt, was as great as her own. With a forced smile, he said that it might be better if they sat apart, then he could pretend to be conducting a tutorial, and keep his questions to the end. That made it easier, and she found it easier still if she did not look at him, but stared into the fire as though talking to a stranger. Nevertheless, there were things left out, her sexual reactions particularly. In retrospect they were shameful, and her response to men he knew was bound to be upsetting. To make it less painful for Nick she carried on with the story.

But his frown deepened when she described that terrible dream, the one that still seemed to her to have been more reality than nightmare; and when she mentioned the name of Sarah Stalwell, he gave a sharp exclamation.

'What do you know about her? Where does she come into all this?'

'Why – she – I've just told you. I had these words in my head, *By the Grace of God, Amen*, and once I'd set them down, once I'd given in to them, they turned out to be the beginning of her story . . .'

From the edge of his seat, Nick leaned towards her. 'But who is she – do you know?'

Natasha shifted uncomfortably. 'Well, yes, I think so.' It was hard though, given her past beliefs, to put into words what she now felt. It constituted an about-face with which she was still not easy. 'I've never believed in these things as you know, and – well, it's all a bit circular, I suppose. You see, I associate her with the woman in the barn, and I think they're one and the same person. It seems to me,' she added, taking a deep breath, 'that somehow – and I don't know how – she's been *using me* to write her story . . .'

'You mean like a medium?' he whispered.

She nodded, unhappy with that description, but unable to provide another. 'But I can't prove it, can I? I mean, any sensible person would say that I've been suffering a minor breakdown or something – taking refuge in my work as a sort of cure . . . I'm not even sure they wouldn't be right.'

Nick shook his head emphatically. 'Natasha, darling, I have to say I might've thought that too, had it not been for the name. Rest assured, you didn't make that up – Sarah Stalwell really existed.' He laughed suddenly, a laugh of wonder and astonishment. Leaning back in his chair, he said: 'Tell me about her.'

But Natasha was dumbstruck for a moment. 'You're serious? You mean you've *heard* of Sarah Stalwell? How?'

'No. You tell me. I have one or two facts – let's see if they tally.'

She reached for her cigarettes. 'Well, let me see. Her maiden name was Kirkham, and she was born in Hammerford. She married young – at sixteen – a farmer by the name of Richard Stalwell. He'd been married before, and was quite a few years older. But he died young – in fact he and his nephew died in a snowstorm, coming back from York, between here and Brickhill. I think Sarah went slightly mad with grief. They didn't have any children.'

'What year, do you know?'

'1723, towards the end of January, if I remember correctly.'

Releasing a long, slow breath, Nick stood up and began to pace the room. 'Well, you're right. She was married to Richard Stalwell, and he certainly died about the time you claim. The local rector made a note of it in his journal – I saw it only a couple of weeks ago. Apparently they had a long wait to bury him, because of the frost and snow.'

'Yes, that's true . . .' Absorbing that, Natasha was not quite sure how to react. It seemed thrilling and terrifying all at the same time, and as she started to smile she felt threatened by a rising bubble of hysteria. Clutching her mouth, she fought it down. Eventually, she said: 'Remember the Whiteheads? Remember Mrs Bickerstaff saying they'd always lived here?'

'Yes . . .'

'And your doubts about that?'

'What about them?'

'Well, they were Richard's in-laws . . .'

That shiver, which seemed to have touched his soul, galvanised Nick into action. He had to ask questions, and he wanted to be able to check the answers, so he went first for a notebook and pen. Slightly light-headed from the wine, he suddenly realised that it was after half-past ten, and neither of them had eaten since lunchtime. If they didn't eat soon, they would both be flagging from exhaustion.

He made sandwiches and coffee, let down one of the arms of their ancient sofa and drew it closer to the fire. 'Here, have something to eat, while I make some notes.'

In the next half-hour he took Natasha through the story again, clarifying all the relevant points. She was looking better all the time, he thought, warming to him as she spoke, meeting his eyes as they talked, in a way that she had not done for months. She still had that feverish look, but seemed so much her normal self that he kept wanting to stop and kiss her, and found himself smiling for no other reason than that she was there, and looking at him, and they were together.

In spite of the subject-matter, and in spite of that terrifying experience outside, Nick felt light-hearted and happy, happier than he had ever expected to be again.

He asked whether she would mind him reading her manuscript, and at that she smiled and said that she would mind very much if he didn't. As she brought it to him, he caught her hand and pressed it to his lips. 'You must be tired,' he said softly, 'do you want to go up to bed?'

'No.' She shivered and bent to the fire. 'I think I'll just stretch out on the sofa, while you read. When you've finished – or when you get tired – just wake me, and we'll go together.'

Sensing that underlying fear, Nick found himself thinking of the weekend he had just spent in London with the boys; and the other nights that he had spent with Sally. It shamed him to think that he had left Natasha here on her own. 'You must have been frightened while I was away.'

'I was,' she admitted, reaching out to stroke Colette. 'But the work took my mind off it.' With a little laugh, she said: 'I just didn't go to bed, that's all. I sat up all night in the kitchen, working.'

'Why the kitchen?'

'I felt safer in there.'

He drew her up and into his arms. 'Never mind,' he whispered, touching his fingers very lightly to her cheek, 'there's two of us now. Together, we should be able to solve it.'

'And then?'

With what he hoped was a reassuring smile, Nick laid a finger across her lips. 'Let's tackle one thing at a time . . .'

Before he started reading he went upstairs to check all the rooms again, and to look out of each window. On both sides of the house all seemed quiet, the white frost providing an illumination all of its own. He could see no hulking black shapes, no eyes glowing like coals in the darkness; but, he reminded himself, that did not mean the thing was gone for good, or even very far.

He shuddered at the thought. What was that god-forsaken thing? Spectral hound, mystical beast – or the manifestation of a damned human soul? However incredible and implausible it seemed, if the connection between Reynard and Reynald were true, then he had looked into the eyes of something that had suffered eight hundred years without rest, eight hundred years of an eternal damnation . . .

It was impossible not to feel, amidst the horror, the smallest stirrings of pity. How had that brutal Norman warlord been so transformed, so cursed, so stamped with the mark of eternal displeasure? By the incantation of some twelfth-century priest? Surely not. By divine interference in the laws of nature and mortality? Such thoughts hardly bore consideration, and yet he had seen it; and that small fact altered every concept, every learned notion of the possible and impossible. It changed everything.

He stood by the window, pondering the questions of eternity and damnation. As he looked out over the village, at the lights visible here and there between the trees, he heard the church bell begin to toll the call to Midnight Mass. The last half-hour of Christmas Eve, the holiest night of the year; and yet evil had been abroad tonight, he could testify to that. Although who would believe him, other than Natasha, Nick could not imagine.

Her voice called to him, drawing him out of his reverie. He answered, pulled the curtains shut, and went downstairs.

They talked for a while, and wished each other a slightly ironic merry Christmas as Natasha drained her glass and Nick drank his black coffee. He wanted to stay awake, not just to read, but to be watchful; he felt Natasha deserved that.

The typed pages, fortunately, were numbered, although not in very good order. By the time he had found the first thirty-six pages, and had sorted out the twenty or so handwritten sheets, Natasha had fallen asleep.

He tucked the quilt around her and threw another log on the fire; with the lamp angled to give a better light, and his feet propped on the hearth, Nick settled down to the manuscript.

The opening phrase struck him immediately: *BY THE GRACE OF GOD AMEN*, had a portentous ring to it, rather like the opening phrase of an old last will and testament. Similar, but not the same. Generally, as he recalled, they began in the *name* of God. Intrigued, he read it several times, until the sense of it eluded him completely. With a sigh, he went into Natasha's office for a dictionary, and looked up the word *grace*.

Amongst several meanings given by Garmonsway in the Penguin edition were *favour; mercy; respite; God's mercy or favour;* (theol.) *supernatural power given by God to the soul to enable it to attain virtue and salvation . . .*

At that, his eyes widened. 'Really?' he murmured under his breath. 'Now that is interesting . . .'

Returning to the manuscript, he read on.

Nick was used to reading quickly, and made considerable progress in the first hour; as he took a break to make some coffee and reflect for a few minutes, he realised that he had been totally absorbed by the character of Sarah Stalwell, and the minutiae of her life. He could see the medieval hall of her aunt's house on Goodramgate, decorated for the Twelfth Night feast, and feel her embarrassment at the matchmaking going on behind her back. Most of all he echoed her father's admiration for the young Richard Stalwell, his achievements and his ambition. Richard, after all, had been a member of the family that built this house.

There was an innocence, an ingenuousness, about the tale in its early stages that he found surprising and endearing. What struck him on reflection, however, was the style, which was quite unlike anything that Natasha had written before. The mode of expression could hardly be said to have the stamp of the eighteenth century upon it, it was far too modern for that; but it did not have Natasha's stamp upon it either. And there were details here and there that only a student of the period would recognise as being entirely in context.

Intrigued, and more than a little excited, Nick straightened the growing pile of pages on his left, and picked up a fresh batch. He wanted to know more about Richard Stalwell and Holly Tree Farm.

The man turned out to be an efficient and productive farmer who increased the quality of his stock as well as the output from his fields, and managed to survive the problems of government taxation in a period when many others were going to the wall. The right marriage was obviously important, and that he had found an able partner in Sarah, as well as access to capital, must have seemed like the fulfilment of his wildest dreams; added to that, she was not only in love with him but also sexually compatible. After his shaky start with Caroline, Richard Stalwell must have felt that fate was smiling at last, and that with Sarah beside him, he was destined for a future of happiness and success.

Reading the seventy or eighty pages that covered the decade of their marriage, however, Nick began to feel the slow disappointment, the dying of a hope that one day there would be children to inherit the achievements and carry on his ambition. That such hopes were never to be fulfilled seemed an irony of fate, particularly since the only one of his nephews in which he saw any ray of hope was destined to die with him in that terrible snowstorm of 1723.

By half-past two, Nick was shaking his head over Richard's death, regretting his loss as an interested party, since after that the surge of progress ebbed away. In the years since, the house had remained largely unchanged, and that was evidence enough to suggest that no other owner of house and farm had possessed the energy and foresight of the Stalwells. Certainly none of the Whiteheads.

There was a sadness in Richard's death which amounted almost to grief. It was as though a young and talented friend had died for no good reason, and he could appreciate Sarah's madness, the mind-destroying agony of bereavement.

Nevertheless, that sudden and indiscriminate promiscuity shocked him. It shocked him because it was so out of character, because he liked and admired the Sarah Stalwell of this account, and forgot while he was reading that he had known of her activities from other sources, and had already judged her harshly. Not all the men had been rough and ignorant; from her description, young Jack, the house-servant, sounded rather more intelligent, and she had mentioned one or two of the local gentry, who were presumably educated, although not necessarily more sensitive. He made a mental note to check names and dates, since young Jack, if found to have died by his own hand, would certainly merit a marginal account in the parish register.

Nick read on to the last typed pages, through Sarah's search for Jack and to that meeting with the hound on Dagger Lane. Instantly, his imagination provided all the vivid detail her account lacked; he was back, and facing the thing, and trying to start the car . . .

Caught by an uncontrollable bout of shivering, he knelt by the fire and persuaded the smouldering logs into a fitful blaze. Adding more wood and some lumps of coal, he managed to revive it properly, then poured himself another glass of wine. As he lit a cigarette, Nick tried to tell himself that his reactions were simply those of shock; this was, after all, the last decade of the twentieth century, which was supposed to have a rational explanation for everything.

For a long moment he gazed at Natasha sleeping peacefully with the ginger and white cat curled against the curve of her body. Overwhelmed by love and protectiveness, he wanted to go to her and hold her close; but even as thought and need formed in his mind, he wondered at the powerful influences at work, and the extent of the damage already done. But that was another mystery, one which he was not yet ready to investigate. For the time being, the one before him was enough.

He picked up the final part of the story, mentally adjusting himself for the idiosyncrasies of Natasha's handwriting.

> We knew each other, this creature and me. What is there to say except that I recognised him, I had seen him in all the men who ravished me, who came back, time after time, to satisfy their brutal desires with a woman who welcomed such usage. The creature was part of them, however briefly, just as he had been part of me for a long time.
>
> I knew him, so I was not afraid as some might have been. What had I to lose? I was his already, and he had come to remind me that there was no escape, no going back.
>
> Jack, poor Jack, who tried to comfort me with love, who tried to save my soul when my soul was already past redemption, was dead. They found him next day, hanging from an oak in World's End Wood, dead by his own hand, but they all knew who and what had driven him.
>
> His sister, who had been pretty once, took up Agnes's cry and called me a witch; but she made sure her children were out of sight when she did so. Old Jacob, bitter now and broken, took his plea to the rector that the boy's death was an accident, no more than that. Enough doubt was cast that

it became possible to bury him in the churchyard, but not with his family. His grave, unmarked, lies in the farthest corner of the graveyard, facing north, not east.

The curiosity of that halted Nick's eye for a moment. Was that the old rector's way of settling doubt? Suicides were not entitled to a Christian burial in consecrated ground, he knew that; but if doubt were raised, and his sympathies enlisted, then it would seem the old man had hedged all possibilities by burying the boy away from the faithful, aligning him crosswise instead of in traditional fashion. If that were true, then there should be a note to that effect in the parish register, and possibly one in the old man's journal. Although when he would get another chance to look at that was anyone's guess.

He turned his eyes back to the manuscript.

Just after dark on the eve of Michaelmas, with all the farmyard chores finished, I took myself indoors for a meagre supper of bread and cheese. My idle labourers had been paid and were gone already to York to seek fresh employment at the hirings, and would no doubt celebrate their freedom between times. Tomorrow or the next day I must go there myself, and find some good men to work the farm. Supplies were needed too: I could not survive the winter on what I had, and must needs consult Richard's lawyer regarding necessary funds.

I ate my supper while thinking on these matters. There being no ale in the house, I drank some wine from the last remaining cask, and thought: as soon as I have these new men, I must devote some time to brewing. The necessity of keeping hunger and thirst from the door, and of keeping my new servants fed, had begun to impinge in ways that had not concerned me for many a long month.

It may be that I slept; I know I came to with a start. A log fell in the hearth, or a door creaked, and as I turned in my chair I remember thinking, no, please, not Tom Whitehead again. My bones ached from the labour of the day, and that night my strength was not equal to his pitiless attentions. Like a torturer he would threaten and cajole, all to the end that I must give up the farm and leave the village. And when I refused, and spat at him, and fought off his lecherous assaults, he took pleasure in forcing me across a table, or to my knees, or occasionally on my back on the stone floor. He would leave me gasping and full of hate, my lustfulness roused but rarely satisfied. And that was when I missed Jack, who in that respect at least had been useful to me.

But as I turned that night it was not Tom Whitehead I saw in the doorway, but Agnes Stalwell, a more shameless drab than I, since she had supplanted her own sister in what passed for Tom Whitehead's affections, and subjected herself willingly to his perverted tastes. But I had diverted him, and now she hated me more than ever, malevolence glittering from beneath those lowered brows.

There was excitement in her eyes, the excitement of evil intent, and I was on my guard immediately. As I stood up, my back to the fire, I cast around for something to use as a weapon, for I was certain I should need it. On the hearth was the stone flagon of wine, and half-burnt logs in the grate.

I forced a smile of greeting. 'Why Agnes,' said I, 'to what do we owe this pleasure?' Bending to the hearth, I picked up the flagon, seeming to offer her a drink, but as I straightened, Jack's sister moved silently into the room, to take her place beside Agnes; and as I stared, taken aback, the wife of Dick Howsham appeared, an evil little slattern whose invective I knew well. She grinned, although I knew not why, for I swear her husband had serviced me more often in the last six months.

There were a dozen in all. I could name them, but it serves no purpose, except to say that most of them had been present when I hooked Tom Whitehead in the lane at harvest time; and all of them had husbands whose rods I knew the length of.

They were mostly common, ignorant women whose society I would have despised when Richard was alive; and, when Richard was alive they would scarce have dared to approach my door, much less cross the threshold uninvited.

I challenged them, ordered them out, but not one of them moved. Doll Howsham sniggered, and Jack's sister, Mary Collitt, spat on me, her once-pretty face contorted with hate, her fingers working with the desire to tear and hurt and pummel me into submission. But she would never do that.

Very slowly, while Agnes smiled, I wiped the spittle from my bodice. For the first time I began to be afraid, for I sensed a unity of purpose here, and I dreaded what that might be. Pain, certainly; punishment, no question. It seemed to me that I was to be hurt and humiliated in some way, to the extent that I would have to abandon my home, my life, all that I had once held dear. It meant little without Richard, but I would not give it up for pride's sake; and I would not give it up to Agnes Stalwell.

But that edge of fear made me hasty. 'Get out, Agnes – I've no patience with your games. Get out of my house, and take your *sisters* with you!'

At that, I took a step forward, thinking that if I ousted her the rest would follow. But she stood her ground. Not only that, she grabbed my arm and twisted it. 'Whose house?' she hissed. 'This house belongs to the Stalwells – you're nothing but an interloper here!'

The twelve surged forward, surrounding me. As I struggled to free myself from Agnes, Doll Howsham grabbed my bodice, and Mary Collitt my hair; someone else wrenched the flagon from my grasp, and before I knew it I was on the stone floor, my clothing ripped from my body by those venomous hags. And hags they were, screeching with glee as they punched and kicked, scratched and tore at my naked flesh.

Battered and bleeding, I was yanked to my feet, then forced into the chair. Agnes produced a pair of shears.

Mary Collitt, almost drooling in her desire to humiliate me further, took them like a communicant takes the cup at the altar-rail, holding them out for a moment before pressing the cold metal to her lips.

My hair was snagged and knotted from the fight, my scalp cold yet burning where great hanks had been pulled out by the roots. I saw those shears and I quailed, unable to bite back a sob of grief and terror as she set her teeth and started hacking at what remained. My hair, my yellow hair that Richard had praised and adored, that he had trailed across his body like a silken skein, twisted in his fingers, touched to his lips – my hair was hacked from me with less regard than a fleece from a struggling ewe.

I cursed them then. I cursed them like the witch I was purported to be, until Agnes clamped my jaw with her fingers and stuffed a balled-up remnant of my shift into my open mouth.

There was no need to tie me down. Enough hands were there to hold me, to scratch and nip and twist my flesh, to take turns at making me jerk and kick like a strangled marionette.

I thought they would leave it at that. I thought humiliation was the aim, that they would turn me out with nothing, to suffer such shame that I would never return. But my estimation fell far short of reality. They knew me, you see, knew that I had shamed myself and cared not a whit, and that not even in a bloody, shorn and naked state would I seek shelter away from my own hearth and home.

And Agnes knew, of course she did, that if I was driven out in that state, that even if I had to crawl and beg my way to York I would have the law on them, all of them. I had the power of my position as a freeholder, and I had money – apart from the farm – to pursue them through the courts and make the charges stick.

So they could not let me live.

I should have realised that.

If hysteria had prompted the first violence, and revenge the humiliation, there was a cold-blooded detachment about the preparations for my death that spoke of careful planning.

They were wives, these women, servants in their own homes, and they knew about stains and cleaning, and the trouble it is when a man kills a pig badly, and the blood misses the pot and spreads across the floor. So they spread a fine woollen blanket from my bed, and covered it with my torn and raggy clothes; and aside they stripped off, one by one, and laid their clothes on the settle. Between times, for courage, they drank my wine.

I saw them, I knew what they were about. I would have screamed except my mouth was stopped. Although what good screaming would have done, with no one to hear, I do not know. I struggled to no avail.

It was like some pagan ritual, in which the victim's sins must be chanted before the killing commences. Each incited the others, but Agnes, armed with a butcher's knife, delivered the first blow.

A dozen wounds in chest and back, and I know not which one killed me. At first I was not even aware of dying, only of a cessation of pain, and the curious fact of being apart from them, of watching that series of blows, the knife passed from hand to hand, and the sobbing that followed.

They behaved as though they grieved for me, these terrible, ignorant women. Only Agnes did not weep. She, in cold ferocity, slapped faces, issued orders, had water brought from the well, and started cleaning up. The body that had been mine was soon ignored, avoided, spreadeagled as it was across the bloody, rumpled blanket. It occurred to me how often I had lain like that before, while some man pulled on his breeches and stumbled away into the night.

They could not have done it without Agnes. She was the clever one, the one who issued orders, who knew what to do. Mary Collitt was sent away while the others dressed, got rid of the bloody water, took hold of their senses and listened to Agnes drilling them in what they must do next.

Some went upstairs. A couple of trunks were packed with clothes, books, a few precious items of silver, all things which caused bitter haggling amongst women who were too poor to own pewter, let alone silver. But Agnes slapped them down.

'Do you want to *hang*?' she hissed at them. 'If one single thing – *just one* – be found in your home, that should be here, then we invite suspicion. Sarah Stalwell has gone, left for York or Hull or London, we don't know – but it must be seen that she took her traps with her.'

'We could sell them,' whined Doll Howsham.

'And have the pedlar say he bought them from a poor woman in *Denton*?' Agnes demanded with contempt. 'You're such a fool, Doll Howsham! No, we pack the trunks, and we bury them, where nobody will think to look.'

And where would that be? I wondered in my detached, untouchable state. The question was soon answered. The men, my ex-gallants, former stallions, crept in fearfully in twos and threes, to be herded in the passage between front and back doors. When all were there, including Tom Whitehead, Mary Collitt let them into the room where lay the body of Sarah Stalwell, now decently wrapped and covered.

Between them, I noticed, they were carrying spades.

'She's dead,' Agnes announced, and in her voice I heard for the first time the quavering of fear. 'We all killed her.'

'And now,' the bitter tones of Mary Collitt went on, '*you* are going to bury her.'

There was a babble of voices, husky disbelief amidst thunderous protests. A few tried to get out of the house, but two of the women stood guard on the door, and at their alert, wives dragged their husbands back.

'You'll do it,' Agnes said, all determination again, 'because you're as much to blame as we are – and if you don't, we'll likely all hang.'

Her words penetrated and after a discussion that was once

more dominated by my redoubtable sister-in-law, the men filed out to begin their work, followed by wives who could no longer bear the sight of what they had done.

Tom Whitehead held Agnes back. 'In the name of Christ, woman – what have you done?'

'Done? What have I done?' She shook off his restraining hand. 'I've got you what you always wanted – this house, this farm, the Stalwell land. Only in trust, of course,' she added with a high, slightly hysterical laugh. 'Unless I *marry* and have *children*,' she taunted him, 'it will go eventually to Matt.'

'It will go to Matt anyway . . .'

'Not in my lifetime,' she promised him, 'you can be sure of that!'

He fell back, knowing what I now knew: that he was saddled with Agnes Stalwell, his dead wife's sister, for good. He could not marry her, for the relationship, in law, would have been incestuous; and he could not turn her out, because she was Richard's nearest living kin, and, as such, quite likely to be given control of the property for the next seven years, until my death could be safely assumed. If he wanted control of the farm until his eldest son's majority, then he must put up with Agnes; and she must put up with him, knowing that I had destroyed his passion for her.

In that respect, I had my revenge on them, for I knew they would not prosper. Nor did they. I think my presence lingered between them more effectively than any haunting.

In the yard, the men closed the gates and shifted the cows out of the byre, cleared the straw and droppings from two of the stalls, and started digging. A couple of hours later, the job was done: the body in one grave, the trunks buried in another. With the excess soil carefully disbursed about the garden and a neighbouring field, and the straw and droppings replaced in the byre, it was difficult to tell that anything had been disturbed. Impossible, once the cows were back. The poor beasts, which were to be left until their complaints at not being milked alerted the neighbourhood, munched quietly at their feed.

As the conspirators made their way, in silence, back home, it seemed to me that I should be going too. Richard would be waiting for me, waiting to greet me, waiting to show me the way home . . .

Light with love, I sought to be free, but it was as though I was held fast to the earth by a great weight. And then, in my new awareness, I saw him: not Richard, but the darkness that was my captor. I saw him, the instigator, he who existed by fomenting evil in the hearts of men; he held me fast, as he had held others and would hold more in the centuries to come.

It was not Richard I was meant to meet, nor any of those I had loved on earth. No, I must wait, in my turn, to greet the captive souls of Tom Whitehead and Agnes Stalwell . . .

My body lies still in unconsecrated ground. My soul, unshriven, begs absolution and release . . .

By the Grace of God, Amen.

Thirty Five

NICK AWOKE, shortly after eight, with a painfully stiff neck. As he massaged life into his aching muscles, he was visited by a memory of transatlantic flights and nights spent in armchairs when he was very much younger. He even had the sour aftertaste of too much alcohol and the crumpled, sweaty feel which came from sleeping in yesterday's clothes.

Bending forward to rub his neck, he saw the bottle, the empty glasses, and the manuscript on the floor beside the hearth. With a cold chill the murder sprang to mind; he glanced up and realised that Natasha was missing. At once, with no thought for his protesting body, he crossed the stone-flagged hall to the kitchen; and there she was, in her dressing-gown, making coffee.

Relief brought a shaky smile to his lips. He wrapped himself around her, kissing her hair and rubbing his cheek against hers, but she winced and smiled and pulled away, reminding him that he needed a shave.

Facing her across the table he was aware that barriers had been erected, that after last night's closeness, they were behaving almost like strangers. He was conscious of her reluctance and his own hesitation, and was reminded again of student parties, the embarrassment of meeting someone next morning while recalling all too clearly what had been said and done the night before. But to recognise such things by day gave them a credence they did not always deserve, made them issues to be acted upon; it was a similar kind of reluctance that held them silent now. Unspoken, the events of last night could be ignored for a time; once acknowledged, they were bound to take over.

The inevitability of that stuck in his throat, making conversation impossible. Pushing his chair back, Nick said that he would go and take a shower.

The water, blessedly, was hot, taking the ache out of his muscles and the apprehension from his thoughts. Beneath those searing flashes of memory, his mind was asking questions, still demanding to know what was going on; and as he towelled himself dry he went back over the last few months, trying to chart the clues, trying to spot the vital piece of information he might have missed.

But it was no good. He would have to look at his notes, jot things down on paper; he always thought better that way. Tucking the towel in around his waist, Nick ran some hot water into the basin and prepared to lather his face. With the razor in his hand, he paused, staring at his reflection in the mirror. What was it he had said that day they went to Brickhill? *Just a little bit of historical detective work* . . . And Natasha, in cynical mode, had replied: *Which won't produce a corpse or a culprit, or even a crime . . .*

He blinked hard and released a long, slow breath. Every instinct cried out that Natasha's manuscript was fact, not fiction, and that a crime had been committed and the culprits named. To prove it, all he needed was the corpse.

Quite how Reynald de Briec fitted into the conundrum, Nick was not sure, nor did he wish to pursue that aspect for the time being. It was enough to know that the beast had been seen in Denton in the 1720s, and that it was still around now, 270 years later.

They had to talk, and soon. Before anything worse happened.

'But we don't know what's going on here,' Natasha reminded him as she dried her hair. Staring at her own reflection, she thought of Sarah Stalwell, and her plea for absolution and release. That stirred more doubts than she felt able to face this morning. 'I'm not at all sure that we're competent to deal with this. Couldn't we –' She paused and swallowed hard. 'Couldn't we just put the house up for sale, and rent somewhere in town for the time being?'

That she was merely putting into words the fears which had struck him only a short while before made Nick gentle with her. 'Could you do that? Could you simply ignore all this, pretend it never happened?'

'Maybe I made it all up,' she said defensively. 'Maybe it's just a series of coincidences. That barn is early nineteenth century, you've always said so.'

'The present building is, I'll grant you that. But it was more than likely built on the same site as a previous construction. And don't forget – you saw her originally in the barn doorway.'

But the more Natasha thought about that, the less she liked it. The building where they parked their cars, the one they always referred to as the barn, had certainly been used as a byre in the past. She knew that from the old wooden stalls which had still been in place when they bought the property. If what she had written was to be believed, then the remains of Sarah Stalwell lay beneath that hard-packed earth. But she did not want to believe it. Right now she preferred to think that the barn/byre of Sarah Stalwell's day was elsewhere, on another site, one she did not have to think about every time she climbed into her car.

But whether that was so or not, Natasha knew that in her eyes at least the sitting-room would never be the same again. Last night, wound-up on adrenalin and insulated by varying degrees of shock, it had all seemed rather exciting; but she shuddered whenever she thought of those worn stone flags the builders had taken up, and which were still stacked by the wall outside. On those stones, Sarah Stalwell had been murdered, and right in front of the hearth . . .

She dressed hurriedly, finding it difficult to control a powerful desire to flee. While Nick buttoned his shirt and straightened his collar, she turned abruptly and left the bedroom. It was warmer on the landing, with sunlight streaming through those southern windows, and she paused, tensely, to look out across the yard. In the sun, the frost was starting to melt, although the barn doorway was still deep in shadow. With a startling flutter of black and white plumage, two magpies alighted on the pantiled roof, uttering their rapid, machine-gun call at the sight of the prowling outdoor cats. Natasha shivered.

A moment later, Nick joined her by the window. After one darting glance at her, he let his eyes rest on the scene before them, the sunny yard, the reddish-brown hedges, the frosty fields beyond. 'I know,' he said softly, 'it just doesn't seem possible. But the thing is,' he added, 'I know what I saw last night, and you know what you've written – '

He broke off, and she saw his mouth harden, the slightly pugnacious jaw come up as he turned to face her. 'We have to talk. We have to decide where we go from here. I think it's important to get to the bottom of it.'

'Oh, yes?' she challenged, her voice squeaky with nerves. 'And where do you suggest we start?'

'Look, if we try, Natasha, we can do it. But we have to trust each other, we have to be honest about everything that's happened to us in the last couple of months. Before that, everything was all right. It was, wasn't it?' As she nodded, he went on: 'Well, we take it from where things started to go wrong – that way, we might see some kind of pattern.' He paused for a moment, gripping her fingers between his own strong ones. 'Don't you see – that way we might find out what it is we're up against.'

Drawing her hand away, she said: 'I should've thought that was obvious. God, Nick, you came face to face with it last night – wasn't that enough? I think we should leave, get the hell out of here.'

'And let somebody else suffer?'

'But will they?' she demanded, hearing her voice rise. 'Don't you think it's just *us* – you and me, living together in this house? I used to think things like this were just claptrap – hauntings, objects being flung about, even Helen seeing an old dear sitting on the end of her bed. I thought they were just attention-grabbing *stories*, Nick. Or that there was some kind of rational explanation. But now it's happening to me, I realise there *isn't* an explanation. And that is bloody scary. I don't want to know – I just want out.'

He watched her as she paced the landing, but said nothing for a moment. Then, as she came back to sit on the windowledge, he shook his head and said: 'Look, I understand – I really do understand what you're saying. But the point is, we know more about this than anybody has known in the last eight hundred years. I can't ignore that. I can't just walk away and forget it.'

She knew that look. The drawn-down brows, the upward glance, the stubborn set of the jaw. It was what she termed his bloodhound look, when he was determined to pursue a course of action or line of thought of which other people disapproved. Now he would insist on staying, whatever she decided to do; and if she were to leave he would be susceptible on two fronts. Not just to whatever was lurking out there, but to this other woman, Sally.

Biting her lip, Natasha looked away. Threatened from the same two quarters she was angry enough to want to hit him. Couldn't he see the quandary she was in?

Abruptly, she stood up and went into the bedroom. Finding her cigarettes she lit one and smoked furiously for a minute, balancing one fear against another. Eventually she went back to him. 'All right. So what do you propose?'

He grinned at her, relieved now that he had her acquiescence. 'Some breakfast,' he said lightly. 'A high-cholesterol special – how about that?'

'Only if you're cooking it.'

Laughing, he led the way downstairs.

She was stacking plates in the dishwasher, afterwards, when the conversation turned to Sarah's sexual obsessions.

'Although really,' he said, 'when you think about it, it was more in the nature of a spiritual possession, wouldn't you agree?'

'I couldn't say – I don't know enough about it.'

'Well, who does? I'm just going on things I've read, and Sarah would seem to be a classic case. Not only did she turn her back on God, she cursed Him – and apparently left herself wide open to possession by –' he broke off and thought for a moment. 'I don't know – Reynald de Briec, I suppose, in the guise of Reynard, the hound . . .'

Remembering the cold, emotionless nature of Sarah's hunger,

the relentless pursuit of satisfaction, Natasha shuddered. She busied herself at the sink, trying not to think of the sexual heat she had experienced, the death of love, that turning away from Nick . . .

'She'd probably be called a nymphomaniac today,' Nick went on, 'but what does anyone know about the cause of something like that? Maybe this kind of thing is more common than we realise.'

She heard him light a cigarette, and could feel him watching her from his seat by the table. After a little while he said, not quite jokingly, 'But you weren't affected like that, were you? I mean, I can see similarities between you and Sarah Stalwell – up to a point, that is – but it seems to me that, unlike Sarah, you were turned off sex completely . . .'

Natasha felt herself growing hot with embarrassment, although had their relationship been back on its old footing she thought they might have laughed, made a joke of it. As it was, she was tempted to lie, to just agree with him and change the subject. But then she recalled her twin fears and his determination to see this thing through; and if being honest would help solve the problem, then she wanted it solved, and the quicker the better.

'Well, yes, in many respects that's true.' She turned to look at him, but he had his back to the window, and the smoke from his cigarette was making a blue haze in the sunlight. 'Something turned me off sex to begin with, and then – as I said last night – things started to happen, and I thought I was going mad. But that's what you thought too,' she added accusingly, 'so it wasn't exactly a turn-on, was it?'

'No,' he agreed sombrely, 'I don't imagine it was.'

She hesitated, wondering how much of the truth he could take. Not Giles, that much was certain, nor even Craig Morrison. 'But there were moments when I wanted sex,' she admitted, 'moments so unexpected, and so *bizarre*, I really did think I was suffering from nymphomania.' She paused to let that sink in, then said calmly: 'I even had the unspeakable experience of fancying Charlie Cramp.'

'What? *Charlie Cramp*?' He was so aghast, he started to laugh. 'I don't believe it!'

'Well, I can assure you it's true. And it wasn't funny – it was *dreadful.* The worst part about it was that he wanted me too. As soon as I looked at him I could see the – well, the *speculation* in his eyes.'

Nick's laughter died at the expression on her face. 'You mean you were really lusting for him? My God, how . . .'

'Disgusting? Yes, it was. I was disgusted, Nick, and appalled. I didn't know what was happening to me. You see, he wasn't the only one – there were quite a few more before it stopped. Complete strangers mostly, people I just happened to see in town.'

'But they turned you on?'

'Well, something did. Physically, I wanted them. In fact,' she added wanting to shock him now, 'I could have dropped my knickers there and then – it was horrible and very frightening.'

He winced. 'But your mind wasn't involved?'

'No, not really. Not beyond the usual sort of thing – you know, catching sight of someone and thinking how attractive they are.'

He glanced up, frowning, and she could see that he was disturbed. 'But Charlie Cramp's no Robert Redford, is he?'

'No, he damn well isn't, that's the point. In fact I find him repulsive in every way.' Sitting down at the table, she took one of Nick's cigarettes. As he flicked his lighter, she said: 'When I think about that evening, that's what I can't understand. I mean, why him? Why not Graham Fish, for instance? He's not bad-looking in his way, although he's not my type – and I actually *like* Professor Benson –' She broke off as Nick laughed again, but this time his laughter was infectious. 'Yes, I know, it gets ridiculous, doesn't it? But what I'm saying is – why Charlie Cramp, and not the other two?'

'Maybe it's something to do with the men themselves – their levels of susceptibility, perhaps.'

If that was feasible, it was also unpleasant. 'You mean Charlie Cramp's a dirty old man on the quiet?'

Nick shrugged. 'Well, he might be, but I didn't really mean that. I mean perhaps they were susceptible to similar forces – or just to *you.*' He studied the table-top, worrying a mark with his fingernail, and then glanced up. 'But what I can't understand is the barrier between you and me – '

'Divide and conquer,' Natasha said without thinking.

'Yes, of course,' he agreed, pausing to consider that. 'And if we're to fight back, we must be united – *in every way*.' Taking her hand in his, he said earnestly: 'Natasha, we have to be honest with each other . . .'

The question in his eyes made her snatch her hand away. Between gritted teeth, she said: 'No, I didn't, if that's what you're asking! I'd like to tell you I had sex with every single one of them, but as a matter of fact, I didn't. The opportunity never arose!'

His fingers curled and clenched. When he looked up again his eyes were hard, his lips a thin line of repressed anger. 'Don't,' he said quietly, 'I can do without all this. I'm just trying to establish what's been going on – '

'Then perhaps you should bring yourself into the equation – ask yourself about your own sexual inclinations over the past couple of months. You've admitted to one, but what about that girl at the party? And how many more were there? Or did you just get a hard-on,' she said brutally, 'and not do anything about it?'

Shaking with fury as sudden as it was inexplicable, Natasha thrust the chair back and leaned across the table. 'But you see, Nick, in men it's acceptable – they're allowed the instant turn-on, so nobody thinks twice about it. But the dictionary has all sorts of colourful and derogatory terms for women who follow their inclinations – and the least of them is *whore*!'

With that, she turned on her heel and flung out of the room before her fury could give way to humiliating sobs.

With the subsiding of his first angry reaction, Nick tried to think calmly. Reflecting on what she had told him, he tried to imagine what it must have been like for her, at the mercy of sexual whims that he could only liken to those of his own adolescence. Those sudden priapic urges had been difficult and embarrassing at times, but also exciting; particularly when there came an answering response. Had she felt that excitement too? Was there someone else she had responded to, someone younger and rather less repulsive than Charlie Cramp, who had found her looks and sensuality as breathtaking as he did? Although he had dismissed the idea before, on the grounds that Natasha hardly knew anyone and was generally too busy working to build up a circle of fresh acquaintances, Nick began to reappraise that theory. If the fact that she was a woman was discounted, if he set her in an average man's shoes, Nick suddenly began to see that almost any member of the opposite sex might have attracted her attention, not just a select group of people who shared a similar background, outlook and tastes. It might have been a man she met on the train, going to or from London; someone she met by chance in a café or supermarket.

The opportunity never arose. That was what she had *said*, but he had only to look around him to see that opportunity had been here all the time, especially when he had been in college all day.

But she had been so vehement about it. Did he believe her? On balance, he thought he probably did, in spite of the jealousy burning like fire in his throat and chest. Nevertheless, he would stake his life that there had been someone with whom she had wanted to go to bed, someone who had stoked the sexual flames in earnest, whether or not they had been satisfied. But who, Nick wondered; what was he like?

On the heels of that furious thought came a fleeting picture of Sally, and he had the grace to feel ashamed. Sally had not been a passing fancy, Sally had been for real; he had been to bed with her, made love to her, and she had made love to him. Nor did he consider the word love abused; there had been more than just an element of caring about what they had shared, however briefly.

He had heard other men claim that casual sex was meaningless, that it made not a whit of difference to how they felt about their wives. It was probably true, since in spite of that affection for Sally he was not aware of feeling differently towards Natasha. Or if he was, it was a question of caring more, rather than less. No, he thought, what these people failed to appreciate – indeed, what *he* had failed to appreciate – was the effect on the other party, the serious wounding involved. Did it really matter, ultimately, whether the adultery was comprised of caring sex, or sex purely for the thrills? It hurt, it hurt like hell, and he was not proud of the fact that he had flung his affair with Sally in Natasha's face, with every intention of wounding her.

Well, he had an inkling now of what it felt like, even if it was largely a blow to his masculine pride. It was no longer fashionable to claim that a woman belonged to you, that she was yours and yours alone; but, politically correct or not, that was exactly how Nick did feel, and he could not bear the thought that his wife, the woman he loved and with whom he was still so very much in love, had been sexually aroused by other men. Whether she cared about them or not really did not enter into it.

Quietly he went upstairs and opened the door of their bedroom. She was lying on the bed, and as he sat down on the edge of it she turned away, not wanting him to see her tear-ravaged face. He sighed and stroked her shoulder, further mortified by the evidence of her misery. On the floor was a box of tissues; he handed her a couple to replace the damp and crumpled ball she was holding in her hand.

In a voice deep with regret, he said: 'I'm sorry, I didn't mean to upset you like this. I didn't realise . . .' Without finishing the sentence he turned her gently and drew her up into his arms. 'Come on now,' he whispered against her damp and tumbled hair, 'stop crying. You've had a hard time, I know, and I didn't mean to put the pressure on . . .' He breathed in the scent of her hair and skin, the hint of citrus blossom from the perfume she used, and the familiarity was instantly arousing. 'Please, darling . . .'

'I'm sorry – '

'I know,' he murmured, 'we've both said things we shouldn't . . . Can't we just forgive and forget, make a new start . . .' His voice was low and soothing, but beneath his hands Natasha's body was awkward and unyielding as she fought to control those shuddering sobs. He moved to hold her more easily, and found it easier still to lie back against the pillows, her head cradled against his arm. He kissed long wet lashes and the tear-stained softness of her cheek, and thought how much he loved her, and how very much it hurt. He reached the salty warmth of her mouth, and thought was banished then by a deep and urgent thrill which went right to the core of his being.

For a moment they were both poised, barely touching, hardly breathing; then those softly parted lips touched his again, and he was aware of aching need, a burning desire to be deep inside her, forcefully erasing every other memory, each passing, illicit desire. The strength of it shocked him; on a deep breath he drew away, just far enough for self-control, while with trembling fingers he touched her cheek and the outline of her mouth. He searched her eyes and saw them widen at his intensity, her nostrils flaring a little as he ran his hand down over her breast and down again to the slender curve of her waist. Under sweater and T-shirt he found the warmth of her skin, felt the shiver of acquiescence as he tugged at her waistband and released the fastening. As she reached up to kiss him it took every ounce of his restraint not to tear at her clothes and force his way into her.

'I want you so much,' he admitted huskily, knowing she wanted him too, but not quite in that way and not for those reasons. 'Take your clothes off – I can't bear it like this – '

It was a relief to be free of restraints. He felt easier, more in control, although when she touched him he begged her to be easy, pulling her back with him across the bed. Pressing the length of his body against her, he felt her desire mounting to match his own, yet still held himself in check, touching and caressing with hands and mouth until she was open and quivering on waves of ecstasy. She was almost at the point of orgasm before he plunged into her, thrusting hard and deep to reach a long and shattering release.

Thirty Six

THE HALF MOON was, for tall people, an obstacle course of flamboyant Christmas decorations. Great swags of them hung from every blackened beam, while glittering arrangements of fir cones and baubles vied with the glassy stare of stuffed animals from the innumerable niches. A heavy-laden Christmas tree took up one corner by the chimney, and the place was crowded too, by a largely masculine clientele, local inhabitants today rather than the sober-suited businessmen who formed the bulk of lunchtime trade throughout the year.

Preparing to fight his way through to the bar, Nick squeezed Natasha's hand and left her in a comparatively free space between the two main areas of the best room. Nevertheless, she was hemmed in on both sides by groups of men with big hands and bigger voices, mostly farmers by the sound of them, commenting on the Christmas fatstock sales. Several looked at her and smiled, while she tried to avoid their eyes and studied the elaborate trimmings. Absently fingering the gold chain Nick had just given her as a Christmas present, she thought about their recent love-making. He had surprised her, since after her outburst earlier, she had expected cross words or an angry silence; but something of what she said must have gone deep to call forth that level of intensity. Could it be that he was so afraid of losing her? That this Sally woman meant so little to him? Or was it to do with Sarah Stalwell, and the parallels they had discussed – particularly the sexual obsession?

She raised herself on tiptoe, trying to see past the gathered heads to where Nick was being served at the bar. Catching sight of him, his thick dark hair and broad shoulders, Natasha had the feeling that what she had just experienced with him was not purely an act of love, but one of reclamation, and while part of her could understand that – was even turned on by it – a hard little kernel of detachment refused to be softened. Once again something important had been side-stepped, and she had compromised herself because of it. And yet without that –

Startled by a hand at her waist, she almost cried out. She jerked round and looked straight into the eyes of Craig Morrison.

'Now then, how's things? Hoping for a Christmas kiss, are you?'

'Certainly not, I'm – '

But he kissed her anyway. No more than a friendly peck on the lips and a surreptitious squeeze of her bottom in the skin-tight ski-pants, but Natasha was not pleased. Laughing at her consternation, Craig glanced up. 'Sorry, couldn't resist it – not only do you look good enough to eat, sweetheart, you're standing underneath the mistletoe!'

She swore, looked up, saw the bunch of green twigs with its berries like pearls, and moved hastily away from that ancient symbol of sexual invitation. With her face on fire, she laughed and said: 'I wondered why they were all grinning at me like Cheshire cats!'

'You should have wondered why this spot was free,' he laughed, raising his glass to her. 'Anyway, Merry Christmas to you – it's good to see you. What have you been doing with yourself?'

With a fleeting image of all that had taken place since their last meeting in her kitchen, she shook her head and said lamely: 'Oh, you know, this and that.' After a short pause, she added: 'Working, mainly. Finishing a story.'

'Oh?' Grinning wolfishly, he said: 'That sounds like good news. I hope you're going to take my advice.'

'I'm sorry?'

'You know, like I told you – get out and discover some real

life for a change. Have a bit of fun while you're still young enough to enjoy it.' He grinned again, the lapis lazuli eyes leaving her in no doubt as to his meaning. 'Like I said before, any time you want to break out, you know where to find me . . .'

She bit her lip, suppressing a rude reply. Lighting a cigarette she said: 'Anyway, what brings you here? I thought your local was the Drovers?'

He laughed. 'It is, but the old man's called a truce since it's Christmas, and invited me to dinner.' Jerking his head, he indicated a group in the corner behind them. There was a family resemblance between three of the men that suggested they were all Morrisons, while the much older man was shorter and more wiry, his face harder than any of them.

As he glared in their direction, Natasha turned away. 'Well then, Craig, you'd better not let your dad think you're making up to me or you'll be in trouble again.'

With a quizzical frown, he said: 'And what would you know about that?'

She turned to look for Nick, but he was almost upon them, his questioning glance resting first upon her companion, and then upon Natasha. Smiling brightly, she relieved him of her drink, then issued a warning about the mistletoe before introducing him to Craig Morrison.

Although the two men nodded and agreed that they had often seen each other up and down the lane, they did not shake hands; and Nick's smile, Natasha thought, just failed to reach his eyes. For his part, however, Craig could not have seemed more himself, standing there with his pint, passing comments here and there upon the gathered company.

'How's old Toby going on, then? Haven't seen him about for a while.'

'Fine, last time I saw him,' Nick said. 'Out with his gun, as usual. I don't know how he survives this weather.'

'Aye, he's a tough old bird, is Toby. But you know what they say – only the good die young. And by that yardstick,' he added cryptically, 'he should be with us for a long time yet.'

Nick frowned, and Natasha could see the question forming on

his lips; but before it could be uttered, Craig Morrison was saying he had to go. A moment later he had rejoined the group in the corner, and one of his brothers was taking orders for the next round.

'What the hell did he mean by that?'

Natasha took a deep breath and said: 'I could tell you, but I'd prefer not to do it here. Forget it till we go home.'

The frown deepened. 'Is our young friend a bit of a trouble-maker,' Nick asked laconically, 'or is my judgement biased by what I noticed from the bar?'

The look he gave her brought a guilty flush to her cheeks. 'Yes, well, I'm sorry about that. You might say I was taken advantage of – stupid, really, I should have noticed the mistletoe.' Giving him a sidelong glance, she forced a smile and said: 'But thanks, anyway, for not making a song and dance about it.'

He raised his eyebrows, as though that had been the last thing on his mind. 'Should I have?'

'No, no, of course not –' But she was aware of his jealousy, despite his attempts to conceal it, and knew that had circumstances been even slightly different, he would have had just cause. She was never more glad that Craig Morrison had been mostly in the mind. Eager to divert the subject, she said: 'But you're right, you know – about him being a bit of a troublemaker, I mean. Mrs Bickerstaff couldn't find a good word to say about him . . .'

Leaving the pub later, they walked arm in arm along the road to Sheriff Whenby, enjoying the cold, dry air, and an illusion of warmth from the sun.

Having disposed of Mrs Bickerstaff's gossip while they were in the pub, Natasha went on to give an abridged version of Craig Morrison's second visit to the house, stressing how unexpected it had been, that it had occurred during an obsessive day of work at the typewriter. Nick knew her well enough to judge her reaction to that. He listened patiently, tempering his stride to hers, turning his head occasionally to look at her, his demeanour so controlled that she was reluctant to break it by reaching the point. She brought Mrs Bickerstaff back into the tale, reiterating the sparse comments she had made about Toby, reminding Nick of the attitude he had always found so offensive.

'But you see, she wasn't wrong, not really. I know she's a funny woman, and you don't like her, but if one of your relatives had been convicted of murder I dare say you'd be reluctant to talk about it, too . . .'

'What?'

He stopped abruptly, and she turned to face him, forced to repeat at last what Craig Morrison had told her that afternoon. She tried to soften it by painting a picture of what she imagined were the circumstances; nevertheless, the shock was obviously profound.

'Oh, my God,' he whispered, turning away from her.

'I know, it's – well, hard to comprehend the kind of rage that would prompt somebody to do a thing like that . . .' She sighed and held his arm. 'But you see now why I was suddenly afraid of him. You know, when I came upon him in the lane that day.'

He seemed bereft of speech or movement, so still that she wondered for a moment whether he had taken in what she was saying. He stared across the shallow vale towards the ruined castle on the hill, and then he turned, looking south, to where the road to Brickhill was just definable by a line of trees. When he spoke, it was with such apparent irrelevance that Natasha was taken aback.

'I always wondered why there were two castles here, so close to each other. What's the distance – three miles? Do you know what's just occurred to me? That Reynald de Briec's castle – the original one at Brickhill – was so imbued with evil that nobody could live there. It's my guess that they abandoned it, and built a new stronghold on the hill nearest to it. That one,' he declared, pointing to the crumbling stone keep visible above the red-tiled rooftops of the village.

'But what about the church? That's built on the same site, isn't it?'

'There would have been a church there in de Briec's time, probably made of wood, like the castle . . . Or was it? I don't know. But it's my guess they rebuilt in stone and used the consecration as an antidote to the evil of the place.'

With a sudden shiver she remembered the grotesque carved into the church doorway, that head of a snarling hound which so resembled a modern Rottweiler. 'Well,' she remarked fearfully, 'if your theory about de Briec's right, the consecration doesn't seem to have made much difference, does it?'

He shrugged and said: 'Hard to say. Without a church, maybe things would have been much worse.' He stood for a little while longer, considering all the implications. At last he turned and took her arm. 'Come on, let's go home.'

They had walked some distance before she plucked up courage to mention Toby again, and when she did so, Nick shook his head and sighed. 'I don't know,' he said dispiritedly, 'I suppose it must be true. It certainly fits with what Dr Wills had to say. But what really gets to me is the fact that he obviously haunts that horrible little spot – I mean, I've heard of murderers going back to the scene of the crime, but for God's sake, that is really *sick*.'

It seemed to Natasha that there was nothing she could say to that. They walked on in silence, the beauty of the afternoon destroyed. It was not until they turned into Dagger Lane that he said: 'And you know, I really liked the old boy . . .'

After all the shocks and upheavals of the previous twenty-four hours Natasha expected a restless night, but in fact she slept remarkably well. Waking to an awareness of Nick beside her in the bed, she realised yet again how much she had missed him, and just how comforting his presence could be. Left to herself, she did not think she could have spent another night in this house, but together with Nick she was willing to stay a little longer. Although the ideas he had outlined last night were daunting, she could see the logic behind them; her only wish was that she could share the same kind of faith.

For a while, in the warmth and security of bed, it was easy to convince herself that she was worrying unnecessarily, but she had only to think about getting up and going downstairs for apprehension to clutch at her throat. While in the grip of that obsession with Sarah Stalwell, there had been neither time nor space in her mind to consider the implications; since Nick's encounter with the beast on Christmas Eve, however, she had the feeling that events were catching up, that it was just a matter of time before something else happened. The truly dreadful thing was not knowing what it might be.

Nevertheless, Giles and Fay were expected about lunchtime, and she had a lot to do. In some respects it was a good thing, since the idea of sitting about and waiting for something to happen was unbearable, but she also felt pressured, in need of some time to herself.

Leaving Nick asleep, she gathered her courage in both hands and went down alone. To her surprise and vast relief all seemed as normal. Colette was stretching herself before the stove, and all the ground-floor rooms were just as they had been left the night before. Across the yard, the barn looked as it always did, except that Nick had closed the doors and the cars were standing outside. She was glad about that.

It was another frosty morning, white and cold and still, with the sun rising through the mist. In another hour the mist would no doubt be gone, and it would be bright and sunny. With a sudden desire to be out and walking, Natasha felt invigorated. She would do the chores quickly, prepare the lunch, and then go out for half an hour before Giles and Fay arrived.

Only as she walked into the pantry and saw the pheasants hanging there did she feel another twinge of unease. She had not wanted to accept them, but it seemed stupid not to use the birds, since they would no doubt be delicious. Suspecting that she was being over-fastidious about the whole thing, she went back upstairs to call Nick; when he was up and dressed, he could see to the job of plucking the bloody things.

Just before eleven, with preparations for lunch well under way, Natasha pulled on an extra sweater and a pair of boots. 'I won't be long,' she said to Nick, while reaching for her coat, 'I'll have my shower and get changed when I come back.'

'Okay,' he said lightly, coming outside with her to load the coal scuttle, 'I'll get the fire going now and set the table.' He dropped a kiss on the end of her nose. 'Enjoy your walk.'

'I will!' She laughed and bent to stroke one of the cats, then strode off across the yard and down the lane.

Just a short walk, she thought, to appreciate her own company and this frosty illusion of a white Christmas: the oaks with their crystal trimmings, the holly still flaked with rime, and the sun still veiled by a distant haze as it approached its low, midwinter altitude. It was even colder than she had imagined, much more so than the day before, and in a field below the house a mournful group of cattle were standing in a fog of their own making, as though frozen to the landscape. She pitied them, picturing other cattle in the stuffy warmth of winter byres, and wondered at the wisdom of farming methods which allowed them to be left out in weather like this.

Ahead of her on the stony lane a solitary robin hopped away under the hedge; a moment later there was a sudden clatter of wings as a pair of pheasants wheeled away across a white, stubble field. Thinking of the plucked pair at home, waiting to go into the oven, she felt guilty, and even, for a moment, considered turning vegetarian.

Two or three spots of red in the hedge caught her attention, and turned out to be miraculously surviving rose-hips. Instantly, she thought of Sarah and her rose-hip syrup and, on the heels of that, pictured her riding down the lane in search of Jack. Jack, poor Jack, who had stayed with her almost to the end, who had had his heart and spirit broken in Sarah's cause, and finally crawled away to hang himself from the oak in World's End Wood . . .

World's End Wood, where a younger Toby Bickerstaff had caught his woman with another man. Enjoying him – or being raped by him? Craig Morrison hadn't defined the act, but Nick, last night, had queried it. It seemed less horrible somehow – more a brutal form of justice – if Toby had killed and butchered a rapist. Not right, no, but understandable, particularly in the heat of jealousy and rage. And what had happened to the woman? Not local, gone away, Craig said; which she would have done, Natasha thought, with her man sentenced to life imprisonment. A year or two earlier and he would probably have hung for that murder; as it was, he'd done fifteen years, and when he came out he was on his own. Solitary, reclusive, no doubt changed beyond recognition from the man he had been.

Considering the violence and tragedy this lane had witnessed, Natasha shivered inside her thick coat. She thought of Sarah Stalwell, coming face to face with the beast, and her steps slowed; she thought of Toby in his pathetic caravan, and was certain that in a way he'd been just as much a victim as young Jack. She was frightened, suddenly, being here on her own, but even more ashamed of having been frightened of Toby. His caravan was no more than fifty yards away; she thought it would do her good to knock on his door and ask if he was all right, and whether he needed anything.

Before she could change her mind she strode forward purposefully, determined to overcome cowardice with this one good deed. But as she tried to hold that fear in check, others started to rise around it. She found herself thinking about the beast, the nature of it, and what might have happened to her had she not started writing Sarah's story; and she started to panic about Nick, who had met the thing face to face – what would it do to *him*?

That sense of panic stopped her almost in mid-stride. She was about to turn and run back to the house when her glance was arrested by a Land Rover parked outside the gate into Toby's field. A battered vehicle, oddly familiar, which she suddenly recognised as belonging to Craig Morrison.

What was he doing here?

Her view of the caravan was obscured by the hedge. She hesitated, then advanced slowly; a moment later, she saw Craig dragging the gate shut. He turned and saw her; across the intervening twenty yards his gaze held her transfixed. She started to move forward, but so did he, his arm raised to warn her.

'Oh, God, what is it? What's happened?'

'Toby,' he gasped, holding on to her arm, 'he's dead – the poor old bugger's dead . . .'

'How? What – what happened?'

He shook his head. 'Jesus, I don't know. He's dead – been dead for days by the look of it – '

'He *can't* be! I mean – I saw him – we saw him –' She started to push past Craig, but he held her back. His white face, roughened by a day's growth of beard, was very close to her own.

'Look, he's dead – frozen stiff across the bloody doorstep – there's nowt you can do . . .'

'Was he –' It was hard to get the words out. 'Was he – *attacked*?'

The dark-blue eyes gazed uncomprehendingly for a moment. 'Attacked?' he repeated. 'No . . .'

She sagged for a moment and he held her, his rough cheek pressed to her own. He seemed, Natasha thought afterwards, as glad of that brief reassurance as she was. As she pulled herself together and away from him, he told her to stay there, he would get the Land Rover.

He backed and turned it with difficulty in the narrow lane. As she climbed in, Natasha noticed the bales of hay stacked up behind the seats. 'I was just going down to feed the sheep,' he said by way of explanation, 'but they'll have to wait . . .'

Nick came out of the house as Craig pulled up in the yard. They stood by the gate explaining what had happened, until Natasha suddenly realised that she was shaking with cold, and turned abruptly to go inside.

'. . . I don't know, a heart attack, I expect,' Craig was saying to Nick as they followed her into the house. 'God above, I was only saying yesterday, wasn't I – '

'Yes, well, never mind about that. Look, sit down for goodness' sake. Could you stand a drink? I'm going to have a shot of whisky.'

Nick was shocked, Natasha could see that. They exchanged a look and she knew what he was thinking: after dark on Christmas Eve, something had been prowling along Dagger Lane. Nick had seen it face to face, from the protection of his car, and it had frightened him half to death. What had it done to old Toby?

Cringing under the force of her own imagination, Natasha lit a cigarette and drew on it deeply.

Turning to Craig, Nick said cautiously: 'I know this might sound like morbid curiosity, but before we phone the police, I'd like to have a look myself, just to make sure . . .'

'Look, he's definitely dead, there's no doubt about that,' Craig declared; but when there was no reply, he simply shrugged and drained his glass.

Nick reached for his coat, 'You'd better stay here,' he said gently, squeezing Natasha's shoulder, 'I won't be long.'

'Dead animals don't bother me,' Craig admitted as they drove back down the lane, 'but dead people are different. I've never actually seen anybody dead before – it gave me a bit of a turn.'

'I'm not surprised. You wouldn't have been expecting it.'

Nick, who had been with his mother when she died, and had seen his stepfather's body before it was interred, felt that he knew what dead people should look like. Nevertheless, remembering what had terrified him on Christmas Eve, he was expecting something horrible, a face set in a rigor of fear, an arm raised to ward off attack. Toby's death was too much of a coincidence. Nick was convinced that what had frightened him, had also, literally, terrified the life out of old Toby.

As he opened the gate he saw the body at once, partially on its side, splayed legs hanging down across the step, tatty old trousers thick with frost. One arm was wedged up by the narrowness of the entrance, the other clutched at the chest. Careful not to touch anything, Nick edged closer to see the old man's face. His head was thrown back, which made that difficult, but his beard, like his jacket, was encrusted with rime. That was the worst aspect, since it verified his deadness, negated any possibility that he might still be alive. Otherwise, from what Nick could see, there was no sign of physical attack, and he thought old Toby's face was much the same as other dead faces: devoid of expression, waxen in its stillness, the eyes sunk back.

The slyness of his darting glance was not even a memory.

As soon as they returned to the house Nick dialled the number of their nearest police station. After a minute or two of conversation, he broke the connection and turned to Craig and Natasha. 'They'll be here soon.'

They were. Two uniformed men arrived within fifteen minutes, parking their car alongside the barn.

'All right if we leave the car here, sir? Don't fancy testing it any further down the lane.'

The necessary details took some minutes. As Nick and Craig

Morrison set off yet again to go down the lane, this time in company with the police officers, another car pulled into the yard. Giles and Fay, bemused and a little alarmed by the presence of the police.

Natasha ushered them into the house and had barely begun to explain when a detective arrived, followed by the police surgeon and an ambulance, all seeking directions to the caravan. Then Nick came back with Craig, to say that when the van was searched the first thing the police produced was Toby's shotgun.

'"Did you know Mr Bickerstaff owned this?" they asked me. Of course, I said yes, so the next question was: "Do you know if he had a licence?", to which I said I hadn't a clue. Of course, that produced mutterings and grumblings about it not being in a safe place, *etcetera, etcetera* . . .'

'Well, that's the bloody police for you,' Craig Morrison chipped in, 'all heart, they are. Didn't seem to give a shit about the poor old bugger lying dead across the doorstep!'

At that, he received such a look from Nick that he decided it was time to go. And then, when he had gone, Fay was bristling with curiosity, eager to have Natasha alone so that she could ask whether *he* was the one who had propositioned her a few short weeks ago.

They went into the kitchen, and Natasha explained in brief why Craig Morrison was no longer on the list of local attractions. But she was interrupted by the telephone. Mrs Bickerstaff this time, apologising for the trouble, but wanting to know all the minor details that the police – who had just paid her a visit – had not seen fit to divulge.

Natasha was on the phone for half an hour. Afterwards Nick said: 'Don't tell me – she's worrying about who's going to pay for the funeral?'

'Well, yes, funnily enough – '

'I hope you told her that nobody gets left above ground?'

But Natasha was not amused. 'Oh, damn it all, Nick, they are his nearest relatives, and they don't have that kind of money!'

'Rubbish. Anyway, I wouldn't mind betting that when they go through that caravan of his, they find more than enough money to bury him with. He was drawing a state pension every week, and what the hell did he spend it on? No rent, no rates, very little on fuel, and at least half his food was foraged from the woods. He can't have been short of a bob or two – just didn't like spending it, that's all.'

'He spent plenty in the pub!'

Although the dinner seemed to have come a very poor second to the drama of the day, Natasha was determined that what she had prepared would be cooked and eaten. A little later, when the pheasants were finally in the oven and they were fortifying themselves with nuts and crisps and smoked salmon, Nick said: 'There'll be a post mortem, of course, and possibly an inquest, but no doubt the verdict will be death from natural causes. There certainly wasn't anything I could see to contradict that.'

'Well, what else could there be?'

With a rueful smile, Nick said: 'Ah, but you see, Giles, you haven't heard the full story yet . . .'

The course of that tale continued throughout the afternoon. It was almost dusk when they sat down to eat, and, remembering Toby with the pheasants, they drank a somewhat maudlin toast to the old man's memory, forgiving him a past which for them was but hearsay, and wishing him peace in the next world. If two of the four had reservations about that, they allowed the cushion of alcohol to smother such doubts, and did not give voice to them.

Discussing the events of recent weeks with Giles and Fay had the effect of reducing fear and distancing the realities. It became a rather exciting Christmas ghost story, with the added piquancy of being true. Until, that is, questions started to arise about what Nick and Natasha intended to do.

'Well, for a start,' Nick said, leaning back in his chair and blowing rings with the smoke from a Christmas cigar, 'I'm going to get hold of Joe Rathmell tomorrow, and see if I can't persuade him to help us in a little archaeological dig . . .'

Thirty Seven

'JESUS, NICK, you're not serious? You mean you're going to dig up the barn to look for a body?'

'Bones, Giles, that's all they'll be by now – that's if they're there at all.'

'But you obviously believe they are?'

'I think they probably are,' Nick corrected. 'The point is, we'll never know unless we look. If they're not, well fair enough, it's been no more than an inexplicable coincidence. After all, coincidences happen all the time . . .' He shrugged and tried to make it seem as though the matter was of small importance, but Giles was not to be put off.

'And if you find the bones – what then?'

'Then I think we must give the poor woman a Christian burial, don't you? Get the rector to say prayers for her soul or something. It's the least we can do.'

Fay shivered and reached out to grasp Natasha's hand. To Nick, she said: 'Are you sure you know what you're doing? I don't like the sound of this at all. And what about Natasha? It seems to me as though she's been through enough.'

'Well, what are the alternatives?'

'Get the police in,' she said vehemently, 'let them do the dirty work. Sell up and leave.'

'Oh, yes, the police,' Nick said slowly, pouring himself another drink. 'I can just hear their reaction, can't you? *You mean to say, sir, that you want us to dig up your barn floor because you* think *there may be bones buried under it? And what is it that leads you to this conclusion, sir?*' He laughed at himself, while Fay flushed with annoyance. 'They're not going to be interested in a murder that was committed more than 250 years ago!'

'If you find what you're looking for,' she said sharply, 'you'll still have to report it.'

'Yes, I know.'

'And they're still going to ask you some very awkward questions.' After a short pause, she said: 'Why don't you just sell the house and move back into town?'

Staring at his glass, Nick slowly shook his head. 'We can't do that, Fay. If it were a simple, straightforward haunting, I might be tempted to agree with you. But it's not simple, is it? There's something very strange about all this, and I feel that we're getting close to the nub of it. I don't want to abandon it now.'

'Why? Because you think you're the only person who can solve it?' After a short pause she said: 'Pride, Nick. Be careful it doesn't come before a nasty fall.'

Frowning at her, wondering why it was that Fay should be singling him out for attack, Nick said: 'You're forgetting Natasha's part in all this. Without her story, Sarah Stalwell would just be a name in the Reverend Clive's journal!'

Cutting into the tense silence, Giles laughed and said: 'And who knows where a writer's inspiration comes from? Kipling swore by his *daemon* – when it was working well, apparently, he wrote like someone possessed!'

'Is that true?' Fay asked.

'But of course, didn't you know that?' Glad of the change of subject, Giles launched into a mini-lecture on Kipling and the source of his inspiration, ending up with the assertion that Kipling attributed his *Jungle Book* stories, and much other material, to that familiar spirit.

Nick said: 'So it's not unusual then? The fact that Natasha's written what amounts to the biography of a dead woman – one she had no idea existed – that's not unusual?'

'Ah, well, I didn't say *that*,' Giles stressed. 'She's written a story, hasn't she, about a woman who lived in the eighteenth century? So far, that's all it is – apart from the coincidence of the names which, admittedly, is odd. But the inspiration for the story, as she says herself, could have come from several different sources – the woman she saw in the barn, the mysterious hound that everyone was talking about, even the house itself – '

'Except,' Natasha interrupted, 'I didn't know what it was all about. I didn't know *what* I was writing – I just had to keep going . . .'

'Well, that *may* be the equivalent of Kipling's *daemon*, we just don't know.'

'Just as we won't know how true it is,' Nick said ironically, 'until we dig up the barn floor and find those bones!'

Next morning, over breakfast, they were all a little thick-headed, and tempted to believe that Nick's enthusiasm for such a grisly project was no more than alcohol-inspired bravado. When he started making notes against the names of people he planned to telephone, however, it quickly became clear that he was serious. Giles tried, half-heartedly, to dissuade him, while Fay took Natasha to one side and pressed her to come and stay for a few days.

'Look, if Nick's determined to go ahead with this *dig* of his, I really think you'd be better out of it. I've finished decorating the spare bedroom, and it's yours for as long as you need it.'

Thanking her for the offer, Natasha said she would not forget. 'But in the meantime,' she added gently, 'I think I'd better stay here . . .'

When they had gone, Nick disappeared in the direction of his study, saying that for the moment he was just putting out a few feelers. He rang Joe Rathmell, one of his opposite numbers in the Department of Archaeology, and, without being too specific, sounded him out on the possibility of help and advice with an urgent project. Initially, Joe was pessimistic, saying he was overworked as it was, but Nick refused to fall at the first fence. 'Joe, I need help. I know what we're looking for, and I don't want to go at this half-cocked, and make a mess of it. If you can't give me the time, do you have a couple of students, third-years who might have a decent idea of what they're about?'

There was a lengthy silence. Eventually, his colleague asked again, with weary patience, exactly what the project involved. Underlying the weariness, Nick sensed a spark of interest; with crossed fingers, he decided to go for broke. 'I have grounds,' he said bluntly, 'for believing there's an eighteenth-century body buried under the floor of my barn.'

Afterwards, he realised how lucky he was that Joe Rathmell liked and respected him; without that, Nick felt that he might easily have been dismissed as just another historian who was prepared to go to any lengths to prove a point. As it happened, it had been necessary to admit to some weird occurrences, and to elaborate considerably upon the journal of the Reverend Clive. Natasha's story, Nick suspected, would not have carried a lot of weight with Joe Rathmell, whereas he was impressed by an honest desire to see those bones interred in a proper place. The fact that the dig would be under cover was an additional point in its favour. At last, he said that he might be able to organise a couple of students, and that he would ring back later. Taking that as an affirmative, Nick looked at the other names attached to his notes. Dr Wills, however, reminded him of Sally Armitage, and he experienced a sharp pang of guilt that he could have forgotten her.

He dialled the number and it rang for a while. He was wondering whether she was back from her holiday when she answered, a little breathlessly, having just come in.

'Yes, I got back last night,' she said, but he thought she sounded none too pleased, especially when she reminded him that it was over ten days since he had phoned her last, and she had been wondering how things were in Denton.

Apologising, Nick tried to explain the difficulties involved. The boys had been to stay, and he had taken them to London; and then, when he got back, Natasha had seemed so ill. 'I couldn't understand it – I suddenly noticed how much weight she'd lost, and then –' He broke off, realising too late that Sally could hardly be expected to share his concern for his wife. 'Anyway, that's not important, except that I didn't find out *why* until Christmas Eve –

and I didn't discover that until after –' But that thing in the lane was hard to describe, it made him feel cold just to think of it. '... scared the hell out of me, I can tell you ... came right up to the car – stared at me through the bloody window, can you believe it? No,' he answered a moment later, 'it didn't seem solid at all – more like a shifting mass of black mist ...'

He went on to tell her of Toby's death, and his conviction that the old man had also come face to face with the beast, and that the shock of it had killed him. 'So, we're both feeling a bit bloody jumpy, as you can imagine, especially since –' But then he realised that he hadn't told her about the story Natasha had written, and when he mentioned the name Sarah Stalwell, Sally was aghast.

'You're sure she hadn't been reading your notes?'

'Positive. Anyway, there must be nearly two hundred pages of it – and she wrote it in a month. That's incredible in itself, especially when you think she's just finished *Black Earth*, and that's taken her two and a half *years*.'

'And what's it like? This story, I mean.'

'Excellent,' he said without hesitation. 'Details are spot-on. Not in her usual style, either. And I'll tell you something else – I might not be a very good judge of fiction, but I found it bloody compulsive reading. I sat up all night with it.'

Sally was impressed. But when he told her his plans for the barn, she sounded as apprehensive as Fay. 'But it's the only way to prove anything,' he told her. 'And I honestly believe it's the right thing to do.'

'I dare say it is, Nick, but I still think you should be careful ...'

'I intend to be, don't worry. It's just that I feel ...' He hesitated for a moment, wondering whether he could admit to Sally what he would never dream of admitting to Natasha: that he was seriously worried by the coincidence of those events of Christmas Eve; that every night there was that feeling of being under siege, and a sense of time running out.

In the end he kept his fears to himself, and said: 'I don't know, it's just that time seems to be important here – I don't think we should waste it.'

But she seemed to understand anyway, and offered a hesitant kind of sympathy which embarrassed him. With an assurance he did not feel, he said that everything would be all right, and he would keep her posted; he wanted to see her in order to talk things over, and was planning to come up to Ghylldale just as soon as the present crisis was over.

At that, however, Sally became evasive. A visit wasn't really necessary, she said, and probably not wise either, if he was trying to patch things up with Natasha. She would like to know the progress of the story, and its outcome, but a phone call would do, there was no need for him to come in person. It was said pleasantly enough, but he had the feeling she was upset, and that bothered him too. But how could he explain his feelings on the phone? Impossible. Regretfully, he shook his head and replaced the receiver. Pondering for a minute or two, Nick decided that things could not be left on a phone call. Just as soon as he could he must go and see her, and say goodbye with some sort of grace.

He returned to the matter in hand, and phoned his old friend Haydn Parker in the hope that he could give him some advice. But an answering machine informed him that Haydn and Isabel Parker were not available just now. Feeling frustrated, he left a message, and turned to the last name on his list, Dr Wills. From her he was less in need of advice than the simple confirmation that he was not completely off his head.

To his surprise, she answered almost immediately. He had the strangest feeling that she had been expecting his call, a feeling strengthened by the fact that she exhibited no real surprise at what he had to tell her. They talked for some time, her comments confirming many of his own conclusions. They agreed that something had to be done about Reynard, and preferably very soon; where they differed, however, was with regard to method. She advised a strong, experienced medium, one she could recommend, and spent some minutes trying to persuade him to her way of thinking. But her experience and belief in spiritualism were not Nick's. Before he committed himself in that direction, he wanted to talk to Haydn Parker, and if Haydn was unable to help, then he would go to his sons' school and find a Catholic priest.

Later that day, Joe Rathmell called back to say that he had arranged for two keen third-year students to assist Nick in his little project. But they were not free until the following Thursday, almost a week away. Although Nick was disappointed that it could not be sooner, he realised that there was still much else to organise, and thanked Joe sincerely for the favour.

It was Sunday before he heard from Haydn Parker. They exchanged pleasantries for a minute or two, but as soon as he understood the nature of Nick's problem, Haydn cut the conversation short, saying that he would prefer to discuss details in person.

It was agreed that he would come to the house the following morning, and, on discovering that, Natasha immediately felt awkward. Although they had met several times before, in the past she had resisted Haydn's friendly overtures, largely out of a stubborn mistrust of his calling. Nick had always said that she was being silly, since Haydn was not the hearty, evangelical type, nor the petty despot Natasha dreaded. Nevertheless, she worried now that he would think her attitude personal rather than general; and then she was concerned that he might not take their problem seriously.

In the event, her worries appeared to be unfounded. He arrived wearing jeans and an elderly Barbour jacket, his sandy hair ruffled by the wind, and looking much younger than his thirty-five years. In fact he looked, she thought, more like a recent graduate than a priest, and that immediately set part of her fears at rest. If he had arrived in clerical garb, she felt she would not have been able to talk to him at all.

Taking a seat at their kitchen table, he listened calmly and attentively to their jointly told and often disjointed tale. That too was impressive. Almost in spite of herself, Natasha began to warm towards him.

'Well,' he remarked at last, when it seemed they had given him all the facts and not a few suppositions, 'I can't say I've come up against a problem quite like this before.' Adding cream to his coffee, he said mildly: 'My experience in the past has been mainly to do with students playing dangerous games – ouija boards, things like that. Either they frighten themselves silly by the power of their own imaginations, or – in just a few cases – they have actually managed to call in something rather unpleasant.'

His unruffled, matter-of-fact tone was, Natasha thought, very reassuring. She felt so much calmer for having set the problem before him, and suddenly realised what a gift he must be to a confused and frightened student. There was something so comforting and approachable about him, she wondered that she'd never noticed it before.

With a sigh of regret for her own prejudices, she turned her attention back to the matter in hand. Haydn Parker was talking about hauntings, about the presence of unquiet spirits in people's homes, and the fact that it was largely fear that made them call in the Church to persuade these spirits to leave. He was so rational about it, as though these were everyday matters with straightforward solutions, that he managed to make what had been happening at Holly Tree Cottage sound almost normal.

'You mean ghosts actually exist?' Natasha asked wonderingly. 'They're not the product of an overworked imagination?'

'No, decidedly not. They do exist.'

She regarded him with some amazement, and not a small amount of relief. 'So what do you do about it?'

'Well,' he said carefully, 'we don't interfere unless specifically asked to do so. Generally, that's because the people concerned find the presence frightening.'

Sensing in him a reluctance to go into detail, Natasha pressed him, nevertheless. 'And how do you go about persuading a presence to leave?'

He scratched his ear and smiled at her. 'Well, in most cases,' he said gently, 'all they need is permission to go. Reassurance, absolution, and – well, just permission to leave. And, in the case of your Sarah Stalwell – if she was indeed murdered and buried here, as it would seem that she was – then I could say that she's in need of precisely that.'

She would have gone on, but Nick said: 'And in the case of Reynald de Briec?'

'Ah, yes.' With a frown, Haydn Parker studied his empty cup, and then carefully set it back upon the saucer. Watching him, Natasha sensed that his attitude had sharpened considerably. That impression was confirmed when he looked up and said: 'I'd like to ask you both a question, and I trust you won't take offence. But it must be asked, and, if I'm to help you, then it must be answered honestly.

'Have either of you – or indeed, anyone that you know – been dabbling in the occult?'

Aghast, Natasha shook her head, while Nick issued a firm denial.

'You haven't heard of any local witchcraft, or desecration of graves – anything like that?'

'Witchcraft?' she repeated incredulously. 'In this day and age?'

'Oh, yes,' came the terse reply, 'you'd be surprised to know how much of it goes on. In fact, in the last few years, since the abolition of the laws on witchcraft, the services of the Church have never been so much in demand!'

It was hardly credible, yet Haydn Parker was so far from jesting that he had to be believed. In an unpleasant state of astonishment, Natasha heard Nick ask what they should do next.

'Tackle one thing at a time. Look for the bones, get that problem sorted first. In the meantime I'll consult with a colleague of mine regarding the other matter. There may be some difficulty, since the haunting isn't confined to a specific place – hard to tell a spirit to leave when it's not actually there!'

'Yes, quite,' Nick murmured. 'So there's nothing else we can do?'

'Pray, Nick. And be assured that I'll do everything possible to help you. As a matter of courtesy, of course, I must speak to your local priest – I presume you haven't spoken to him yourself?'

'No, we haven't. I must confess we don't know him very well.' Nick smiled and shrugged. 'He seems all right, it's just that – '

The chaplain laughed. 'I know, I know – you don't have to explain!'

He was suddenly, Natasha thought, warm and good-humoured again. Gathering up her manuscript and copies of

Nick's research notes, he said he would read and return them as soon as possible, perhaps on Thursday, when he came to help with the dig.

'He's not really going to help with the dig, is he?' she asked after Haydn had gone. 'Surely he must have better things to do?'

'He's a man of many parts,' Nick said enigmatically, then, with a laugh, added; 'You should see him on the rugby field – he's a brilliant full-back.'

'Full-back? Which one's that?'

'The last line of defence . . .'

Thirty Eight

THE FOLLOWING day, which was New Year's Eve, seemed to be one for telephone calls. Dr Wills rang first, for an update on the situation; then, when Nick had finished talking to her, the twins called to wish him and Natasha a happy New Year. They were going to Manchester for a few days with their mother, to visit Grandma and Grandpa, and did not feel they could telephone from there.

That accurate judgement made him smile, but he was touched by their thoughtfulness. Wishing them both all the very best, he gave a jocular reminder about their New Year resolutions, and hoped they could get together for an afternoon at a rugby match before term started. The suggestion went down well, and, saying goodbye to them both, Nick returned to work on his desk.

Within half an hour the telephone rang again: Oliver Duffield this time, asking to speak to Natasha. Nick shouted down to her, and she said that she would take it in the kitchen.

A few minutes later a slight *ting* told him the call was over; he wondered what it had been about. With the excuse of stretching his legs, Nick went down to ask.

'Oh, nothing much. He just wanted to know when I could make it to London – I cancelled the last date, if you remember. Anyway, I told him it was a bit awkward at the moment – I said I'd call him back next week.'

'Why does he want to see you?'

'Oh, you know – to discuss their plans for *The English*

Lesson, introduce me to one or two new people at Oasis Books. I haven't been down for ages, as you know . . .'

'No, you haven't,' he said, feeling a slight concern for that relationship with her publishers. 'You should go. It's a compliment to be asked – '

'I'm not going anywhere,' Natasha said firmly, 'until this situation is resolved. OK?'

'Yes, right, OK,' Nick murmured, backing off and heading for the stairs. He was halfway up when he heard the phone ringing again.

'It's all right,' she shouted after him, 'it's for me . . .'

With relief, he made another attempt to settle down to work, but it seemed he was destined not to make progress. As soon as the call was over, Natasha came up to relay the message.

'It was Mrs Bickerstaff. She says they've done the post-mortem, and she's been to collect the death certificate. Myocardial something-or-other – anyway, it means old Toby died of a massive heart attack.'

'Bet it doesn't say what caused it,' Nick muttered, turning to face her. 'Are they having an inquest?'

'No, the body's been released now, and she's trying to arrange the funeral for Friday. Church service,' Natasha added with an ironic twist of the lips, 'and then the crematorium – '

'Well, my God, if that doesn't beat all!'

'Yes, that's what I thought. It's the old, old, story, isn't it? Mustn't speak ill of the dead, and now he *is* dead, they can all forgive him.'

'I don't know,' he said wearily, 'they're such bloody hypocrites. If they'd paid as much attention when he was alive, I wouldn't mind so much . . .'

With a sigh, he turned back to his work.

They went to Giles's that evening, but although the party was as good as any of his previous New Year gatherings, neither of them felt able to enter into the spirit of the thing. It was hard to kiss the old year goodbye, and look forward to the new when so much was still hanging over them.

That sense of something threatening was inadvertently accentuated by Haydn Parker, who telephoned the following afternoon. He had read the research notes and Natasha's manuscript, and felt it would be helpful if he could talk to them both again, but separately this time and in more detail.

He arrived a little after four, and while Natasha made herself scarce, Nick took him into the sitting-room. It was still decorated for Christmas and a roaring fire was burning in the grate, but, as he glanced around, the first thing Haydn mentioned was the murder of Sarah Stalwell. Had they experienced anything unusual in here? Or indeed in the rest of the house?

Nick felt gratified that Haydn was taking things seriously; there seemed no doubt in his mind regarding the authenticity of Natasha's story, and that made it easier for Nick to answer him. He shook his head and said no, he didn't think anything untoward had happened in the house, other than Natasha's strange dream just before she started writing. Haydn made a note of that, and then reiterated the problem of pinning down something that was apparently not confined to a particular time and place. Certain aspects, he said, needed clarifying, not least of which being the circumstances of the beast's first sighting. Nick explained that old Toby had been the first person to encounter it, at dusk on 31 October, then Natasha had seen it later that night, as they returned home from the Hallowe'en party.

'Was that the college party?'

'Yes, it was.'

He thought Haydn's expression tightened, but all he said was: 'I want you to tell me what happened that evening. Anything that may have seemed even slightly unusual or disturbing.' At Nick's hesitation, he went on: 'Regard it as a confession, if you like. I'm not here to judge, only to help . . .'

Embarrassment caused further hesitation, but eventually Nick started talking and the more he said the easier it became. He described the atmosphere in the hall that night, the fact that he had found himself an extraordinary focus of attention, particularly for the female students. Mentioning the incident with Jane Bardy, he was embarrassed enough to treat it lightly, attributing the cause to drink.

'Are you sure it was the alcohol that made you feel like that?'

'Well, that and the atmosphere, I suppose . . . and the encouragement, of course,' he added wryly. 'Although –' He broke off, thinking hard about that evening. 'I remember an odd sensation before we set off. When I was dressing, in fact. I looked in the mirror and didn't recognise myself. To be honest, it was a bit unnerving for a moment. Not only did I *look* different, I felt different too – as though the real me had taken leave of absence, and this stranger was free to do anything at all . . .'

Haydn frowned. 'I see. What about afterwards – when did that feeling leave you?'

'Hard to say. Natasha and I had a row when we got home, and the next day I had a king-size hangover. To say I was full of remorse,' he added with an ironic smile, 'would be an understatement.'

'And what about the girl?'

At that, Nick's smile disappeared. 'Ah, yes, the girl. Unfortunately she pursued me for quite a while. I felt bad about it, but I managed to discourage her.'

'You didn't have a sexual relationship with her?'

'Good lord, no, absolutely not.'

Shifting position, making a few notes, Haydn then began to ask about his relationship with Natasha, whether it had remained normal during that time, or had suffered in any way. Those questions were difficult for Nick to answer, particularly since Haydn had always been more of a friend than a spiritual adviser. He hated having to admit that his wife had rejected him, and was able to do so only because that side of their relationship was now under repair. What was even worse was admitting to that brief reunion with Sally, which made him feel that he had not only let Natasha down, but himself too.

Although Haydn offered neither sympathy nor recrimination, he did ask whether all aspects of that breakdown had been discussed, and, when Nick shook his head, advised him quite strongly to do so.

'Not just for the sake of your marriage – which is of prime importance in the long term – but in order to overcome this present trouble. It seems to me you've been divided, not just by external forces, but by some inherent weakness in your relationship.

'I don't know the cause,' he went on, 'but it strikes me as a kind of *separateness*, a withholding of some kind, which is preventing you both from making the right kind of commitment. Do you see that?'

'Well,' Nick sighed, 'that's certainly true of recent times, although . . .' He shook his head, remembering the closeness they had enjoyed and wondering at that present, lingering awkwardness. It was, he thought, like trying to communicate through a plate-glass screen.

'There is something, isn't there?' Haydn pressed. 'A kind of self-containment, perhaps, which might be perceived on your part as male pride . . .'

'Oh, surely not,' Nick said quickly. As he looked up, however, he caught Haydn's small, quizzical smile, and suddenly realised that he could not afford to be either defensive or dishonest. 'Well, perhaps,' he conceded.

'Yes, perhaps. And the trouble with pride is that we're all tempted to see it as a form of strength, even – as men – as an admirable toughness. But it's not, you know, it's really a great weakness – it obscures our view of ourselves and those around us. It gets in the way, Nick – it sets up barriers for our real selves to hide behind – it creates the very opposite of unity.'

Nick pondered on that. 'Are you saying,' he ventured at last, 'that with regard to Natasha, I'm lacking in honesty and perception?'

Haydn smiled. 'Not at all. I'm asking you whether your perception of your role in this relationship is correct.' While Nick digested that, Haydn suddenly became sharper. 'You made a lot of excuses for yourself when you talked about Sally. In effect, you were blaming Natasha for refusing to sleep with you. But how many times did you try to talk about that problem? Once or twice? It seems to me that you gave up without really trying, which isn't like you.' He paused for a moment and then said speculatively: 'Could it have been because it was easier in this case to take refuge behind your injured pride, rather than face up to some uncomfortable answers?'

Nettled, Nick started to reply, but Haydn stopped him. 'No, *I* don't need to know the answers – *you* do. Ask yourself this, Nick – what is it about your relationship with Natasha that really worries you? When you find the answer – and I know you will – lay that anxiety before God, and pray that the burden may be lifted.

'It might also help,' he added more gently, 'to confess those fears to Natasha. Women don't need us to be strong and invincible all the time – in fact I'm sure they find us easier to love when they know our weaknesses . . .'

Facing Haydn Parker for the second time, Natasha was distinctly nervous. That afternoon, instead of sporting jeans and a well-worn sweater, he was rather more conventionally dressed for an Anglican clergyman, in a black shirt and stiff white collar under a plain dark suit. Although he apologised for the formality, and explained that he had come straight from a clerical meeting at the Minster, his first serious question made Natasha think that the clothes were deliberate.

'I wish you'd tell me why,' he said gravely, 'you feel such antipathy towards priests.'

She felt herself staring, her eyes growing wider as she searched for an inoffensive answer to such an astonishingly direct question. It was as though he had said: 'I wish you'd tell me why you dislike me . . .' , and she felt guilty and dismayed that her feelings were so obvious.

'It's not you personally,' she said at last, but although she stopped and started, and tried to be evasive, Haydn would not let her off the hook. He kept on tugging until she began to tell the truth. In that, he reminded her of a particularly forthright journalist, one who would not let go and who never flinched before an insult. But, having been a journalist herself for a while, she found the image familiar and understandable; she clung to it in preference to the more disturbing one before her.

After that, she was able to speak with some degree of honesty about her early life, and to explain about the priest who had managed to instil such feelings of guilt and fear and loathing. Even so, Natasha felt herself switch into what she termed her story-telling mode, felt the subtle detachment that accompanied the change and that enabled her to tell the truth as she saw it without becoming too emotionally involved. It was rather like talking about somebody else.

'Of course, what you must understand is that Father O'Gorman was an Irish priest of the old school, a man used to remote country parishes where he could rule with a rod of iron – where people were less sophisticated, not used to challenging authority. And, as I remember, the Catholic families in our part of East Anglia were few and far between, so it would have been difficult for them to band against him – even if they'd thought of it, which they probably didn't.

'He was a tyrant,' she went on, 'as simple as that. But he had conviction on his side, and the weight of the Church behind him – and he obviously believed he had a mission to draw that lapsed and scattered flock together. He set about it as soon as he arrived.' She paused to light a cigarette, aware of the differences between then and now, the awe-struck ten-year-old gazing up at the imposing figure in black, wondering why her mother addressed him as *Father* and looked so nervous as she asked him to sit down; and why her own father was so angry behind that glittering smile.

'I don't know where he got the information from, but somehow he discovered that my mother Celia was one of the strayed sheep, and that her daughters had never been baptised. So he came to see us.'

'What about your father? Was he a Catholic too?'

'Good grief no! He was an atheist. He was also a doctor, and a very clever and articulate man. When he was young,' she said, trying to recall the youthful photographs full of life and laughter, and not the shrunken figure he had been latterly, 'my father was a Pathfinder pilot – he led the bombing squadrons to their targets over Germany. He joined up in 1943, when he was eighteen – rather miraculously, he survived.' Not to tell the tale, she thought painfully, but to die a slow, self-inflicted death from alcohol more than thirty years later. Pushing that memory aside, she added: 'He studied medicine after the war – I often think it must have been in reaction to all that death and destruction . . .'

She heard a sigh and looked up, but Haydn Parker simply shook his head and glanced away. After a moment, he said: 'So he wasn't a young man when he married?'

'No, he was in his late thirties when he met my mother – she was fifteen years younger.'

'So,' Haydn commented, 'a little bit like yourself and Nick – a clever and articulate older man, and a much younger woman . . .'

Having warmed to that fleeting impression of sympathy, she now bridled at what he seemed to be implying. 'I do have a degree,' she reminded him, 'and I am able to string a few multi-syllable words together.'

'And was your mother clever too?'

'Well, she didn't have the benefit of a first-class education, if that's what you mean, but she was a state-registered nurse, and she certainly wasn't lacking in intelligence!'

'But what was she like as a person? Describe her for me.'

Natasha sighed and stubbed out her cigarette, wondering what all this had to do with their current problem. Remembering Father O'Gorman, however, she said: 'Impressionable. She was a good mother, and I know she always meant well. But she was easily impressed by men. Not sexually, I don't mean that, but in an intellectual way. She had such a low opinion of her own ability to think for herself that she allowed the men in her life to make decisions for her. She wanted somebody to lean on, somebody to tell her what to do, what to think – unfortunately, my sister's much the same.'

'And you don't approve of that?'

'What, in this day and age? You must be joking!'

Haydn smiled and spread his hands. 'Just clarifying a point. But tell me,' he added, 'about your mother's religion. She was a Catholic, but lapsed, I understand. Why was that?'

'Well, I imagine my father managed to convince her that it was nonsense. That's certainly what he believed, and he was not a man to keep those opinions to himself, not even when the priest came to see us. In fact I seem to recall he showed Father O'Gorman the door, and told him not to come back.'

'But he came anyway, in spite of that?'

'Oh, yes. Except he made sure to come when my father was out on his rounds, and usually when my sister and I were at school. But we soon started to realise what was going on, because my mother was always in such a state when he'd been. Then there would be arguments and rows – and my father, who had always been a heavy drinker, became much worse.'

Although she knew that her mother must have been under a terrible strain at that time, especially during Alex Crayke's last illness, Natasha still found it hard to forgive her mother's gullibility. It was that gullibility which had allowed the priest a foothold, and that foothold had led to the stresses and strains which brought about her father's death.

Natasha suddenly realised that she was trembling, and that her detachment was breaking down. She lit another cigarette and tried to distance herself again, but it was difficult. 'He was a hateful man,' she said, referring to the priest. 'He wouldn't leave us alone, even when my father was ill and dying. In fact I blame him for my father's death. He drove a wedge into our lives and forced us apart – he wasn't a man of God, he was evil.'

She heard herself say those words, and the truth of them seemed to echo in her ears. Evil masquerading as good, fear where there should have been trust, force trampling sensitivity underfoot, and a total abuse of power.

'Then, when my father died, he just seemed to leap in and take over – he turned everything upside down.' Remembering, she felt the tears pouring down her face, but was powerless to control them. 'I couldn't believe it – it was as though my father didn't matter any more – he was dead and buried and we were supposed to forget all the things he stood for. Helen was only young then – she just went along with it – but I was twelve, nearly thirteen, and I wanted to remember him as he was, full of humour and ideas and –' She broke off to dry her eyes, sniffing a little as she recalled her father's slightly bent, wiry figure, hunched over the wheel of his car as he took her with him on his rounds during the holidays. He rarely mentioned his youth, but sometimes, passing one of the old, deserted airfields, or a churchyard where airmen were buried, he would tell her of his friends . . .

'He was sad sometimes, and bitter about the war. And he drank too much, I know that, but he was my father and I loved him. I hated my mother for years, because she didn't seem to want to understand how I felt. She had us saying masses for his soul, and down on our knees every night, praying for his sins to be forgiven.' Shaking her head at that, Natasha took a deep breath and continued: 'I screamed at her. I had tantrums. I told her I didn't want to pray for his soul, I just wanted him back. I said I wished she was dead, and then we wouldn't have to go through all this religious sham.

'I couldn't win, though, could I? No, I was wicked to speak to her like that, *wicked* to think that way, God would punish me, etcetera, etcetera. And then Father O'Gorman got his teeth into me. He used every trick in the book to break my will. He even managed to imply that my prayers would be more valuable than anybody else's because I was such an unbeliever, and that my conversion would be so much more precious, because I was such a terrible sinner.

'Do you know, I started to believe him? I couldn't believe my father was wicked, because to me he had seemed such a *good* man – but I began to feel that I was guilty of all the sins in creation, and that if I didn't give in, I really would burn in hell for all eternity . . .'

She glanced up appealingly, seeking Haydn Parker's denials, but he had his head bent and his eyes were shaded by his hand. He seemed to be staring into the fire, unaware of her distress.

Feeling let down by that apparent detachment, wondering whether he even believed her, she turned away to find another tissue. But a moment later, as she wiped her eyes and nose, she heard him say gently: 'My dear Natasha, I'm so terribly sorry . . .'

His sympathy, sincere but understated, prompted such a surge of gratitude and relief that the tears came flooding back. Fighting hard to control them, she bent to mend the fire. As she placed a log carefully to catch the blaze, he said: 'And do you still blame your mother for all that?'

It was a difficult question to answer. She sat back on her heels, thinking about the book, and Helen, and the emotional upheavals of the last few months. Slowly, shaking her head, she said: 'I don't know.' Only a few weeks ago she had been convinced that what she had written had settled the years of pain and anger; that through the novel she had managed to come to terms with what she saw as her mother's inadequacies. But talking to Haydn Parker seemed to have dredged everything to the surface again, and now she was just as confused as ever. With difficulty, she said: 'I don't want to blame her, but it's hard not to. I mean, I can see that she was a victim too – of her own upbringing, of a powerful and persuasive man. And it's not her actions that I find hard to understand or to forgive, but the results of those actions – the pain and distress she caused, not just to me, but to my father. You see, before that, they never argued – well, not that I remember – and yet they argued all the time about this priest. It was almost as though he saw this new desire of hers as some kind of betrayal – as though she was being unfaithful to him . . .'

The words slipped out easily enough, but their aftertaste was like bile, burning her throat and chest and innards as though they'd been etched in acid.

'And was she?' Haydn Parker asked.

His cool, matter-of-fact tone shocked her. 'No, no, of course she wasn't!'

'Are you sure?'

'Of course I'm sure – it would have been unthinkable!'

'Why?'

'Well, he – he was a priest, and celibate, and – and – and he was *old*, for heaven's sake!'

'Maybe not so old as he seemed to you,' Haydn pointed out reasonably. 'And he was also a man – don't forget that.'

As she stared at him, frozen with shock, he said quietly: 'Is it really so unthinkable, Natasha? Sadly, it's not only priests in fiction and the tabloid press who have affairs with married women – real ones fall prey to that temptation too. Sometimes, they're people we know. It's terribly wrong, a great sin, an abuse of the love and power invested in us by God – but it's not uncommon, I'm sorry to say, and it has been going on for centuries.

'And the ones who fall into that temptation,' he went on,

'aren't all young, good-looking blokes with attractive personalities. A lot of them are apparently tough old buggers knocking on for retiring age . . .'

She gave an involuntary gasp and turned away.

'Don't think I'm siding with him – I'm not. Nor am I making light of it,' Haydn said firmly. 'What I'm trying to do is help you to realise that it's not unthinkable and it *may* have happened. If you honestly think it did, and you want to talk about it, then I'll be here again tomorrow. But now,' he added, setting his notebook aside, 'I'm going to ask Nick to make you a hot drink.'

For quite a while after Haydn Parker had gone, Natasha was silent, hiding behind the wall of shock and contemplating the panorama of knowledge in fragments, until she was sure she could look at it all and not be destroyed by what was there.

It was a barren landscape, that much was clear, with most of the protagonists dead, gone, or so far deserted that they were no longer a threat. But the waste and the damage, the painful scars of those old battles, filled her with rage and anger and the bitterest kind of sorrow. The rows and arguments, that rebellious adolescent need to be herself had been no more than the outward and visible aspect of something far more distressing, a deep-seated suspicion which in the beginning had been only half understood, and later too revolting to contemplate.

But still, she'd been aware that something was going on, aware that her mother's love and loyalty and support were being diverted from their natural course and towards a man who should have had no such claim on her. That awareness had given rise to anger and jealousy and a terrible sense of betrayal, emotions which had expressed themselves in her own mind as a cry for comfort and understanding, but, being frustrated, had come out in tears and temper tantrums and moments of petty destructiveness. The attention-seeking hadn't worked, except to alienate her mother even further, and to strengthen the clamps of an increasingly strict regime. After that had come the silence of despair.

In the years of conformity which followed, Natasha remembered coldness and a sense of isolation, Helen's smug self-confidence in being the favoured one, and her mother's occasional attempts to draw Natasha back into the fold. All quite fruitless, because no matter how much Natasha wanted to, she could not respond while Father O'Gorman was still looking on.

By then, when she was in her mid-teens and looking to university as a means of escape from that barely tolerable situation, the priest was much more circumspect in his comings and goings. He called in the afternoon, for tea; or stayed for an evening meal with them, while Helen simpered and smiled and hung on his every word, playing up her image of the sweet, devout child, so satisfactorily biddable in comparison to her abrupt and awkward older sister. But Natasha had resented his presence in the house and at their table, his assumption of the role of *Father*, which was constantly emphasised by his title.

That he might have taken her father's place in other respects was not something she had ever allowed herself to think about, but now, with Haydn Parker's reasonable tones still ringing in her ears, Natasha found herself looking back and remembering things from those early days; looking back and seeing them with the eyes of an experienced adult. The rows; her father's jealousy and despair; his slurred insults, her mother's tears and bitter recriminations; and then the silence when it was all over. The silence of death, when he could plead no more.

She began to sob then, knowing that what she had said to Haydn was true: her father had been betrayed, and Celia Crayke's unfaithfulness had not been just a matter of belief. She saw the tall, gaunt figure of Father O'Gorman in her mind's eye, and remembered the power of his personality with an involuntary shudder; for the first time she realised that what had so frightened and repulsed her might have had a sexual basis, and that it might well have been attractive to a susceptible older woman. Especially if it were used deliberately.

The priest had always struck her as an evil man, but that thought made him more so, making her writhe and exclaim with revulsion. Desperately, she turned to Nick, and as she sobbed and clung to him he had never seemed so safe and protective, so absolutely vital to her existence.

Feeling that depth of anguish as though it were his own, Nick drew her even closer, comforting her like a heartbroken child. The outpouring of words and tears was like the bursting of a dam, behind which the grief of knowledge and bitterness and pain had been pressing for too many years. Holding, stroking, soothing, he made no attempt to stem the tide; he simply held her in his arms and listened to the disjointed memories, suffering with her as he began to grasp what she had withheld for so long.

It had never occurred to him before there might have been a sexual relationship between Celia Crayke and the Catholic priest, but as Natasha told him what Haydn had said, and described the priest's personality, Nick saw that it was possible. And, as she went on to relate various incidents which had followed on her father's death, that it was more than likely.

The priest had been frequently at the house, and often very late at night. Grief-stricken, unable to sleep, Natasha had heard his voice. When she challenged her mother, she'd said that Natasha was mistaken, it was only the television; but on one occasion Natasha had crept downstairs and surprised them with their arms around one another. She had seen, as they sprang apart, the look of loathing in the priest's eyes – quickly veiled, but unmistakable and never forgotten.

'He couldn't fool me, you see – just as he couldn't fool my father. We both knew him for what he was, which was why he hated us so much. He tried to be as nice as ninepence to me after that,' she added bitterly, 'but I never forgot that look . . .'

'But what did they say?' Nick asked. 'How the hell did they explain themselves?'

'Oh, my mother said something pathetic about having been upset – she claimed he was just comforting her.' Natasha sniffed with disgust and brushed her tears away. 'I had to believe her, though – the alternative didn't bear thinking about.'

Nick nodded, struck by the aptness of the phrase. He lit a couple of cigarettes and gave her one, and they smoked in silence for a while. A little later, she said: 'Then there was another time. I woke up – I don't know what time it was, but it must have been well after midnight. I heard somebody cross the landing and go down the stairs – somebody trying hard to be quiet. I opened my bedroom door, but it was too dark to see anything. Then a moment later, the front door opened and closed. My room was at the back of the house so I never saw who it was, but I knew, deep down. It wasn't a ghost or a burglar – it was *him*.'

She was trembling and he held her close, saddened by those old sins as well as irate on her behalf. The evidence wasn't conclusive, he realised that, but it was damning enough for him, and he knew very well that children often have an instinct for the truth where their parents are concerned. And Natasha had not been a young child, she'd been a girl verging on puberty, beginning to be aware of the physical relationships between men and women, and sensitive enough to find the wrong ones repulsive.

Obviously, that relationship must have continued for some years, and how on earth it had gone undetected, Nick could not imagine. But if Natasha's conscious mind had forced her to ignore it, there must have been others who had turned similarly blind eyes, presumably to avoid a scandal.

If that aspect remained a mystery, Nick found that the more he thought about the illicit affair, the more he understood about Natasha. So many private questions were solved that he wanted to exclaim as each separate item slotted into place, and it was difficult to restrain himself to a sudden nod or a sharp release of breath. It explained her hatred of the priest, and that hangover of revulsion which had touched every man in clerical garb ever since. And, remembering the awkward, prickly, vulnerable girl he had known nearly ten years ago, he realised now why she had been like that; and why, at the age of twenty, she had never had a steady boyfriend. Looking back, he could see that her growing love for him had been largely idealistic, so lacking in the usual sexual undertones that his own sense of what was right and wrong and potentially disastrous had failed to come into play – until it was too late.

He had a sudden recollection of the evening that changed everything: those first kisses, her willing yet unpractised response which had aroused in him such a heady combination of tenderness and passion. He'd loved her, yes, but he thought now that he should have let her walk away. She should have been allowed a gradual awakening, instead of that sudden wrench from innocence into the adult world of sexual passion. He hadn't been a boy, chancing things with her, he had been a man, knowing very well what he was doing.

It was unpleasant, seeing his own behaviour in that light, and he felt ashamed. Full of unspoken regrets, he sighed deeply and stroked her hair, kissed her forehead and tried, unsuccessfully, to close his mind to the painful awareness of what he had done. Unwittingly, he must have inflicted a lot of damage, and all because he had loved her and wanted her, and needed the gratification of that love.

That gratification had wrought damage elsewhere, but he knew all about that and had no need to go over it again. Nevertheless, it came to him that he had deceived Bernice – and the boys – in much the same way as Celia Crayke had conducted her deceptions. The circumstances didn't matter; in Natasha's eyes she had been as guilty of hurting his wife and children as the priest had been guilty of hurting her family. For that she had been unable to forgive herself. No wonder she had said, all those years ago, that she felt besmirched by the affair.

Pondering on that, Nick was no longer surprised that she had always avoided the topic; the miracle was that she had ever felt able to love him again. But when she said tearfully that she could never bear lying and deceit and the hurting of other people, he understood something of the conflict under which she had laboured. And, recalling his earlier conversation with Haydn Parker, it seemed to Nick that all this pain and guilt had created enormous barriers between them; barriers of misunderstanding against which love was largely ineffective, particularly in a crisis.

He saw, in that moment of insight, just how much he too had contributed, and that there were burdens he had carried alone which might have been eased if he had shared them with Natasha.

What fools we are, Nick thought as he gently caressed her, nursing our secret pains like shameful scars which must be hidden from the world. Perhaps it was better for the world not to know such things, but lovers should be braver and more forgiving. It should be possible, he reflected, to bare all in an emotional sense with no more hesitation than it took to discard a suit of clothes; and yet he knew from his own experience just how very difficult that could be.

He was touched by Natasha's courage; and, with the easing of her distress, uplifted by her trust in him. She had turned to him for comfort, and he had been able to provide it; that alone lightened his sense of guilt, and her need of him now was reassuring in ways that she could not begin to comprehend. She took a small, shuddering breath and clung to him, and on a wave of tenderness he buried his face against the softness of her hair. He was aware of an exhausted sense of calm, and knew that the worst of the fury had passed. She might weep and grieve again, but the violence of it was over.

They lay quietly on the old sofa, staring into the fire. In spite of the sadness, they were one and at peace. Nick found himself thinking of Bernice, trying to recall a moment when he had felt as relaxed as this with her. He supposed there must have been such moments, but he could not remember them. In those days, when he'd needed love and comfort, somehow it was always missing.

A little while later, Natasha broke into his thoughts with another memory of her mother, less traumatic than the others but, in the light of what had gone before, no less painful. It concerned a conversation which had taken place not long before she died, and while Celia Crayke had not been ill as far as anyone was aware, it seemed strange that it should have occurred just then.

'It was a couple of years after you and I parted,' Natasha said slowly, 'and I'm certain I never told her about – well, about our affair. Although I suppose I must have talked about you quite a lot prior to that. But it seemed so odd that she should ask about you after all that time.'

Intrigued, Nick said: 'She asked about *me*? Why?'

'Well, at the time I didn't see the connection either – more to the point, I'm sure I didn't *want* to see it, although it makes sense now.' She paused for a moment, then said: 'My mother must have guessed about you and me. It wasn't mentioned at the time, but suddenly, two years later, she was asking me whether I'd recovered from being in love with you.

'I said yes, of course I had – it wasn't strictly true, but it seemed so extraordinary that she should ask such a thing, I didn't know what else to say. Then she went on to say something about life and love and how difficult they both could be – she said she hoped that I was beginning to understand . . .'

'But you didn't want to understand . . .'

'No, I didn't. So I just stood there,' Natasha said, a tremor in her voice, 'and looked at her. And then, would you believe, she asked me to forgive her . . .'

Frozen by the coincidence, by words which had also been spoken to him as his own mother was dying of cancer, Nick did not take in what she said next. For a moment he could neither move nor speak; alarmed by that sudden tension, Natasha glanced up, her words tailing away as she read his expression.

'What is it?' she whispered. 'What have I said?' But he could only shake his head and reach for her, hugging her warmth as he closed his mind to the chill of memory.

'Later,' he murmured, 'we'll talk about it later . . .'

But Natasha turned to look at him, and he saw the intensity of concern in her eyes. 'No, we won't,' she said softly, reaching up to touch his face, 'I've heard that one too many times before. Tell me now, Nick – it's important.'

And so it was that he came to tell her at last about his own mother. After all the anguish of Natasha's experience he found the facts surprisingly easy to relate, although his feelings were another matter entirely. But she understood the difficulties and held him close, saying only that she wished he could have told her a long time ago.

Thirty Nine

In spite of the day that lay ahead, they sat up talking until the early hours, discovering parallels of experience in two quite separate lives. They were able, at last, to discuss the differences between them, the things that had driven them apart, the love and yearning which had kept them reaching for each other across a seemingly bottomless void.

If honesty was painful, Nick found it less so once the subjects were broached and the words under way. He was strengthened by what Natasha had told him, and by the inner light of knowledge; it gave him courage to expose some of the less edifying aspects of his own life, and to express the doubts and uncertainties which had beset him ever since his mother's death. He hoped Natasha would not only understand, but find a similar light in what he had to say, and that she did so was evident from the first. He was able, ultimately, to describe the sense of shock which had followed that revealing of the truth, and the disorientation which had dogged him for several months afterwards.

'And all this happened just before we met?'

'Yes. It was at the beginning of the autumn term. My mother was ill all the previous summer – in and out of hospital, you know how it is with cancer. But she seemed to be getting better,' he said briskly, 'and we were all talking about Christmas and a big family get-together . . . then, in October, she had a sudden relapse and died shortly afterwards . . .' He shook his head, choked by the memory of those last few days, the desperate journeys to and from Leeds, the telephone calls to Australia; and the shock of his mother's revelation, which had blunted his ability to accept her death.

'For a long time afterwards, I didn't know where I was – I didn't know who I was, either, which is probably more to the point. I could see what I'd become though, and I didn't like it. All the things I'd based my life upon, all that striving for success, seemed to have no reason, no foundation in anything worthwhile. I looked back, and I felt so *guilty* at the way I'd behaved – thoughts, actions, all the stupid things I'd said and believed. I felt a *bastard*, Natasha, in every sense of the word. And the thing was,' he added, 'I couldn't talk about it. I wanted to, but – somehow, I just couldn't.'

'Not even to Giles? And what about Bernice?'

Nick shrugged. 'I don't know – maybe I should've talked to Giles – I don't think I even considered it at the time. And as for Bernice – well, I tried. Several times. But she didn't even understand my grief – it irritated her. I don't say it was all her fault, it wasn't. She and my mother didn't get on, and I – well, I tried to keep the peace by keeping the two halves of my life apart. It became a habit – and then it rebounded on me when my mother died. It was difficult to talk about her to Bernice – and it became impossible to talk about the secret she'd kept all those years, and what it had done to me to learn the truth.'

He turned to face Natasha, regarding her intently. 'I always said that my marriage was on the rocks before we met, but I can see now what helped to drive it there. I don't know that Bernice would have understood even if I'd been able to tell her – but the point is, I kept ducking the issue with you as well. I nearly let the same thing happen again.'

She hugged him fiercely. 'Oh, my darling, I'm sorry – sorry it happened, sorry for both of us – '

'Don't be,' he said, 'there's been enough of that already.' He held her close for a moment and then drew away to look at her. 'Remember this – you came into my life when I needed you. You jolted me out of my miserable existence and made me feel worthwhile again. All right, I was bloody devastated when you walked out, but in a strange way I felt I deserved it. I'd overstepped the mark with one of my pupils, and I felt I was paying the price. Unlike the other misery, it had a certain logic – and it was one of the reasons I stayed with Bernice, and tried to make a go of it.'

He sighed and shook his head. 'After a while, I learned how to put you out of my mind – work helped, as it always does – but you were never far away, or for very long. I used to remember how you were,' he said softly, 'remember your eyes and the shape of your face – the way you laughed, the things you said – the good times we had together . . .' He wrapped his arms around her and pulled her close. 'God, but I missed you!'

'Did you hate me?' she whispered against his chest.

'No – never.'

She sighed. 'I hated you sometimes.'

'Mmm, yes, I think I rather guessed that . . .' He smiled and touched his lips to her forehead. 'But you know, don't you, that I was never like that callous, cynical character you described in *The English Lesson*?'

With a shamefaced grin, she looked up at him. 'Yes, I know that. The stupid thing is, I think I always knew, deep down.'

He considered for a moment, frowning. 'Then why on earth did you give it that ending? You were the one who finished things between us, not me – so why did you turn it around in the book?'

It was a while before she answered him. Then she said seriously: 'It was just a reflection, Nick, of all the things I saw around me. I didn't trust men – you'll understand why, now. But on the other hand, I wasn't exactly impressed by the intelligence of the women I knew – even those who were supposed to be clever. I saw them as victims – and I didn't want to be one, not any more. And yet there I was, gullible as the rest, falling in love with you and being used, just like all the others.

'That was how it seemed, anyway,' she added quietly. 'You see, I didn't understand about love – I only knew how bloody cruel it could be, how much it *hurt* . . .' She shook her head as if to cast off that painful memory, and then, with difficulty, she said: 'I expected you to end it. I was waiting for the inevitable moment, at the end of term, when you'd have to explain to me why we couldn't see each other any more. And I felt I deserved that – it would have been a just recompense for all the damage I'd caused to your wife and children. But I forestalled it, of course, and ended it myself.'

'But the book wasn't like that – '

'No, it wasn't. But don't you see, it was all to do with changing the sex of the characters? I made the victim a boy, and his lover an older woman – *she* was the one calling the shots, running the show. She was the one doing all the manipulating – I don't think she was particularly cynical, but she was very selfish, very self-orientated. *She* was my protest, if you like, against the traditional role of women in this world, and it wouldn't have been right for the book to have the tables turned upon her by the victim.

'You see, that book wasn't *just* about you and me. It started off that way, because I needed to get it out of my system – but it turned into something more than that. It was a way of looking at an old and tired situation from a fresh angle – in the end, I wanted it published because I wanted to make people *think*.'

'Well, it certainly did that,' he said, remembering the book's success and his own reaction to it. A moment later he frowned. 'So the ending wasn't really very much to do with you and me?'

She hesitated. 'In one way, no, it wasn't. But in another it had everything to do with what happened nine years ago. As I said before, it was a reflection – I gave it the ending I felt I deserved.'

Distressed by that comment, Nick held her close. 'No, you didn't deserve it – I couldn't have done that to you.'

'What would you have done?'

He shook his head. 'I don't know,' he said honestly. 'And it's impossible to say, now. Whichever way, it would have been bloody painful, and the longer it went on, the worse it would have been.' Pondering on that, he added gently: 'Perhaps, in the end, your decision was the right one . . .'

They were both tired the next morning, reluctant to leave the ease and comfort of bed. Nick suggested that she might like to stay there, but Natasha wanted to be with him, taking part in the job to be done.

The archaeology students arrived just before ten. The ambiguously named Lesley turned out to be a young woman, short and sturdily built, with a bright, good-humoured face which Natasha liked at once. Her companion was a tall, gangling young man with a deep forehead and a serious expression; he introduced himself as Dave, and it was immediately obvious that he was the straight man to Lesley's bubbling good spirits. To Natasha, they looked and sounded like a comedy duo, the girl wise-cracking about Dave's old banger of a car and the terrible journey they'd had coming up from Lincoln, while he kept protesting that at least it got them to York in one piece.

Natasha tried to apologise for dragging them back from holiday, but Lesley shrugged it aside. 'No, Mrs Rhodes, it's all right – we wouldn't have missed this for anything, would we, Dave? It's great old Doc Rathmell picking us for the job – makes a change from his yelling at us all the time!'

Dave glanced at them nervously, but Nick simply laughed. 'I know – he even shouts at me sometimes! Anyway, enough of the formality. This is Natasha, and I'm Nick. You're the bosses on this dig, and the rest of us – that's Haydn Parker and Giles Crowther when they arrive – will be the labourers. If any of us start getting in the way, I'll expect you to say so – all right?'

'Yes, sure,' Lesley agreed, looking awestruck. 'I didn't know the Rev was going to be here, though.'

'Yes, well, he's kind of interested,' Nick explained. After a moment, he added: 'You do know what we're looking for? And why?'

For the first time, Dave spoke up. 'Well, Dr Rathmell did tell us you thought there might be human remains buried in the barn, but he didn't go into any detail.'

As Nick was giving the students the same edited version of events that he had given Joe Rathmell, Haydn Parker arrived, followed a couple of minutes later by Giles. Haydn was suitably dressed in what looked like his oldest gardening clothes, while Giles, whose knowledge of gardening was limited to what could be grown in a few pots on his concreted patio, was in the Burberry raincoat he wore to college, and carrying a brand-new pair of Hunter wellingtons.

'Good grief, Giles,' Nick exclaimed, 'we're digging up the barn floor, not going to a bloody point-to-point!'

'Look, just piss off, will you? You said I needed boots – I bought some. All right?'

'Don't mind Nick,' Natasha assured him with a laugh, 'he's only jealous! But I think you should borrow one of his old jackets, otherwise you'll ruin that Burberry . . .'

When he was adequately kitted out, Giles patted her arm in gratitude. Their eyes met for a moment and he smiled again before going out to join the others. With a surge of relief and affection she realised that their relationship had at last returned to its old footing.

Laughter and light-heartedness lent an air of adventure to what lay ahead, although as soon as they entered the barn the jocularity died down a little. Nick had cleared out the old horse-plough and harrow, together with the gardening and decorating materials, which were now covered with an old tarpaulin; empty, the barn looked surprisingly large. Above their heads was a half hay-loft, and, to one side of the open door, the place where straw had been stacked. When they first came here, Natasha remembered, there had been masses of it to clean out, and it was underneath the straw, buried under several impacted layers, that Nick had discovered the original fire-back. Wondering what else might be buried here, she felt a chill touch her spine.

Nick, catching that moment of apprehension, gave her arm a little squeeze. 'Are you sure you want to do this?' he whispered. 'Nobody would mind if you didn't . . .'

'Yes, I'm sure.' She summoned a smile and glanced at Haydn, who had already suggested that they should talk later; for the time being, she did not want to think about that. It was enough just to be with Nick, to remember last night's closeness, and to know there was hope for the future.

'Well, where do we start?'

Giles's question startled her, and Nick, who had been studying the wall where the old stalls had been, turned abruptly. But before he could speak, Dave said: 'Well, always allowing for the fact that this is not the original barn, I think we have to assume that the layout would have been much the same, and try to avoid the area where the animals were kept. If somebody was burying a murder victim in a hurry, they wouldn't have time to shift the cows first.'

'Ah,' Nick interjected, wondering how to get over that little detail. 'Well now, let's think a moment. If you'd committed a murder, with the help of some accomplices, and you wanted to hide the body where it wouldn't be found, wouldn't you take the trouble to shift a couple of cows?'

The young man flushed, but did not give ground at once. 'What about the noise, though?'

'Oh, I don't think these people would've been too worried about a few mild protests – this house is a fair way from the village, you know.'

'Perhaps they fed them hay to keep them quiet?' Lesley suggested, earning herself a frown from Dave, who could see his arguments being demolished. With some reluctance he turned to survey the length of the stalls. Arrow slits of light from above competed with the electric bulbs, but it was still dark in the far corner.

'Wherever we start,' he said, 'we'll have to have more light.'

'OK, no problem – I bought a couple of angle-lamps the other day.' Nick strode away to fetch them, while Dave and Lesley hauled their equipment out of the ancient Volvo estate-car in the yard. And the yard, Nick thought as he made his way between the parked vehicles, was beginning to look like a garage forecourt. But at least it was a decent day, sunny and relatively mild after almost two weeks of below-zero temperatures. He was glad of the sun; it went a long way towards redressing the more macabre elements. Doing this job under a louring sky would have been like taking part in a horror movie.

It was decided to begin in the middle of the barn and work outwards. Dave and Lesley marked out the positions of a trench, 6 feet wide by 12 feet long, running 6 feet in and parallel to the long wall facing the doorway. While Lesley and Natasha lined up a motley collection of buckets and barrows, Dave swung a pick at the compacted debris of the last three centuries. During the intervening years that mixture of straw and cow-dung had set like concrete; breaking it up was hard work, and for the first time Natasha was seeing the initial stages of archaeology. She had viewed various archaeological digs in York, and, without giving it much thought, had imagined that such work was all tiny trowels and the sifting of fine soil. This exhibition of brute force was almost shocking; but exciting and contagious too. When Dave began to flag a little and Lesley begged to take over, Natasha was not surprised: she wanted to have a go too.

But the men wanted their turn first. As a sweating Dave handed over to Nick, the two women indulged in some vociferous objections, until Nick, with a humorous glint in his eye, handed the implement to Natasha. In his hands, the pick did not look so very heavy, but it was all she could do to lift it; after a few ineffectual jabs at the unyielding floor, she laughingly conceded defeat and handed it across to the more experienced Lesley.

'My dad's a farmer,' she said between swings, 'and we've always had to help in the holidays. Haymaking and potato-picking . . . mucking out the animals in winter.' She paused for breath. 'Amazing what chucking straw-bales about can do for your muscles – no need to work out with weights . . .'

Sitting at a desk and pounding a typewriter all day was hardly the best way of keeping fit, Natasha acknowledged, but there were other things she could do besides wielding a pick. Ignoring the light-hearted banter, she took a garden spade and began shovelling the loose material into one of the barrows. Taking his cue from her, Dave then started to organise them into a team, designating jobs on a short rota system, so that no one became either overtired or bored.

Since it was not an archaeological site, it was possible to work with relative speed, clearing just over a foot of accumulated debris and compacted cow-dung before reaching the dark soil of what had been open fields before the barn was built. They were agreed that the accomplices would not have dug the grave very deep, and took the dig down from there in spits of a foot at a time, four of them lifting the soil while the other two sifted it. Once it was cleared, the soil was barrowed outside to a heap by the wall.

Broken up and sifted, there seemed to be a vast amount, and Giles, easing back with the barrow, remarked on it wearily. 'Just think, Nick – whether we find what we're looking for or not, we've got to get that lot back into the hole!'

'Yes, I know. It'll be like getting a quart into a pint pot.'

'Hate to say this, matey, but your barn floor's never going to be the same again . . .'

They took it in turns to make coffee and tea, but the work didn't stop. At lunchtime Natasha said she would make soup and sandwiches, and Haydn volunteered to help her. Nick knew that his desire to talk to her was motivated by concern, but as he watched them go he was pierced by a different kind of concern, a fear that Haydn would press her too hard when what she probably needed was to be left alone for a while.

She seemed composed if subdued over lunch, and he could not help wondering what had been said. There was, however, no real opportunity to ask, and he decided to leave it until later. But he watched her closely as they worked on, noting her pallor and the evidence of fatigue around her eyes.

By four o'clock they were all tired. Outside the light was going, and after six hours of hard physical labour the trench was over 4 feet deep, 3 feet below the natural soil level. In spite of the lack of success, both Dave and Lesley were pleased by the progress made, and felt it augured well for the next day. Giles was less convinced. Easing his aching back, he hazarded a guess that they would all be too stiff to do a hand's turn in the morning.

'Try a nice hot bath,' Lesley suggested, 'it works wonders. Then a couple of painkillers before you go to bed – you'll be right as rain in the morning!'

Giles groaned as he climbed into his car. 'I hope you're right,' he said pathetically.

'He's a hero, really,' Nick declared with a grin as his old friend drove away. 'In fact you all are. You didn't have to do this, but I'm bloody glad you volunteered – thanks.'

He waved them away with a smile, but as the Volvo's taillights disappeared down the lane he felt cold. The sky was black over the fields and the wind was strengthening, and suddenly the barn seemed a sinister place. Turning back, he switched off the lights and closed the door, stumbling a little as he returned to the house.

Only Haydn lingered and, as Natasha announced that she was going upstairs to soak in the bath, Nick asked him to stay for a drink. He made some coffee and poured two small whiskies, but drank his own almost at once. With a second measure he began to feel a little better.

It was no surprise to him that Haydn wanted to talk about Natasha and what had transpired the previous evening, nor that he was interested in Nick's reactions. After a day of strenuous activity in which such thoughts, of necessity, had been largely pushed to the back of his mind, he found it an extraordinary relief to talk about them, to put into words some of the insights that had come to him as he listened to the story of Natasha's mother and her relationship with Father O'Gorman.

'Was I shocked? Yes,' he admitted softly, 'I suppose I was. Not so much by the sexual aspect, as by the fact that it had never occurred to me before. I'd just assumed that Natasha's mother was suffering from some form of religious mania which blinded her to the damage she was doing. But that, of course, is how Natasha described her mother to me, so it's perhaps not so surprising after all. If I'd ever met her myself, I might have thought otherwise . . .'

'So how does Natasha feel about it, do you think? I gather she's accepted the possibility that there may have been a sexual relationship between them?'

'Oh, yes. From what she's told me, I'd say it was more probable than possible, and Natasha herself is convinced of it. Being brought face to face with it was a terrible shock for her, as I'm sure you're aware – but in some strange way it seems to have made sense to her at last . . . Just as it did for me – except for me the sense is much broader, because it encompasses things in my life too.' He smiled suddenly, then said: 'If I say that it's been like finding the key to a set of hieroglyphics which has baffled me for years, you might understand why I feel so much lighter for what's happened, rather than completely sad.'

Haydn raised his glass. 'Yes, I do understand. And I'm glad you've found the good so quickly – evil often clouds the issue for an awful long time. As indeed,' he added reflectively, 'it has in this case . . .'

Evil, Natasha thought, surveying her chapped and blistered hands; so much of it in the world, and not just in war and terrorism and the torturing of dissidents. It existed in small ways and in small places, in isolated Fenland communities and tiny North Yorkshire villages; it was mean and cruel and deceitful, and it spoke in judgment through the ages, from court benches and church pulpits and from the kitchen tables of the lowliest households. It twisted and manipulated the innocent, tempted and trapped the worldly-wise, and nobody was immune.

She thought of her father, a good man, but so shattered by the evidence of evil in this world, by his own contribution to those horrific air raids over Germany, that he could no longer believe in God; and she thought of her mother, so keen to prove her faith that she was prepared to sacrifice both marriage and children to a priest who was proud and unscrupulous. Evil had tainted him and magnified itself through his actions, killing Alex Crayke, ruining Natasha's relationship with her mother, and also with her sister Helen. And it had come very close, she reflected, to killing her love for Nick.

But without him to cushion things last night, the agony of knowledge would have been unbearable. As it was, she had raged and ranted, cursing everything and everyone until sheer exhaustion calmed her down. Nick had absorbed the rage and coaxed every last little piece of the story out of her, until in the end she wasn't angry at all, just achingly sad that such things could have happened.

Unlike anger, sadness could be comforted. She knew that now and the knowledge warmed her, enabling her to feel the forgiveness her mother had asked for all those years ago. Then, as she had explained to Nick last night, she hadn't wanted to understand, and had lightly dismissed a very serious request; now she could comprehend her mother's pain and guilt, even see that moment as an uncanny presentiment of death.

Nick understood that. His mother had known she was going to die, and, before death, had needed to unburden herself, to set the record straight. But although he had managed to say the words, for him, like Natasha, the real forgiveness had been a long time coming.

Until very recently, that fact would have distressed Natasha unbearably, since she would have imagined it as coming too late. But her experience of Sarah Stalwell had forced her to think again, to acknowledge the existence of spiritual life beyond the material world. Perhaps the words she uttered were empty, spoken only to emptiness, but as Haydn said, it was the forgiveness of the heart which counted.

Forty

THE OUTDOOR cats, looking like dispossessed refugees, had returned from yesterday's walkabout to complain vociferously at being turned out of their comfortable home in the barn. Colette watched smugly from the garden gate as her impoverished relatives mewed and howled at the humans gathered in the yard. One rubbed against Giles's muddy wellingtons, while the other rolled over and over in an attempt to attract attention. Haydn, tricked into stroking her, was clawed and bitten for his kindness.

Unable to concentrate on the discussion, Natasha hurried indoors to open a tin of cat-food. Feed them, she thought, then they'll find somewhere to groom themselves and go to sleep. She chopped meat into a couple of plastic bowls and took them outside, where, with an ecstatic growling and swishing of tails, the two tucked into a hearty breakfast. Colette turned her back on them and stalked into the porch.

The diggers had moved into the barn, where Dave and Nick were already inside the trench and attacking the next spit. Giles and Lesley were marking out the position of the second trench, again 6 feet wide by 12 feet long. When excavated, it would cover the entire length of the old stalls. As before, Natasha immediately started hoisting buckets of soil, sifting through each load carefully to look for small bones, phalanges and metatarsals, that the men in the trench might have missed.

By half-past nine they had completed the spit, and taken the level down to 5 feet, 4 feet below the natural soil level. They were all agreed that the hurried burial of a murder victim was unlikely to be deeper than that, and at once began to excavate the second trench. Once the surface was broken up it was easier to terrace the spits from the open face; they were making such good progress that Natasha was more frustrated than relieved when Nick reminded her of the time.

Of course, Toby's funeral. She'd almost forgotten what day it was, never mind the time, and had even been wondering where Haydn was. But he had said that he would meet them in church.

She washed and changed hurriedly and, with half an eye on the clock, dabbed on just enough make-up to relieve the pallor. Nick was waiting with her coat, ready to hurry her into it; with his hand at her elbow, he almost frog-marched her down the lane. Even so, the bell was already tolling as they crossed the Green, and they made it into church just as the hearse was pulling up outside.

Natasha was surprised to see the little church so full. For a moment she hesitated, but Nick had already spotted Haydn, halfway down on the left. He moved along to make room for them, and as Natasha gathered her breath and looked around, she saw the landlord from the Half Moon a couple of rows in front, and Mrs McCoy – she still had no idea of the woman's real name – sitting in the pew beyond that. Amongst a lot of unfamiliar heads, she noticed with astonishment Craig Morrison's black hair in its usual pony-tail. And he was wearing a suit. She was so amazed she barely registered the entrance of the coffin.

With the first hymn, she took the opportunity to look at the family pew, at the front of the nave. Beside Vera Bickerstaff and her husband, Ted, were an elderly couple and a much younger woman, who might have been Vera's married daughter. If there were other Bickerstaffs still living in the area, they were not here today. Somehow, that was unimportant; it seemed fitting that the majority of the congregation should be people with whom Toby had shared a pint or two and helped with the gardening. Whatever their private reservations about the old man, they had at least seen him and spoken to him on a regular basis, and appeared, unbidden, to pay their last respects. With her new awareness,

Natasha found herself hoping that it was not simply a matter of bidding a sentimental farewell to the last of Denton's old characters.

As they all knelt to pray, she wondered how many of them knew about the murder, and what they thought of the circumstances surrounding it. The rector probably felt that Toby had paid his debt to society and was now making his reckoning with God, and Natasha hoped that was the case. She was not sure what Haydn thought, but for her the idea that Toby had been another victim of Reynald de Briec added a chill to the cold church, and inspired a fervent wish for the safety and repose of the old man's soul.

Suspecting that wish of being a prayer, she was surprised at herself and glanced up at Nick, half expecting to see him smile. Instead he reached for her hand and squeezed it. She clung for a moment to his warmth and solidity; this new spiritual sense of hers was unfamiliar, and a little unnerving.

The rector began his address, and with the stillness of the congregation Natasha was able to let her eyes and thoughts settle. Gazing at Toby's coffin, she found herself thinking of her mother's funeral, the Roman Catholic rite no doubt different from this, although she could not recall a word of it. The officiating priest had been young and earnest, and sensing her dislike had confined his sympathies to Helen, weeping like the suitably distraught daughter she was. Natasha had been unable to shed a single tear, and her stony face had raised a number of eyebrows amongst the gathered mourners, as it had invited later recrimination from Helen.

It had taken three months for Natasha to cry, and then she hadn't been able to stop for a week.

The silly thing was, she wanted to cry now. Not for Toby, although his life had been tragic enough to warrant a few tears from somebody. No, she wanted to cry for her mother, who had made so many mistakes and no doubt paid for them in her heart after Father O'Gorman's death.

And if anyone's dying should have been painful and lingering, Natasha thought, his should; but, like the speeding car which killed him, it had come upon him suddenly, on an icy country road.

Now, contemplating justice, she was surprised to find she no longer cared. In the end, the best revenge had been her escape, and if the road to this point had been long and tortuous, at least she and Nick were together.

She met Nick's glance with a silent plea for understanding. It was there and she was reassured. We've been such fools, she thought, remembering all the difficulties of the past few months, and hoping they were well and truly over. But with a clearing of throats and shuffling of feet as they stood to sing the last hymn, Natasha was reminded of why they were here. Old Toby was dead, yet out of this entire congregation, she and Nick and Haydn were probably the only ones who knew how and why he had died. Something black and formless and very, very evil had struck terror into his heart and killed him; it was out there still. That was why Haydn was here, saying his own prayers for the repose of Toby's soul, and giving his protection as they searched for Sarah Stalwell's last remains.

The rector of St Oswald's, Nick decided, was a cleric of the old school, a middle-class, middle-of-the-road Anglican who suited this farming community admirably. As the spiritual shepherd of three small rural parishes, he was probably overworked and certainly underpaid, and would not have much time to devote to the myths, legends and local superstitions so beloved of many of his forebears. With a private income and time on his hands, the Victorian country parson could afford to indulge in afternoon calls and intellectual pursuits; his present-day equivalent was not so fortunate. Nevertheless, the funeral oration was delivered with all the skill of a diplomat, and, as the congregation filed out of church behind the coffin, Nick mentally awarded full marks to the rector for offending nobody, least of all the deceased.

How he was likely to react to what was going on up Dagger Lane, Nick found it impossible to judge, although he had a sneaking suspicion that Haydn was going to have his work cut out, explaining things. Like his forebear, the Reverend Clive, the present incumbent might well feel that such extraordinary tales and superstitions were not to be taken seriously.

People were standing about in groups amongst the gravestones, reluctant to be seen hurrying off, yet equally reluctant to accompany the cortège to the crematorium. The sky was densely overcast and threatening rain; once it began, Nick thought, the mourners would soon disperse, either to their own homes or to the welcoming comfort of the Half Moon. Tony, the landlord, seemed to be attracting a small group of elderly farmers, all, by the look of them, eager for a warming tot of whisky after a bone-chilling half-hour in church. Out of the corner of his eye he caught sight of Craig Morrison making his way towards them, and, having no wish to speak to him, Nick excused himself and moved off in the direction of Mrs McCoy, who seemed to be alone and looking lost.

'How are you?' he said warmly, 'we haven't seen you for a long time.'

'Oh, no, well . . .' She blushed and stumbled over her words. 'No reason to, is there? Now McCoy's gone . . .'

'No, of course not – I'm sorry. It must have been upsetting for you.'

'It was.' She looked away from him, towards Craig Morrison, leaning nonchalantly against a tall memorial stone and chatting to Natasha. 'I can't forgive that young man for what he did. I mean, McCoy did get out, on two or three occasions, but I still can't believe . . .' Her voice faltered a little, and her eyes filled with tears. Searching for a handkerchief, she said: 'I mean, why would he do such a thing? He was well fed – too well fed, the vet told me . . . why would he go round killing sheep?'

'I don't know,' Nick murmured, pitying her despite his embarrassment, and for the first time wondering whether McCoy had been the victim of some form of possession. 'But sometimes they do – and farmers have the right – '

'But did he have to come to my house with the mangled body?' she demanded fiercely. 'It was *horrible* – my poor dog – his lovely head all shot away . . .'

She was crying openly now, and Nick regretted his own thoughtless greeting. He found a clean handkerchief in the pocket of his overcoat and handed it to her, resisting the impulse to take her arm or pat her shoulder. In his experience, too much sympathy made things worse. As firmly as he could, he said: 'Amazing to see so many people here. I didn't realise old Toby was so well liked.'

'Well, I can't say I liked him,' the woman admitted, sniffling a little but managing to control her tears. 'It was just that he was good to me that day I saw that – that *thing*, down the lane. He looked out for me – made sure it had gone before he saw me safely up the lane. He didn't –' She broke off for a moment, searching for words. 'He didn't think I was crazy – he seemed to understand.'

Something about her tone told Nick that other people – her husband perhaps? – had made fun of what she claimed to have seen down Dagger Lane. Wanting to dismiss that idea once and for all, he said: 'No, old Toby wouldn't have thought that. You see, he saw it himself, just a few days before you.'

'Did he?' She looked at him then, hope banishing the tears. 'Did he really?'

'Oh, yes. He told me about it.'

'And what was it?'

Nick shrugged, wondering whether to tell her that he had seen it too. 'I'm not sure. Some sort of ghost, I think.'

She shivered in the cold wind. 'What? The ghost of a dog?'

He forced a smile. 'Something like that. But I've seen it myself, so I'm sure you're not crazy. At least, no more than I am!' He laughed then and turned his head, glad to see that Craig Morrison had gone.

'Thank you for that,' she said firmly. 'I knew what I'd seen – I knew it had to be something very strange to frighten McCoy. I'm glad you told me – it's made me feel a lot better.' She wiped her nose and pushed Nick's handkerchief into her coat pocket; there was something symbolic in the gesture, he felt, as though she had done with tears and soul-searching. She certainly looked better, her expression firmer, her backbone straighter than it had been a minute ago.

Her eyes met his and she smiled. 'Shall I tell you something, Dr Rhodes?'

So she knew his name. Smiling back, wishing he knew hers, Nick said: 'What's that?'

'Now that I don't have the dog to look after, I'm going to look for a job in town. It's time I got out and about, I think. After all,' she added with an apologetic grin at their surroundings, 'we're a long time dead, aren't we?'

'We are indeed,' he acknowledged, shaking the hand that was held out to him. 'You know, I'm sorry to admit this, but you have the advantage of me – I don't even know your name . . .'

'Whitehead,' she said cheerfully. 'Jennifer Whitehead.'

At once, Sarah and Agnes and Tom Whitehead sprang to mind. Momentarily stunned by the coincidence, Nick had to force himself to speak normally and wish her all the best; and then, having done so, not to hurry after her and ask for a breakdown of her husband's family history.

'Of course,' he explained to Natasha and Haydn as they walked back up the lane, 'it's pure coincidence. After all, Whitehead's a common name, and her husband can't possibly be related to that particular family, otherwise they would have inherited the house.'

'But the coincidence shook you,' Haydn commented.

'Yes – yes, it did. Brought them all back, as large as life. Made me remember what we're doing, and why we're doing it . . .' He shivered inside his coat, turning up his collar as the first large drops of rain came sweeping in from the west. The wind was cold, and the rain felt like ice; they started to run towards the house.

'That reminds me,' he said a few minutes later, as he and Natasha were changing back into their old jeans and sweaters, 'what did young Morrison want?'

'Oh, I noticed you sloping off as soon as he came along,' she said with a teasing grin. 'You don't like him, do you?'

'No, I do not. What did he want?'

'Nothing – he was just curious. Wanted to know what we were doing, excavating in the barn.'

Startled, Nick said: 'And what did you tell him?'

'Well, I *didn't* tell him we were looking for human remains,' she replied with some asperity, 'I said we were laying a concrete floor. I'm not at all sure he believed me, though!'

As she stood there, facing him, in the shadowy half-light of the bedroom, he was struck by an acute awareness of her beauty. Her hair was wet from the rain, a little too long for the style she preferred, but she had the most perfect cheekbones, and her mouth was so . . .

He paused in the act of tucking in his shirt; recognising his look, Natasha laughed softly and came to him. 'I know – I love you too,' she whispered, 'but there are people outside, no doubt wondering where we are . . .'

Reluctantly, he zipped up his jeans and tried to be satisfied with a kiss. Before letting her go, he murmured: 'You're so precious to me – don't go away from me again.'

She said there was no danger of that, but the funeral and the work they were doing – even that conversation in the graveyard – had left him feeling oddly vulnerable. From the bedroom window he could see the rain lashing at the village in its tree-shrouded hollow, and, from the landing, that same rain sweeping in across the Vale. As Natasha turned and went downstairs, he felt cold and curiously isolated, and for the first time doubted the wisdom of what they were engaged upon.

After lunch they set to work again. At one end they were already 3 feet down, with no sign of boxes, bones or any kind of disturbance. Here the soil was rich and deep, and apart from a few stones, the earth was well packed, right down to the clay bed. Following yesterday's system, they dug out, sifted, and cleared the soil from the area in barrows. Giles had covered one pile with a weighted plastic sheet, and had begun another; in the torrential rain, however, it was seeping away into mud. Nick suggested that they start filling in the far end of the previous trench, which upset the archaeology students. That was not the way to do things, they said; but to him it seemed the only logical answer to the problem. Piling up soil within the barn itself was out of the question, since they might need to dig underneath; and he did not want his yard looking like a film set for the Battle of the Somme.

Eventually, amidst much muttering and grumbling, they agreed. It may not have been according to the book for an archaeological site, but it did make the work quicker and easier. By half-past two they had completed the spit, and paused before beginning the next. Nick, glad of a break, stuck his spade blade-first into the base of the trench. The metal struck something hard, jarring his wrist slightly; the metallic ring silenced them all. Before he could raise the spade to strike again, Dave jumped down into the trench and grabbed it from him.

'Nick, hold fast! Just a minute – we don't know what it is.' He reached out to Lesley, who, like a theatre-sister at some delicate operation, slapped a trowel into his hand. While he carefully eased the soil away, they all hung over the hole, mouths agape. 'For goodness' sake,' he hissed in exasperation, 'get out of my light – I can't see a bloody thing.'

A moment or two later he sighed and sat back on his haunches. 'All right, cut the excitement – it's just a stone. A big stone.'

It took them a while to dig round that chunk of limestone, and two of them to lever it out of its pocket of earth. They were gasping and sweating by the time they had it clear of the trench, and Haydn promptly sat down on it to gather his breath. From the trench, Dave muttered something about it all being a waste of time, especially as he had just spotted another stone next to the first, protruding from the edge of the trench.

'Who on earth was going to find room to bury a damned thing down here, with bloody great stones like that lying around?'

Nick, who had been cast down by the disappointment, was tempted to agree with him. But as he glanced across at Haydn, something struck him. 'Hang on a minute,' he said under his breath. 'Haydn, just stand up for a minute, will you?'

Dave looked round, his eyes on a level with the stone. 'Well, damn it all,' he declared. 'Have you just noticed what I've noticed? Are we stupid, or what?'

'No, we're not stupid,' Nick muttered, bending over the stone.

It was old and it was pitted, but there was no mistaking the fact that what they were looking at was not just any old boulder, but a stone that had once been cut and faced.

'What the hell is a faced stone – no, *two* faced stones – doing buried under nearly three feet of soil?' Dave demanded. 'There aren't any stone buildings round here.'

'Sheriff Whenby Castle – this is big enough to have come from there. And the same goes for the other one, I'll bet.'

As Nick jumped down into the trench to have a look, Haydn looked around in bemusement and said: 'Is someone going to enlighten me?'

Giles chipped in too. 'Yes – what are two faced stones doing buried under three feet of soil?'

Hugging Natasha in glee, Lesley answered the riddle. 'Buried treasure! Don't you see? According to Natasha's story, they buried two trunks with Sarah Stalwell's body – trunks containing her most valuable possessions – '

'But these are *stones*,' Giles insisted.

'Yes, of course!' Natasha laughed. 'The Whiteheads dug them up again later – '

'And filled the hole with a couple of stones! Easier and less noticeable,' Lesley declared, 'than carting soil about the place.'

'So does this mean,' Giles ventured, peeling off his gloves and regarding his blistered palms, 'that my suffering may not have been in vain? Dare we hope to find the lady herself, do you think?'

'We can certainly hope,' Nick muttered, climbing out of the hole. 'The problem is, having reached this point, where do we go next?'

They stood and considered the situation. Outside, the gloomy afternoon was growing darker, wind and rain gusting under the eaves and rattling the rooftiles. Within the barn electric lights illumined the gaping holes and piles of soil, the keen eyes and weary faces of the onlookers, and the mundane array of spades and tools. Amidst the deepening shadows they looked like a group of conspirators; remembering the original ones, Nick shivered and lit a cigarette. Faced with the impending proof of his own convictions, he was suddenly seized by doubts as to the wisdom of this endeavour. All the eerie tales he had ever read came flooding back, unbidden, with a glaring image of the beast.

With a sharp, involuntary movement, he shook the memory off. Turning to the door, he stood there for a moment, seeking solace in the wind and rain. But the past, like an elemental force, seemed to be all around him. Across the yard, the long, low house appeared dark and brooding beside the primeval track that was Dagger Lane, while the remaining oaks of the ancient Forest of Galtres dipped their branches and groaned. Even the fields, empty and open to either side, assumed an alien aspect in the gathering gloom. Feeling threatened and isolated, his eyes searched the hedgerows for a shadow, blacker than the rest. No sign, but that meant nothing; it could be anywhere, just waiting. What did it want with him?

There was no escape, and the awareness was chilling. Retreating to the path fate seemed to have laid out for him, Nick ground his cigarette underfoot and stepped back into the barn. There, at least, was the comfort of humanity, whatever the grisliness of the task in hand.

Arguing the toss about something, Dave and Lesley were engaged in measuring up. The stones were only 18 inches in from where the second trench abutted the first, while the second stone was protruding from the edge nearest the far wall. Between there and the present brick wall was a distance of 6 feet, but Nick reckoned that the original wall must have stood some 2 or 3 feet in from that. It was decided to dig down, as before, along the length of the present trench. With any luck, they should find bones protruding towards the centre, within another 3 or 4 feet.

They were eager, but they were also tired, so Dave insisted that every care be taken. The sifting operations being performed by Natasha and Haydn suddenly became vital.

An hour later, having divided the trench lengthways, and cleared the soil to a depth of 4 feet, there was still nothing to be seen. Exhausted and thoroughly miserable, they paused for another conference.

'Do you seriously think this bloody woman's here?' Giles demanded, easing his aching back. 'If you ask me, she's hiding in a corner somewhere, laughing her bloody head off!'

Natasha winced, and Nick shook his head. He was aching in places he had not discovered since his last game of rugby, and his hands, unused to all this physical labour, were sore and bleeding. Haydn, who was always the last to complain, peeled off his gloves too, and suggested that it might be time to call it a day. One of his gloves fell into the trench and, with a groan, he climbed down stiffly to retrieve it.

Somebody mentioned a bath, and suddenly they were all discussing the pleasures of a long, hot soak, followed by supper and bed. Haydn's voice cut across them.

'Dave, pass me that light, will you?'

'What is it?'

'I don't know – maybe only stones – you'd better have a look . . .'

Climbing down with the portable angle-lamp, Dave peered at the spot indicated. 'Lesley, pass me that brush . . .'

Again, they all leaned forward, hanging over the hole like Eskimos after fish. Dave, looking like a real archaeologist now, used the brush and picked delicately at the spot with a pointed trowel. Then he brushed at it again. They saw the fine granules of soil falling away, and, under the bright light, what looked like three broken twigs embedded in the earth.

The silence, for a moment, was profound.

'Phalanges,' Dave whispered reverently, looking up at Nick. 'Finger bones. We've found her.'

Forty One

ELATION SURGED between them, dispelling every last ounce of weariness as they hugged each other and praised Haydn for dropping his glove in that particular spot. Lesley even did a little war-dance, punching the air with exuberance as she declared that moments like this were what archaeology was all about. Even Dave was laughing, confessing to Nick that he had thought they were on a wild-goose chase, and would find nothing at all.

The amateurs, having forgotten their aching limbs, were suddenly keen to carry on, and even Lesley was tempted; but Dave shook his head. 'No,' he said firmly, 'we were all pretty well done in a few minutes ago, and Doc Rathmell always says that excitement can make you careless anyway. I don't think that's a good combination for uncovering the rest of the skeleton – we should pack up now and have an early start in the morning.'

Nick, recognising good sense when he heard it, was in full agreement; but before they could turn away and begin clearing up, Haydn asked them to pause for a moment, and to be quiet.

'These bones were once a human being, quite probably a young woman by the name of Sarah Stalwell. If that is so, then she was murdered . . .' he paused to look at them individually, '. . . which is an evil deed by any standards of belief. And then she was buried here, in unconsecrated soil, in a place where animals stood, without so much as a prayer for her soul. Because of that, I'd very much like you to say the Lord's Prayer with me. Say it for the person buried here,' he added weightily, 'if you can't say it for yourselves . . .'

As they all bowed their heads, a corner of Nick's mind was impressed by Haydn Parker's ability to draw the best out of people; but as he joined in the prayer such considerations were forgotten. For him, in a very real sense, the phrase, *deliver us from evil*, had never been so meaningful.

It was a wild, blustery night and, despite physical exhaustion, neither of them rested well. They were both awake about six o'clock, turning to each other in tension and anxiety rather than passion. Afterwards, Nick slept again, to wake with a start at eight as the radio blurted out news of the first Loyalist murder of the New Year in Northern Ireland, and an IRA bomb in London's Oxford Street. The pound was down against the German mark, and the storms which were presently battering the east coast of the United States could be expected to hit Scotland and northern England within the next few days . . .

'I thought they were already here,' he muttered, switching the radio off. Leaving Natasha in bed, he went downstairs to make some tea.

On television a few minutes later, he caught the news again, graphically illustrated this time. It was depressing, but horror and disaster on such a scale made excavating a 270-year-old grave seem no more than a minor pin-prick by comparison.

The crowd arrived as they were finishing breakfast. After coffee in the kitchen, Haydn wanted to talk to Nick about the local rector, and as an aside to that, what they were going to say in the face of subsequent questioning. Nick wanted to keep Natasha's story out of it, so it was decided to stick to the line he had used originally, of a hunch which had developed through his research into the ownership of Holly Tree Farm.

Having been schooled in that, they all pulled on their working gloves over hands which were covered in Elastoplast, and prepared for the last phase of the excavation.

Dave and Lesley, having studied the layout again, came to the conclusion that Sarah Stalwell's body must have been buried parallel to the wall rather than at right angles to it. As they began to clear what lay above the bones found yesterday, it soon became obvious that the rest of the bones were very close to the timber-framed wall of the original byre. Shifting the solid chunks of old cow-dung, they came across the stumps of vertical posts and studs, broken bits of wattle-and-daub infill, and a rotted sill-beam resting on a course of ancient bricks. The difference in levels led the archaeologists to estimate that the original building was between three and four hundred years old, which tallied well with Nick's guess that it had been erected about the time that the house was enlarged and rebuilt in brick. It may even have been, he thought, gazing at the old sill-beam, that some of the timbers from the old house were re-used in the construction of the byre.

It was a slightly better day, with blustery, intermittent showers rather than the torrential rain of the day before. It was mainly brighter too, although the wind, which had come round a point or two, had a tendency that afternoon to shriek through the arrow-slits above their heads. It increased as the day wore on, and finally became unnerving as they uncovered the mortal remains of Sarah Stalwell.

With the skull, scapula and pelvic bones clear, they were all becoming jittery. They were awed and anxious, Natasha could feel it, and wanting the job finished, while for her it seemed to be going too fast. It was almost like coming to the end of a long and difficult piece of writing: she wanted to be sure of the ending, she wanted it over and done with; but she was also afraid of the empty space beyond. Afraid of what might surge in to take its place . . .

It took a couple of hours to clear the earth from the rest of the bones. Dave and Lesley worked in deep concentration, while the others sat or stood around, watching and smoking. Very slowly, as the bones were revealed, it became clear that Sarah Stalwell had been buried on her left side, in a foetal position. Of the makeshift shroud that had covered her, there was no sign.

Dave, as detached and practical as any scientist, remarked in an undertone that acidic cow manure would rot natural fibres more quickly, so it was hardly surprising that only bones were left.

One hand had been tucked beneath her. As Lesley gently brushed soil from a partially exposed femur, the light from the angle-lamp picked out the shape of a ring; and, beneath that, the long, crusted blade of a knife.

Seeing that, Natasha started to shiver. All the extraordinary emotions inspired by the writing of the murder scene came flashing back, and it was as though she felt the vicious pulling of her hair, the chill of nakedness as clothes were ripped from her, and the hot pain of that long-bladed knife as it slashed through vulnerable flesh and jarred, screamingly, against sensitive bone . . .

. . . as though part of her hovered, detached and wonderingly, while the conspirators panicked over the body . . .

She was cold, and her cheeks were wet. Men's voices, muffled . . . a girl's cutting through with an edge of panic . . . something about a doctor . . .

Doctor? Too late for that . . . she's dead . . .

Rough hands, chafing her arms and legs . . . *hurting* . . .

Her words of protest came out as a moan, but Natasha found volition enough to withdraw her hand from whoever was intent upon rubbing it away.

Nick's voice then, husky with emotion and relief: 'Oh, thank God – *at last* . . .' She recognised his familiar embrace and the smell of his sweater, even the unshaven roughness of his cheek, pressed to hers. He hugged her to him, rocking her like a child, and his warmth restored some kind of sense and energy so that she was able, at last, to raise her eyelids and see for herself what was going on.

But her confusion was not clarified by finding herself on the sofa in the sitting-room, half-covered by a quilt, with five pairs of anxious eyes regarding her. Lesley, like a nervous little girl with a bunch of flowers, suddenly smiled and thrust a hot-water bottle into her lap, and said something about never having seen a faint like that before.

'Oh, was that . . .? I'm sorry, I didn't – '

'No, don't try to get up – just stay still,' Nick said, 'it's best to let the circulation return to normal . . .'

A little while later, when they were alone, he told her that when she collapsed, he had only just managed to prevent her from falling into the trench. 'I noticed you were shivering – then the colour just went from your face. Completely.' With a rueful smile, he stroked her cheek. 'I've never seen that happen before – it scared the hell out of me.'

'Oh, Nick – I'm sorry . . .'

'For heaven's sake, don't apologise – it wasn't your fault. It scared me, that's all. Just as well, really – I caught you as you fell. But the thing was, we couldn't bring you round. That was the alarming part. And you were so *cold* . . .'

'Well, I'm all right now,' she said, hugging the hot-water bottle. But in truth she did not feel all right, she felt shocked and drained and extremely tired. She sipped at the tea Giles had brought, and asked, a moment later, how long she'd been unconscious.

Nick shrugged and tried to appear nonchalant, but she could see that he was worried. 'I'm not sure – maybe four or five minutes. It seemed like hours.'

It seemed a long time to her too. Remembering what had provoked it, she shivered again, and when he said: 'Was it the knife?' she just nodded.

'I don't know what I expected,' she admitted a moment later, 'but it wasn't that. In fact to tell the truth, I don't think I expected anything at all. Even last night, when we found the bones, I kept telling myself that they could be any old bones – they couldn't possibly be Sarah Stalwell's, because . . . well, because *I had to have made her up . . .*

'It's crazy,' she said suddenly, running distracted fingers through her hair. 'I mean, the biggest part of me *knows* I didn't make her up, that I couldn't possibly have written that story on my own. Anyway, I was aware of her as a separate entity – and once I'd accepted that, I actually felt *good* about it, it helped me so much to come to terms with this thing about my mother. But still,' she went on passionately, 'there was still this niggling doubt, this hard core of scepticism which kept saying, *don't be ridiculous, you're kidding yourself girl, these things don't happen.*

'But I just found out they do. I saw that knife, Nick, and I *felt* the pain of it. Don't ask me how – I don't know. But it was as though it had happened to me.'

She saw his frown and the slightly distant expression which always came into his eyes when he was weighing facts against feelings, theories against proven truths. 'What are you saying?' he asked at last. 'Are you talking about reincarnation?'

The question surprised her. 'No, I don't think so. No, no, I'm not,' she added abruptly, frustrated by his lack of understanding. She paused to find a way of describing what she meant, but words seemed worse than inadequate, they made everything sound mad.

Eventually, taking a deep breath, she said: 'Sarah Stalwell isn't me – she's separate. If you remember, I saw her looking up at me from across the yard – and even when I was writing her story, it was like being dictated to by someone else. But there was one occasion,' she added slowly, 'which was different. I was on my way into the village – just about to cross the road at the foot of Dagger Lane, in fact – and just for a split-second I saw the village as it must have been in Sarah's time, with all the thatched houses and the mud, and the stream running down the middle of the street. There was a ford, by the way, and stepping-stones, where Dagger Lane crosses the Green – '

'My God,' he whispered, half-laughing in his amazement, '*now* you tell me!'

'Yes, I know – I'm sorry. It was kind of pushed aside by everything else that was happening. Anyway, it didn't seem so important at the time – except it was like seeing through someone else's eyes, and it really shook me. Made me feel quite ill afterwards – in fact I even went to the pub and ordered a glass of brandy, so you can tell how bad I felt.

'But it only happened once – until just now. And when I saw that knife,' she added quietly, 'it wasn't so much what I saw as what I *felt*. It really was like experiencing someone else's *feelings*.'

Nick did not doubt her word for a moment, even though the story unnerved him. And he was extremely concerned about the length of time that she had been unconscious. He felt that things were happening too fast, sapping mental as well as physical energy, and making inroads upon Natasha's youthful resilience.

Anticipating protests, he was reluctant just then to press the matter of a medical check-up; but in the meantime, while the others were busy outside, he persuaded her to speak to Haydn. This most recent experience of hers might prove to be irrelevant, but Natasha still seemed to be the focus for whatever was going on, and Nick's sense of unease was growing, not diminishing.

Returning to the barn, he stood for a moment, watching the two students complete their work on the excavated grave. Then Lesley moved and he saw the skeleton in its entirety, with the knife lying beneath. That tangible evidence of old evil had shocked him too, although his chief awareness now was of the centuries between, the lifetimes which stood between that moment and this.

And yet they were linked; weirdly, inexplicably linked. He could explore theories of circumstance, predestination, even kinks in the loop of time, but there were no clear answers and even less in the way of conclusive proof. He and Natasha might possess their own private certainties of what had happened and when, but he could never write it up. It would always remain a curiosity, a coincidence, an intriguing little after-dinner story; none of it would stand up to professional scrutiny.

The association of ideas made him think, yet again, of the police. Sooner or later, they would have to be informed. Thinking of Natasha, he was tempted to leave it until the morning, but that would mean bringing everyone back again, and it seemed preferable to deal with the matter now.

Remembering Toby's death, Nick was aware that in these instances the police were never tardy. Nevertheless, he was surprised at the speed with which everything happened. After three days of slow, painstaking work, in which they had become a team working to a common end, the sense of triumph and justification was very short-lived.

As before, it was the local police at Strensall who were contacted. Nick launched into his prepared speech, telling the officer at the other end of the line that, in the course of digging up the barn floor, they had come across a human skeleton – very old, he hastened to add – which he felt must be reported. After a momentary pause, he was asked for his name and address, and at that there was another pause, longer this time. As Nick began to give directions to the house, the officer interrupted. Yes, he said, he knew the place, he had been called out there quite recently.

Only too aware of the occasion, Nick said: 'Yes, of course. It was ten days ago, when old Toby Bickerstaff died. We went to the funeral yesterday.'

With no comment, but an assurance that someone would be there shortly, the conversation was over. Replacing the phone, Nick felt like a criminal. Glancing at the upturned faces around the kitchen table, it seemed to him they had the look of conspirators, and he dreaded the questioning that was bound to follow.

The car arrived within ten minutes, its headlights describing an arc around the yard as it pulled in. Followed by Haydn Parker, Nick went to the door. To his surprise, the young policeman who stepped out of the car was not one of the pair who had dealt with Toby's death. Nick introduced himself, and, with a gesture towards Haydn, said 'And this is the Reverend Parker, one of the chaplains from York University.'

The young officer's face was not entirely impassive; Nick thought he saw a flicker of surprise as the notebook came out.

'Right, sir. If I could just have a look at this, er, skeleton . . .'

Nick pulled back the barn doors and switched on the lights. This time it was obvious that the young man was taken aback. The trenches, in stark shadow, looked even deeper than they were.

Finding his voice, Nick said firmly: 'As you can see, we were conducting an archaeological dig. Then, as I said on the phone, we came across human remains . . .'

'Where?'

Haydn picked up one of the angle-lamps and shone the light into the hole. The skeleton, curled like the body of a sleeping child, looked very small. Above and behind it, the rotted timbers of the old wall were almost like a bedhead, but they gave, Nick thought, added credence to the tale of an archaeological investigation.

After a good, long look, the young policeman indulged in a rueful smile. 'Well, as you say, sir, it's obviously not a recent death, but just for the fact of being here, I'd say the circumstances must have been suspicious!'

'Oh, yes. You probably can't see it from here, but underneath the skeleton there's a knife.'

'Is there really?' He leaned forward and peered even more closely. 'Well, we'd better not disturb anything. I'm sorry, but I'll have to tape the area off and ask you gentlemen to leave until CID have had a chance to look at it.'

He went back to the car, and from the boot extracted several metal stanchions and a reel of high-visibility red tape. In other circumstances, Nick thought, he might have been amused by the care with which bureaucracy tied everything up, especially since they had been trampling all over the place for the last three days. At the moment, however, he was simply anxious to have the whole thing dealt with as quickly as possible.

A few minutes later another car arrived, this time containing two plainclothes officers. Without further ado they went into the barn with the uniformed man, and it was several minutes before they came out again. From the porch doorway, Nick heard the crackle of the car radio as one of them reported back to the station. The older man crossed the yard and met Nick at the gate.

'Dr Rhodes? Good evening, sir, my name's Bartlett – Detective Superintendent. I presume the property belongs to you – the house, and the, er, *barn*?'

'Yes, yes it does.'

'Good. In that case could we go inside, and perhaps you might outline the situation for me.'

He followed Nick into the hall, and the other detective followed him, leaving the uniformed man outside. They looked into the kitchen, where the others were sitting around the table, and with a request for somewhere quiet, followed Nick into the sitting-room. As they sat down, facing the unlit pile of logs in the grate, Nick wondered what they would say if he told them what he believed to be the truth, that those bones out there were the remains of a woman who had been murdered in this very room. Not for one moment did he imagine that they would believe him, yet the craziness of the situation prompted an absurd desire to laugh. He had to frown quite hard in order to control it.

'Now, Dr Rhodes, the people in the kitchen – are they involved?'

'Yes.'

'All of them?'

'Yes.'

'Would you mind telling me who they are, and why they're here?'

Nick ran through all their names and occupations, explaining to the Detective Superintendent – while his sergeant took notes – that the others had volunteered to help him with the archaeological dig.

'But what made you dig just there? Why not the garden, for instance?'

After a moment's hesitation, Nick plunged in. 'Because I had reason to believe that a former inhabitant of this house had been murdered, and might have been buried there.'

The face that was turned to him might have been weary, Nick thought, but the eyes were extraordinarily alert. 'You mean you were actually searching for human remains?'

'Yes, that's right, I was.'

There was a small but eloquent pause. 'And what made you think you would find them?'

'Instinct,' Nick replied without hesitation, confident that in some respects his job and the Superintendent's were not markedly different. He went on to say that he had been pursuing two independent lines of research which had crossed, unexpectedly, in the early eighteenth century; and having explained about the Reverend Clive's journal and its mention of the former owners of Holly Tree Farm, Nick then told him about Richard Stalwell's death and the subsequent family feud.

'It's quite clear from the Reverend Clive's comments that

Sarah Stalwell was at this time behaving outrageously. Not to put too fine a point on it, she was behaving like a whore, which provoked a great deal of local hostility. Then, quite suddenly, she disappeared. The Reverend Clive evidently suspected foul play, but was unable to prove it. Of course, he was old and frail at the time, and died not long afterwards, so it's perhaps not surprising that the crime went undetected.'

With a sigh, Superintendent Bartlett raised his hand. 'Yes, I see. But what made you think the body might have been buried in the barn? Why not in the cellar, for instance, or under the floorboards?'

Nick explained that the house did not have a cellar, and that the perpetrators of the crime were due to inherit the house. 'I couldn't imagine them resting easy with Sarah's body under their feet – and it seemed to me they'd choose the barn because they could work under cover – and hide the disturbance of the soil under straw and cow-dung.'

'Mmm, yes, I see.' He thought for a moment, his face impassive. 'Why not the local woods? I presume, in those days, this area had woodland?'

'I'm sure it did – it has today. But in those days, woodland was used, for fuel, farm implements, household utensils – people frequented the woods on a regular basis. I'd say there'd be far more chance of a grave being found in the woodlands of those days, than there is now.'

Those eyes, slightly hooded but missing nothing, bored into him as he was speaking. Although Nick had logic on his side, he still felt that the Superintendent knew he was not getting the whole truth. He no longer wanted to laugh; indeed, he was sweating in a room that was not particularly warm, and longing for the interview to be over.

'Well, that's an interesting theory,' the other man allowed, 'and not one that would have occurred to me, I must admit. But your friends, now – were they aware of all this?'

Nick pursed his lips. 'Well, yes, more or less.'

'And what on earth made them agree to help you? I mean, it's hard work, digging trenches, Dr Rhodes – you'd have to be pretty well convinced of what you were doing, I'd say, before you got started on a project like that . . .' The raised eyebrows almost begged him to continue.

'It is hard work,' Nick agreed with feeling. Conscious of his hands, he tried to hide the bandages on his palms. 'But I think, like me, that our friends felt it wrong that a body should rest in unconsecrated ground, without the benefit of a Christian burial.'

The eyes regarded him steadily. 'Even an eighteenth-century whore?'

'Yes, Superintendent, even an eighteenth-century whore.' He was annoyed by that before he realised that the jab was probably intended. Just as he was wondering what question was coming next, they heard the sound of a car coming up the lane. As it pulled into the yard, the Sergeant looked out of the window.

'Exhibits, I think, sir,' he said, speaking to his superior.

'Yes, well, the forensic pathologist will be here soon, Dr Rhodes, so we'll find out whether or not you're right about those bones. In the meantime, do you think I could have a word with your wife?'

Glad though he was to be released, Nick was rather more concerned about Natasha, and how well she would stand up to questioning. He had no chance to either prime or reassure, however; as soon as he stood up, so did the Sergeant, and a moment later, as Natasha was escorted into the sitting-room, the young policeman from outside came into the kitchen to sit with them.

Nick would have liked a good, stiff drink, but he made coffee instead; the young policeman shook his head, and the others, awash with coffee already, declined the offer. Uncomfortable with the situation, they sat like patients in a dentist's waiting room, staring at their hands and their used cups, anything but each other. Nick switched on the television for the early evening news, but could not settle to watch or listen; he moved to the window instead, peering across the yard at the open doorway of the barn. Against lights which were certainly brighter than the ones they had been using for the past three days, one of the two men inside was using what looked like a video camera.

In some surprise, he turned to their uniformed chaperon, and said: 'Are they filming the site?'

'I expect so, sir. It's standard procedure.'

'In murder cases.'

The young policeman cleared his throat. 'With regard to bodies found in suspicious circumstances, sir.'

'I see.' How times change, he thought, exchanging a look with Giles, who joined him at the window. In an undertone, he said: 'I wonder what our Sarah would have made of that?'

Giles's blue eyes crinkled in amusement. 'More to the point, what will the forensic scientists make of our little find? Could be interesting, don't you think?'

'I'm more interested to know how Natasha's doing – and how long this is likely to go on.'

'We won't keep you any longer than we have to, sir,' the policeman replied.

Nevertheless, it seemed a long time. In the succeeding three-quarters of an hour, they had all, bar Haydn, been interviewed, and he was in with the Superintendent when Nick noticed another vehicle coming up the lane. Its lights illuminated the stone gate-posts at the entrance to the yard, but although there was a pause, it did not pull in. With seven cars already in the yard, there was hardly room to manoeuvre a bicycle. And the vehicle, as Nick could see, was a large van, with POLICE in reflective letters across the back.

A figure got out; there were consultations; cars were moved into the lane. Eventually, with the Rover, two police cars and Dave's old Volvo out of the way, the van was able to back into the yard and up to the barn. Two of the men who got out had the pared-down look of scientists, Nick decided; all they needed to fit into a research laboratory were white coats over their well-worn suits. The third one, however, was different. In an old tweed jacket and sagging corduroys, he was shorter, fatter and older, with a fringe of long white hair blowing around his head like a halo.

'Who are they?' Nick asked the Detective Sergeant as they walked back to the house from the lane. 'Not policemen, surely?'

'They're from Forensic – pathologist, scientist, and archaeologist.'

'Really?' Nick was impressed. With a dry smile, he watched them go into the barn. 'Let me guess – the guy with the white hair is the archaeologist.'

The Sergeant allowed himself a short bark of laughter. 'Well spotted. He's Professor Ord-Bray. I expect you've heard of him?'

'No, can't say I have, but I imagine Dave has . . .' He turned to the young man behind him, who was staring over Nick's shoulder with something very akin to awe in his eyes.

'Ord-Bray?' he repeated. 'Oh, my *God* – wait till Doc Rathmell hears about this. He'll never forgive himself for sending *me*.'

'You mean he'll be wishing he'd done this job himself?'

'Too bloody true,' Dave murmured. 'I didn't like to tell you this before, Nick, but he only sent me and Lesley because we're mates, and we don't live far from each other. I'm in Boston, and she's just outside Lincoln, so we often travel up and down together, you see.'

'No, I don't,' Nick replied. 'What are you trying to say?'

Looking hunted, Dave shook his head. 'Well, you see, we're not quite the star pupils you thought he'd sent. In fact, Doc Rathmell thinks we're pretty bloody useless. I'm sure he only sent us because he didn't think we'd find anything.'

For a moment, Nick was lost for words. It was so typical of academic rivalry and ruthlessness, he should have been furious. But, seeing the ironic twist of fate, he started to laugh instead. Clapping Dave heartily on the shoulder, he said: 'Well, the old bastard was wrong, wasn't he? Come on, get Lesley, and we'll find out just what sort of a job you've done.'

The Sergeant made every attempt to dissuade them from entering the barn, but Nick was having none of it. 'Look, it's my barn and these two were instrumental in finding those bones. If your forensic people don't want us in there, they can tell us to piss off – but just for the moment I want these two to see the great man looking at *their* work. All right?'

From icy politeness, the Sergeant's tone became threatening. 'Sir, if you persist, I'm going to have to charge you – '

'That won't be necessary,' the Superintendent's quiet voice broke in. To Nick, he said: 'If you'll just wait here, Dr Rhodes, I'll have a word with the Professor. He may want to speak to your young friends anyway.'

A moment later he led them into the barn, to stand behind the red tape. Bound to silence, they stood looking down into the trench, now floodlit from all angles, where the Professor and one of the scientists were examining the bones and depth of soil. The other, crouched over the original wall, was busy making notes.

Snatches of conversation came up to them. '. . . No doubt at all . . . ammoniac deposits . . . at least three centuries, wouldn't you say?'

Restraining a desire to tell them the precise year of the murder, Nick watched and listened. The Professor seemed to be peering at the knife.

'All been photographed, has it?' he enquired of the other two policemen on the far side of the barn. Assured on that score, he reached for one of Dave's tools and carefully picked some soil away from beneath the skeleton. A few minutes later, he extracted the knife. 'Well, there you are, boys – the murder weapon, or I'm an Irishman!' Laughing at his little joke, he held it up for all to see. 'Bit rusty, I'm afraid, and the handle's just about gone, but it could still do some damage . . .' Adjusting his glasses, he peered at it again. 'Doubt if you'll get any fingerprints, though!'

There was some dutiful laughter at that; then, looking up, the Professor seemed to notice them for the first time. 'You supervised the dig, I take it?'

Nick cleared his throat. 'Not exactly, Professor. I'm an historian – my friends here are the archaeologists.'

The thick white eyebrows went up as he surveyed Dave and Lesley. Lesley's eager face obviously charmed him, to the extent that he removed his glasses to see her more clearly. 'Well, you've done a nice clean job – made our business easier, I'm delighted to say. The other trench is a bit unorthodox, I'll grant you, but I can see the problems you must have had.' He smiled benevolently. 'But I presume you knew what you were looking for?'

Struck dumb, the other two looked to Nick. 'Yes,' he said, knowing that he was compromising nobody.

'Hmm. Interesting. I look forward to reading the reports.' He turned away, back to the skeleton, and the Superintendent ushered them out.

The two students were almost floating on euphoria as he escorted them back to the house. 'Won't it be gratifying to tell Dr Rathmell how well you've done?' Nick remarked. 'I for one shall enjoy embroidering that bit of praise!'

'And I hope that bastard Joe Rathmell turns green,' he declared to Natasha when everyone else had gone. 'Just wait till he asks me for a favour – I'll tell him to jump for it!'

'Well, whatever he thinks of Dave and Lesley, they did an excellent job – and they were great to have around.'

'They were indeed,' Nick agreed, and added with feeling: 'But dear God, the police! I thought they'd never go . . .'

'Not over yet, though, is it?'

'No, statements on Monday, and then we wait.'

With the remains of a late supper pushed to one side, they sat in pensive silence. Eventually, Natasha said: 'What will happen, do you know?'

'Yes, they said the bones will be dated by their forensic people, and, provided they really are as old as they appear to be, no further action will be taken.'

She laughed with relief. 'Really? I mean, I'm glad to hear it, but why not?'

'Nobody to bring to book, is there? Nobody to punish, after all these years.'

'Of course,' she said slowly, 'you're right – they're all dead. Why didn't I realise that? I've been feeling like a criminal ever since they arrived – expecting a severe rap over the knuckles at the very least!'

'I know what you mean,' Nick said, laughing. 'If that sergeant had had his way, we'd probably have been banged up in the cells by now!' Drawing her close, he gave Natasha a hug and a reassuring kiss; a moment later, glancing at the clock, he said that it was time for bed.

Before they went upstairs, he stepped into the porch, and, opening the outer door, looked across at the unlit barn. The roof and upper walls were in clear silhouette against a bright, starlit sky. The wind had dropped, but frost was glinting across the yard.

'Well,' he murmured, 'they've taken her away. After all these years, she's finally left this place . . .'

It was a moment or two before Natasha replied. 'I do hope you're right,' she said softly.

Forty Two

ALTHOUGH SUPERINTENDENT BARTLETT had warned them that there might be some media interest following the standard announcement to the press, neither of them was prepared for the ringing of the doorbell at nine o'clock the following morning.

It was Sunday, and after a strenuous three days they had both been looking forward to a morning in bed, lunch at the pub, and maybe a drive into town to see Giles and Fay later on. As the ringing intruded into his dreams, and finally raised him from sleep, Nick thought at first that it must be the boy delivering the Sunday papers; but then he realised that it was too early, and that he would not keep his finger pressed to the bell as though the whole village were on fire.

Still bleary-eyed, he answered the door in his dressing-gown, and was not at all impressed to discover a reporter from the local paper on his doorstep, and a photographer hovering by the gate.

They were polite but persistent. Eventually, Nick agreed to be interviewed, but in half an hour, when he had had time to wash, dress, and drink a cup of coffee. Natasha, listening at the top of the stairs, was outraged.

'For heaven's sake, what a time to call! Nine on a Sunday morning – it's ridiculous!'

'I suppose we should be thankful it's not the national dailies – they'd have been here at seven!'

They dressed hurriedly. Natasha insisted on time to do her

face, applying make-up as she drank her coffee. If no other good came out of it, she knew that at least Oasis Books would be pleased: with her paperback due out in a few months, every scrap of publicity for Natasha Crayke, novelist, would be greeted with delight.

Just for a moment she stood in front of the mirror, checked her appearance, and tried to make the mental adjustment from slightly overwrought human being to professional writer. 'All part of the job,' she told her reflected image. 'You've done it before, and you can do it again.' There was additional comfort in the fact that the story was already well rehearsed. Talking to the police had seen to that.

While Nick cajoled the stove into life, she tidied the kitchen, and was just about to ask the reporters in from their car in the yard when the telephone rang. It was someone from the *Yorkshire Post*, who understood that human remains had been found on Dr Rhodes's land, and would Dr and Mrs Rhodes be prepared to talk about it?

'Look, I can't talk to you just now, I've got somebody at the door. Can you ring back in half an hour?'

'Can we call and see you?' the voice persisted.

'What time were you thinking of?'

'This morning?'

Natasha sighed. 'Oh, all right, I suppose so.'

She put down the phone and raised her eyebrows at Nick. '*There might be some media interest*,' she said, quoting the Superintendent.

He laughed. 'Well, all we can do is keep it low-key.'

With regard to both journalists, they kept it brief and very low-key. Nick mentioned his research into the history of the house, but did not give a name to the Reverend Clive; Natasha did not mention her sighting of Sarah Stalwell in the barn doorway, and neither of them breathed a word of the story she had written. Fortunately, as they had hoped, the fact that Natasha was already known to both newspapers as a local author diverted the journalists from delving further. If there was not much to tell about the bones in the barn, they could at least say something about the people who had found them.

With Joe Rathmell in mind, Nick happily gave the journalists the names of Lesley and Dave, the archaeology students, and, for good measure, said that their work had been praised by Professor Ord-Bray, the forensic archaeologist. The remains, he added, had now been removed to the forensic laboratories at Sheffield, where the Home Office pathologists would examine them. Depending on their findings, he understood that the bones would eventually be released for burial.

Photographs were taken of the house and its occupants, of the barn and the archaeological dig, and of Dr and Mrs Rhodes posing awkwardly beside the spot where the bones had been found; after that the journalists were satisfied. By midday, Nick and Natasha were eager to escape to the Half Moon.

But even in the pub there was no peace to be had. Tony, the landlord, had heard about the police and last night's excitement, and wanted to know all the details; they had barely finished telling him, and found a table for lunch, when Craig Morrison accosted them.

'So this is where you're hiding! I've just been to your house to find out what's going on. You haven't been finding more dead bodies, have you?'

His unashamed curiosity amused Natasha. 'How did you know?' she asked, laughing a little at his astonishment.

Nick went to the bar for another drink while she told the story again, his strained smile covering a profound irritation at the young man's continued interest in his wife.

When he returned to the table, Craig said: 'You're a real pair of dark horses, aren't you? But I knew damn well you weren't just digging that floor out to lay a concrete base!'

'So what did you think we were doing?' Nick asked laconically.

'How should I know? Looking for buried treasure – anything!' Bemused by their laughter, he said defensively: 'Anyway, I knew something was up when I heard the police were round again.' With a sly grin, he added: 'I bet your barn floor's a mess now. What're you going to do with it?'

Nick smiled. 'Would you believe, lay a concrete floor?'

Back home again, he phoned Lesley to tell her about the newspapers, and shortly after that Haydn phoned him, to say that their plans for Monday evening would have to be deferred. He had been hoping to speak to the Rector of Denton, and a rather mysterious 'someone else', but neither was available until Tuesday.

'Well,' Nick said, 'make it Tuesday evening if you like – it's all right with me.'

But Haydn was not concerned about Nick: it was Natasha and Sarah Stalwell who were worrying him.

On Monday morning, Mrs Bickerstaff arrived at the same time as the postman. As Natasha opened the door, he handed her a bundle of letters, and then stood talking to the two women in the porch. Envisaging a lengthy exchange this morning, Nick tactfully removed the mail from Natasha's hand and retired to his study to go through it.

There were a couple of expected bills, some late cards, a bank statement, and – much to Nick's surprise – a weighty envelope, postmarked Bristol, from his friend David, the medievalist.

He opened it with a mixture of excitement and apprehension, feelings which increased as he scanned the letter and its enclosures. He paused for a moment to collect himself, before giving those typewritten sheets his proper attention. Never, he thought, had he been so aware of the two halves of himself, professional and personal; at the moment they were at war with one another.

When he thought he had summoned enough of the historian's detachment, Nick picked up the letter and read it slowly.

Dear Nick,

Thanks for your letter (Dec 3rd) – I'm glad the information was of use. Not having heard since, I assume the investigation is still in progress, and that the enclosed will be of interest. I came across it by chance, while looking for something else, but as soon as I noticed Reynald the man of Paynel, *my attention was arrested!*

What follows has been translated (not by me) from

fragments of a chronicle ascribed to the pen of William of Pontefract, who was an obedientiary at the monastery of Jumièges, n.w. of Paris, c.1150.

Both the man and his chronicle were known about in the later Middle Ages, although the complete work no longer exists, unfortunately. These and other fragments came to light in the early 1920s, when some sixteenth-century antiphonales were being repaired and rebound in Paris. Originally, they had been bound in vellum leaves, and those leaves were from the aforesaid chronicle.

I did wonder about the connection between this monk and your man Reynald, but Jumièges was a Benedictine house, like the abbey of St Mary's, in York. As a Yorkshireman, it is possible that William of Pontefract served first at St Mary's before transferring to France. He refers (as you will see) to 'one Ralph . . . who was received at our table . . .' and the context would seem to place 'our table' as being very close to the scene (and time) of the reported incidents.

The reported incidents certainly bear out the comments (already forwarded) of the Monk of Nostell. I would say also that they make the connection with your man's sobriquet: canis venaticus . . .

'*Your man*,' Nick muttered angrily, 'Jesus, he's not *my* man!' Swiftly, he turned the page, summoning what remained of his detachment in order to study what followed.

He was aware that for a monk idleness was regarded as the enemy of the soul, and that for the Benedictines in particular, writing counted as labour. But he reminded himself that their annals were very selective, including only those events which seemed relevant to the religious scheme of things, either guaranteeing the survival of Christian values, or pointing to the imminence of Christ's second coming on earth. Since biblical prophecies indicated the prior arrival of the Antichrist, at the end of the first millennium they were seeking omens, signs and portents, looking for the Evil One in war and famine and evil deeds. And in

1150, after almost fourteen years of anarchy and civil war in England, Nick thought it hardly surprising that for English monks the biblical prophecies seemed to be coming true.

'About this time [other evidence suggests this was the time of the Cistercian Henry Murdac, then Archbishop of York, 1147–1153] the evil deeds of the Lord Reynald reached the ears of the King [Stephen] who sent for some who should know him and enquired of them what manner of man he was. And they told the King he was no man but more a wolf, a rabid dog, who preyed upon the people and would not desist whatever came of it. At this time the two daughters of the Lord of [either illegible or unrecognisable] travelling by day with their nurse and men-at-arms, were seized by the Lord Reynald where the road to Hotune crosses the water beyond Bulemar. [villages within striking distance of Brickhill, I believe???] He took them to his castle, where he caused the men-at-arms to be killed treacherously except one. This man he sent back after he had cut off his hands to his Lord with the word that the Lord Reynald should have his satisfaction before the Lord should see his daughters again. [A large section here is wholly illegible]

'. . . and dreadful it is to know that when the Lord Reynald that night considering what he had done, determined to repent and was in earnest conversation with a holy man, the devil seized upon his soul again as he had often done and in far more terrible way, insomuch that the Lord Reynald sent for the daughters of his enemy and for their nurse . . . [another illegible section]

'. . . gave the nurse to his serving-men and the two children he caused to be chained in his hall for a night and a day, and in such insane fury none could come near him but he cursed them from him. He pleasured himself with these innocents and when the one was dead he slit the throat of the other and in his madness sent them in a cart to their father with his defiance . . .

'It happened that the Lord Reynald's own daughter who was then about twelve years of age, protesting at her father's cruelty and lasciviousness, was locked in a high room and none allowed to come to her. And when Lord Reynald had supped upon the innocents, straightaway he went to his daughter and violated her, as men say, and cut out her tongue and put out her eyes that she might not thereafter tell of it to any man. But some hearing marvelled and fled the Lord Reynald's wrath and came to the Lord Bishop and he forthwith sent to the King . . .
[There is much missing from the chronicle at this point.]

'At that time, which was about the Feast of St Martin the Bishop, the Lord Earl [could be Albemarle – noted by the Monk of Nostell] sent to the beast to ask of him if he would surrender himself to the King's mercy, but Lord Reynald caused the Earl's messenger to be spitted on a roasting spike and set him over the castle gates so that in his mercy the Lord Earl commanded one of those about him to shoot the man with an arrow and so put paid to his suffering . . .
[Another large section missing, but one assumes there must have been some fighting in and about the castle – resulting in some sort of mutiny.]

'. . . the soldiers [Reynald's soldiers?] seized upon him [Reynald?] and carried him to the fire they had made in the bottommost part of the tower, and there cut off his feet and hands and threw him upon the fire and kept him there at their swords' points until he no longer twisted or turned and was silent. Then they surrendered to the Lord Earl who caused them to be taken in chains to York . . .

'The King he would not consent for the Lord Reynald's body to be buried, and there being no gate to the castle it being burned, he commanded the charred remains to be hung from a gibbet on the road that all men might witness the King's displeasure . . .

'. . . At the Epiphany one Ralph who was Steward to the Lord Earl was received at our table and told of the fate

which befell the Lord Reynald of whom I have spoken, and said about the time the castle was consumed by fire, a black dog men took to be the Devil and some said was no more than the Lord Reynald's spirit sent for with demons to be conveyed away, issued out of the fallen gate and ran wildly along the road to the north as if consumed by fire itself . . .

'. . . a dreadful thing to see so foul a creature . . .

'Indeed it is,' Nick whispered, feeling the hairs prickle at the back of his neck and down his arms. The road to the north: from Brickhill, in those days, that road could only be Dagger Lane . . .

He shivered and turned the page, but there were only a couple more lines:

'. . . even his own soldiers must be God's instruments when no other would avail, and they as black as him and long in his service . . .'

Feeling stunned, he sat back and lit a cigarette, but it was difficult to concentrate. Every now and then he glanced at the words before him, rereading a couple of lines here and there as though to confirm their meaning. What he had was no more than a translation, punctuated for the sake of sense and typed out on cheap modern paper by a computerised machine. But Nick had a mental picture of the original, and soft and costly calfskin leaves turned brittle by the centuries, a cramped Latin script laboriously penned – perhaps in York? – by someone who was alive when those events took place. A man who was living at the same time as Reynald de Briec.

Those words were older than the present Minster, older than the walls of York; they had been written when those grassy mounds behind Brickhill church were a charred and crumbling ruin, while the birds still pecked at de Briec's bones and the countryside sagged into an exhausted peace.

That was what stunned him. When he thought of the age of those words, mere fragments from a chronicle written eight hundred years before he was born, they seemed like a bridge across time, destined for his eyes to read, his mind to unravel. They were not just clues to the mystery, they were the mystery itself; proof – if proof were needed – that he had been right all along about de Briec and the beast.

That afternoon, on their way to the police station at Strensall, Nick insisted on taking the small detour into Brickhill village, just to look at the church and the site of Reynald de Briec's castle.

They parked in the gateway, as before, but this time, instead of climbing the path between that avenue of yews, they branched off to skirt the hill, to follow the broken but discernible line of the castle bailey just within the churchyard wall. In places, those low, grassy mounds looked like a series of irregular, unmarked graves above a shallow ditch; in others just the grassy ditch remained. Time had done its levelling, and, where the hill was steepest, only the ninteenth-century wall suggested a much earlier fortification.

A path of sorts led up between the trees. Taking Natasha's hand, Nick helped her up the muddy incline until they were standing on the crest, surrounded by more low mounds which marked the castle keep. A sudden gust of wind rattled the sycamore branches above their heads and Natasha shivered, as much from nerves as with cold; it was a bleak, alien place, and she wanted to get back to the car. But Nick, still in thrall to the chronicle, wanted to look and see and absorb every feature; he wanted to use his imagination to visualise de Briec's hill and castle as it had been in de Briec's day.

With the words of the chronicle still at the forefront of her mind, Natasha did not have to try very hard; her difficulty lay in ignoring those evil deeds, pushing back the idea of rape and torture and mutilation, brutal soldiers and violated children, and the ravening insanity of a man possessed.

She looked across at the churchyard, and thought that she would not like to be buried here, no matter how well-consecrated the ground; and she looked down into Craig Morrison's garden, with its shrubs and jasmine and that ancient yew tree, and thought she would not like to live there either. Below, the end of Dagger Lane disappeared into a ploughed field, but it had once continued south across the desolate expanse of Strensall Common and towards the distant city. From here she could see the towers of York Minster, pale against a scudding grey sky, and experienced a sharp desire to be there, away from this place with its brooding atmosphere and its ancient history of evil.

With a sigh of impatience she turned to Nick, longing to urge him away. He responded at last, his frown disappearing into a satisfied smile as he took her arm.

They were halfway down the avenue of yews when he suddenly stopped and pointed across the village street to where Dagger Lane emerged. 'You see – the road to the north, virtually facing the gate.'

'You mean – the church gates – they're in the same *position*?'

'As the old castle gate? Yes, I'm almost sure of it. Those mounds either side of the path are probably the old foundations.'

'Oh, my God – how could they?' For a moment she stared in horror, remembering the impaled messenger, the fire, the man – Reynald de Briec – with no feet and no hands, being burned alive . . .

Nauseated, she hid her face against Nick's shoulder. 'It's horrible – I wish David had never sent that letter. Get me out of here – I can't bear it!'

A little way down the road he stopped the car and took her into his arms. 'Look, it's all right – don't panic – it all happened one hell of a long time ago – '

'I know, I know. It's just that place – *knowing* about it. Somehow it makes it all seem so *recent* . . .'

'Yes, I'm sorry,' he whispered against her cheek. 'I shouldn't have brought you here – but it was on the way, and I thought – '

She sniffed and straightened and pulled away from him. 'I wish you'd just leave it alone now – forget about it. I'm frightened – frightened of what it's done to us – what it might still do to you.'

He sighed and started the car. 'I know, but I have to see it through.'

When they arrived at the police station, Giles was already there with the two students; Haydn arrived a few minutes later.

Having been forewarned by Nick's phone call that morning, he read David's letter and the accompanying account while they were waiting, but although he seemed grimly impressed, he was reluctant to comment in front of the others.

'We need to talk about this,' he said quietly. 'Unfortunately, I've got another appointment in York this afternoon, so I can't come back to the house.' He glanced at his watch. 'Do you think we could go across to the pub when we finally get through with these statements?'

As Natasha nodded and said yes, Nick glanced across at Giles; catching the look, Haydn said: 'I'm sure the others will understand. We just need a quiet corner and a few minutes to talk.'

The opportunity came eventually, although the statements seemed to have taken forever. Natasha looked drained, and Nick was badly in need of a drink. Haydn, however, insisted on orange juice.

Scanning through the translation again, he said: 'You know, you must both get this into perspective. Historically speaking, it's impressive stuff – but Nick, you don't need me to remind you that this is *not* an eye-witness account. Not a statement of fact that would stand up in a court of law – it's hearsay. And –' he held up his hand to stem Nick's interruption, 'and even if it were *not* embroidered in any way, you should beware of drawing the obvious conclusions.'

'Which are?' Nick demanded, irritated by that reminder of the truth.

Haydn shook his head. 'You've told me already,' he said calmly, 'when we spoke on the phone. You said de Briec and the beast were one and the same – that you'd thought so all along, and this evidence confirmed it.'

'But surely,' Natasha began, 'it makes the link – '

'The link, yes – but not the fact. This is an account of an evil man – a man who may have been possessed by evil, but who was essentially human –' He broke off to refer to the translation, and quoted from it: '*The Lord Reynald that night considering what he had done, determined to repent* . . . Well, that might not be strictly true, but it illustrates what I mean – that he still had a grain of good in him, enough to know that what he had done was wrong. He was human, but evil is not – and you must beware of making the assumption that what you have seen and experienced recently has anything to do with the human spirit.' He glanced at Natasha and said: 'We've talked of this already with regard to Sarah Stalwell, and I must remind you again that she – it – might not be what it purports to be.

'Your feelings of concern and pity do you justice, but they might be misplaced – I have to warn you of that. Nothing's clear here, and that's what makes me so cautious. Evil likes to trick and confuse, to play its little masquerades – and this could be one of them.'

While they each considered that, Haydn glanced at the papers in his hand. 'If you don't mind, Nick, I'd like to borrow this to show to a friend of mine – I won't keep it long and I know he'll be interested. In the meantime, though, I want you to put it from your mind – I know it's hard not to give it the credence you feel it deserves, but believe me, thinking about evil only increases its potential.'

Although he did not want to argue with Haydn, particularly in front of Natasha, Nick was annoyed. He had asked for advice, but felt that he was being treated like a schoolboy; and that borrowing of David's letter was like having a bag of sweets confiscated by a teacher. Not even Haydn's apology, hastily offered before he left, alleviated it.

'He was in a hurry,' Natasha said quietly. 'He hadn't time to be tactful.'

'Even so . . .'

It was a relief to join the others. Now that all seemed to be over, they were obviously feeling slightly silly, and after one drink in the pub at Strensall, Giles suggested that it would be preferable to continue into town, where they could drink as much as they liked and walk home later.

'Twelve miles?' Natasha said with mock reproof.

'But you don't drink anyway,' Giles protested. 'At least, not so's anyone would notice!'

She laughed. 'It's all right – I don't mind. Anyway,' she added in an undertone, 'I think it would do Nick good to unwind a bit . . .'

The atmosphere improved his temper, and he was soon laughing and joking with the two students, who were enjoying their day of fame. Their names had appeared in two newspapers, and Joe Rathmell had almost choked over his congratulations when they phoned to tell him.

After an hour or so spent sampling the excellent beers in the Spread Eagle, Nick was feeling expansive and reluctant to cut the celebration short. He insisted that Lesley and Dave join them for a meal, and then regaled them with the history of Walmgate's former hostelries as they walked the length of the street into town.

Natasha was as amused as the rest of them, even though she was sober; but in the back of her mind lurked that conversation with Haydn Parker, refusing to be blotted out. In spite of his firm and confident exterior, she could tell he was anxious about their situation, and that worried her. Nor was he convinced that Sarah Stalwell was the power for good that Natasha believed her to be; and that dented her confidence alarmingly. He had asked her twice to let go of that belief and place all her faith in God; he had even asked her, after their last discussion about the destructive nature of guilt, to make her confession . . .

But she was not quite ready for that. He understood, and regretted only the current situation, which seemed to be pressing them all too fast along roads that were fraught with pitfalls. Aware of those they had negotiated already, she looked at Nick and was pierced by love and fear and a desire to protect him. He would probably laugh at that, she thought, just as he was laughing now; but she moved to his side and slipped an arm under his, and when he bent his head to lightly kiss her, her response surprised him.

'All right?' he asked softly, hugging her close.

She smiled and nodded and he was reassured; a few moments

later they were crossing the road by All Saints Pavement, and entering the narrow passageway which led to the restaurant. It was a place that Giles had discovered, tucked away in its own little courtyard, and where they had often dined. That they were greeted like old friends added to Nick's exuberance.

He wasn't drunk, Natasha knew that, just reacting to all the tensions of the last few days. She watched the curve of his mouth as he laughed and talked, the way his eyes creased at the corners, and felt the attractive power of his looks and personality with an acute kind of pain. We used to be happy, she thought; he was often like this before, and not just in company.

Watching the way Lesley was responding to him and Giles, she found herself thinking of that girl at the Hallowe'en party, and the woman, Sally; but she was no longer surprised or even jealous, just sad that such things had happened.

But then Nick, noticing her pensive mood, drew her close to him again, and the sadness passed. By the end of the evening she was as buoyant with good spirits as everyone else. They were still laughing and joking as they left the restaurant at ten o'clock, and only the raw wind blowing from the nearby river made them bid each other a hasty goodnight.

They were pleased to get into the car. Taking his keys, Natasha fastened her seat-belt and turned the key in the ignition. She was aware that Nick was relaxed and happy, pleased by her enjoyment and the spontaneity of their night out; but as they left York behind a silence fell between them, heightened by the buffeting of the wind. As she negotiated the first of a series of tight bends, Natasha was suddenly reminded of that other night, driving home in this same car, after that dreadful party.

Seized by apprehension, she would have given anything to be able to turn round and drive back to York, to say, *bugger the house, we're more important*, and never set eyes on it again.

As though he caught those feelings and needed to fend them off, Nick started talking about the work he still had to do, the fact that there was only a week left of the Christmas holiday, and time was running out on him.

She wanted to say, *time's running out on us, don't you feel it?*

Instead she bit her lip and tried to swallow the fear by concentrating on driving. By the time they reached Denton she was sweating and her stomach was churning. The house was a black, brooding shape as they drove up the lane, and she had never hated it more.

Nick noticed at once that the barn door was ajar, and rattling in the wind.

'Who the hell's been in there?' he muttered, stepping out of the car. 'I'm sure I left it shut – '

'Nick – leave it – '

'Don't worry – it's probably one of the workmen I phoned this morning. One of them must have called while we were out . . .'

But he did not really believe that, and approached the open door with caution. It was possible that the wind had moved it, but more likely that it had been opened deliberately. Remembering the ammoniac smell that he had noticed before, Nick thought of tramps and prepared himself for confrontation.

The Rover's headlights, shining obliquely, gave plenty of illumination as he pulled back the door, but the interior of the barn was black. Tensed, holding his breath, Nick reached in for the light-switches and flicked them on. The light was dim, but he saw at once that the place was empty. Even the trenches, shadowed though they were, hid nothing more than soil.

Sighing with relief, he moved into the barn to make sure, and took another breath. That breath almost choked him. The stench of ordure was so powerful that he had to cover his mouth. The atmosphere was thick with it, so dense and fetid that the impression was of an animal's lair, recently vacated. As he retreated to the door, his glance darted round that great open space, but there was nothing to be seen, and he could not have advanced on those shadowy holes had his life depended on it.

He backed into Natasha, her eyes wide, mouth drawn back in horrified disgust. 'What *is* it?'

But there was no time to hazard guesses. He grabbed her, pulled her outside, and dragged the door shut on its great metal rollers. 'I don't bloody know,' he muttered between clenched teeth, 'but I'm not hanging around to find out. Come on – quickly – let's get in the house.'

'What about the car?'

'Leave it – give me the keys – '

He fumbled with them in his haste, dragging Natasha inside the porch as soon as he had it open, flicking on light-switches as he went. Nothing happened. Everything was dead.

'Jesus Christ –' As Natasha released a gasp of fear, he hugged her to him, feeling his way through into the kitchen. 'Candles – lighter – that lamp of yours – '

It seemed to take forever to gain that small illumination. He stationed Natasha by the window to watch the yard, and picked up the phone to dial Haydn's number. He prayed that he had remembered it correctly, and that he didn't get the answering machine.

After six rings, a pleasant female voice – no machine, thank God! – answered.

'Isabel? It's Nick Rhodes. Sorry for the late call, but I need to speak to Haydn – is he there?'

She said he was, but that he was in the shower.

'Do you think you could ask him to come to the phone? It's urgent.'

The intervening minutes seemed an eternity. He moved as close to Natasha as the telephone cord would allow, and could see her trembling. Eventually, Haydn's voice broke into the tension. Taking a deep breath, Nick described the stench in the barn. 'That bloody thing's been here, I swear it. Trouble is, I think it's still around. We've got no electricity in the house – and I've just noticed the barn lights are off, too.'

Calmly, the voice in his ear urged him not to panic.

'Dear God, Haydn – if you'd seen that thing on Christmas Eve, you'd be panicking too!' Nevertheless, he tried to collect himself, listening to Haydn's instructions as he continued to scan the darkness outside.

'Yes, yes, all right, we'll do that . . . Right, I'll see you soon.'

Replacing the phone, he went straight to Natasha, holding her close while never taking his eyes from the area illuminated by the car lights. But even those seemed less bright than they should be.

'What did he say?'

'He's coming over. And in the meantime he advised us to pray.' He smiled at her quizzical look, and said: 'Don't worry, you don't have to struggle with your conscience – I'll say the prayers, you can just listen.'

Following Haydn's instructions, he closed the curtains and helped Natasha light all the candles they could find. Then he went upstairs to find a copy of Cranmer's Prayer Book.

Forty Three

ALTHOUGH THE print was small, he held the book so that Natasha, sitting beside him at the kitchen table, could read the prayers as he spoke them aloud. Not expecting her to join in, he enunciated the words clearly and with respect, summoning a well of faith which seemed to have lain dormant for too many years. There was strength and beauty in those sonorous, sixteenth-century phrases, and comfort in the fact of praying; but that sense was more than doubled when he heard Natasha's voice, hesitant at first, join his in the reciting of the psalms.

'Thou shalt not be afraid for any terror by night: nor for the arrow that flieth by day; For the pestilence that walketh in darkness: nor for the sickness that destroyeth in the noonday . . .'

He held her hand, giving and drawing strength from her presence, and from that wavering faith which seemed to be growing stronger by the minute. From the psalms Haydn had recommended, they proceeded to the Litany, and they were almost through those prayers when Natasha heard the car.

As expected, it was Haydn, his kind face full of concern. 'Are you all right?'

Rather to his surprise, Nick was able to smile. 'Yes, we are.'

'Good – you certainly sound better.' He stepped over the threshold and deposited a small case in the hall. 'The power of prayer,' he remarked dryly, 'it really does work, you know.'

He made an impressive figure in his cassock and collar, and the long black cloak that went with those garments; but even as he commented on them, Nick wondered at Natasha's reaction. To his relief, she did not avert her eyes, but welcomed Haydn warmly, and earned herself a very special smile.

'It seemed better to come prepared,' he said by way of explanation, 'although I would have preferred to do this tomorrow, as planned, and with the assistance of a colleague. But still,' he added briskly, 'we must do what we have to, and if necessary do it now. But I may need your help, Nick. Is your faith strong enough?'

'To do what?' he asked, aware of a sudden trepidation.

'To help me send this – this creature – back where it belongs.'

For a second he hesitated, but in that moment Nick balanced his belief in the existence of that creature with his faith in God. That faith had never been tested before, and he had neglected it for years; but he had the strongest feeling that if he said no, then that thing out there, whatever it was, would have won.

'Yes,' he said at last, 'it's strong enough.'

'Good. Then let's first discover the lie of the land . . .'

Telling Natasha to stay where she was, to pray if she could, Haydn led the way outside. As they crossed the yard, he said to Nick: 'If anything happens – whatever it might be – don't touch me. If you feel the need to grab hold of anything, grab the wall or the door or something – *but don't grab me*. All right?'

Nick nodded, his new-found confidence taking a sudden dive. Sensing it, Haydn smiled at him. 'Have faith, remember Christ is with us.'

The wind was soughing through the trees, the oaks creaking ominously in the darkness. Just short of the door, Haydn paused to make the sign of the cross. 'In the Name of the Father and of the Son and of the Holy Spirit. Amen.'

Echoing the *amen*, Nick found himself edging closer to his friend; remembering his instructions, he moved away again. With a questioning glance he laid a hand on the door, and at a nod from Haydn pulled it back on its metal rollers. Immediately there was a gush of air, and something rushed past Nick, taking his breath away; he felt the passage of a warm, foul-smelling wind, which caught the chaplain's cloak, bellowing it out like the wings of a great bat. Haydn bent against it, his hands clasped together, while Nick, paralysed with shock, clung to the cold metal handle of the door.

Afterwards, he realised that it could have lasted no more than a few seconds; yet there was that quality of slow-motion about it, an indelible impression of extended time that was almost as frightening as the event itself.

Sinking down against the door, Nick closed his eyes and breathed again, the thin, clean air of winter, sharp with the promise of snow. He dragged great, invigorating gulps of air into his lungs, while his body shook with the release of tension. Haydn too was on his knees, the night wind gently buffeting that heavy cloak. As he looked up, Nick said shakily: 'It's gone – I think it's gone. Are you OK?'

'Yes, thanks be to God. What about you?'

'Like a jelly.' He laughed weakly, and then, still on his knees, poked his head around the open door. The barn was empty, truly empty this time, the air as cold and wintry as ever. Pulling himself to his feet, he stepped inside. There was no anguish, no prickle of fear; that fetid, unclean presence might never have been.

Feeling positively light with relief, he turned and said to Haydn: 'Has it gone for good, do you think?'

'I doubt it.' His tone was uncharacteristically harsh, his mouth hard, his head thrust forward aggressively. Nick had seen him look like that before, but not off the rugby field, and never in clerical robes.

'That thing – call it what you will, Nick – has the devil behind it, and he's not going to give up that easily.' He turned abruptly. 'Leave this – we must go inside to Natasha.'

She was watching from the porch, prayer book in hand, but quite unable to follow Haydn's instructions. Although he was confident and she trusted him, she could not rid herself of apprehension where Nick was concerned. His sense of duty and loyalty to a friend was stronger, she felt sure, than his faith in God. What if that faith let him down? What if his fear broke through? What if he should become possessed, as Sarah Stalwell had been possessed – could Haydn help him then?

Against the car's fading headlights, she saw them pause. Chewing her thumbnail, she watched Nick go up to the barn door, and prayed then, a muttered supplication to all that was good, to protect him. The door opened, and against what remained of the light she saw Haydn's cloak billowing around him. Where was Nick? She couldn't see Nick! Petrified, she saw Haydn fall to his knees and beyond him, Nick collapsing against the door.

'Oh, dear God! Help him – help him!' Shaking like an aspen, she struggled to open the door. As she released the catch it flew back, smacking her on the forehead. She staggered back and cried out, but her cry was smothered by that fetid rush of air. Holding her head in her hands, Natasha bent against the pain, against nausea and the feeling that she was about to pass out. She tried to take deep breaths, but that smell was all around her, the smell from the barn, and it was here, it was here in the house . . .

Oh, dear God. She tried to pray, but no words would come, and the ones in her head were stuck, like a faulty record, on that short phrase. Afraid to look up, she sank to her knees, instinctively moving towards the door; but the door, which had been open, was inexplicably shut.

On a tide of rising panic, she grasped the round, slippery doorknob. Her hands were sweating; it would not turn. Behind her she could hear a strange noise, gravelly, asthmatic, like something struggling to breathe. She turned, pressing her back to the door, but all she could see was the long, shadowy tunnel of the hall, and a faint flow of light from the kitchen doorway.

Then something moved. A gathering darkness, like a dense black shadow, seemed to be taking shape at the far end of the hallway. There was a glimmer of light and she saw that the shape had eyes, huge, imploring eyes that in some strange way calmed her panic. Looking into these eyes she felt weak, lethargic, almost resigned, like someone waiting for death. Her body trembled with exhaustion, while her mind was swamped with pity for this creature, this being condemned for all eternity . . .

'Natasha!'

There was a heavy banging behind her, but it seemed to be coming from a great distance away . . .

'*Natasha!*'

Nick's voice, faint but insistent, and another, exhorting her in the name of God to *move* . . .

Breaking glass; a heavy thud as something dropped nearby; pressure against her back . . .

Pushing with all his might, Nick forced the door wide enough for Haydn to squeeze through, and with a fierce mental effort obeyed his instruction not to touch Natasha as he pushed his own way into the porch. He stepped over her legs, over a broken plantpot and the stems of a large geranium, saw that she was slumped behind the door, her eyes fixed and staring straight ahead.

'Don't look!' Haydn ordered. 'Ignore it!'

But he could not help but look. In the half-light from the kitchen he saw a shadowy figure rising from the darkness, a tall, skeletal shape, the angled bones of arms and shoulders just discernible through a swirling haze of other matter. There appeared the drawn-back grin of a face that was almost a skull, and a pair of eyes so human and tormented that his sense of horror was instantly tempered by pity.

'Nick! The Lord's Prayer – say it! *Our Father, who art in heaven, Hallowed be thy Name* . . .'

His heart was pounding and his throat closing against that appalling animal stench. Crouching beside Natasha, he began to recite the prayer automatically, wondering what Haydn was doing. He faltered at the words: '*And forgive us our trespasses*,' his mind suddenly blank, but Hadyn's voice carried on, strong and sure: '. . . *as we forgive those who trespass against us. And lead us not into temptation. But deliver us from evil* . . .'

Nick glanced at him, and the black cloak was gone. A white surplice stood out against the darkness, and the trailing end of a stole, embroidered with a golden cross, was level with Nick's eyes. 'From all evil and mischief; from sin and from the crafts and assaults of the devil, Good Lord deliver us . . .'

His eyes flickered back to the figure and could not look away. It seemed if anything more substantial, and with horrified fascination Nick saw that apart from that hawklike nose, the strong, bony features of the face were not unlike his own. As he stared, the face became clearer, the figure loomed closer, and in his mind rose thoughts that were not his own, a jumble of words in Latin and Norman French, words he recognised as a plea for some kind of understanding.

'Absolution,' he tried to say to Haydn, but the word came out as a croak. 'He needs absolution . . .'

'Nick, don't waver – remember your promise! Have faith in God and Jesus Christ our Saviour. This thing is *evil*!'

But he did waver. As pity overwhelmed him the figure became more distinct, no longer a thing of skin and bone, but with the tautness of flesh at shoulder and chest and thigh, and the swirl of garments around it. Dear God in heaven, what was happening?

Beside him, Natasha moaned and stirred. As he wrenched his attention back to her, Nick saw her raise her arms in welcome to what his mind had identified as Reynald de Briec. Her lips were parted in the seductive half-smile he knew so well, her eyes were glowing with desire.

Haydn's voice continued, as stern and commanding as ever. '. . . and deliver this place and this woman, Natasha Mary, from all evil spirits and every deceit of Satan the deceiver . . .'

Hearing those words, seeing Natasha's response to the figure materialising before her, Nick suddenly understood. Lies, deceit, trickery and possession. That was how it worked. Natasha was being seduced, and so was he, by an appeal to his sympathy and his intellectual pride. This thing had tantalised him for months, and was now busy confirming all his theories, showing itself as having its roots in suffering humanity, appealing to his sense of justice, his feeling that after eight hundred years it was entitled to release from whatever curse had bound it, entitled to forgiveness and absolution.

And if he gave in to that, if he allowed his pity to hold sway, it would move in and take his wife.

Instinct overrode instruction. He grabbed hold of Natasha,

turning her to face him. When she resisted, he pulled her to her feet. 'I love you,' he declared fiercely, clamping her jaw with his hand so that she could not turn away. 'I love you and I won't let you go. Not now, not ever. You're mine and I'm yours – we are *one*, do you hear me? Look at me, Natasha – yes, that's better,' he whispered, seeing the light of recognition in her eyes, 'look at me, not at it. It's not a man, it was never a man, don't let it fool you – '

'Nick . . .'

He saw her confusion, but at the heart of it was his wife, the woman he loved, and the woman who loved him. Holding her hard against him, thanking God for her deliverance, he cradled her head protectively and closed his eyes. That thing was too powerful, it fed off credulity, on pride, on lustful desires, on all the deadly sins that beset mankind. All he had to defend Natasha was love, and if love was not enough, then he was damned too . . .

'. . . In the name of Jesus Christ, Son of God, I *command you* to leave us now, to leave this place, to harm no one, and *go to your own place*, never to return . . .'

Nick felt the surge, a split-second of anguished resistance, and then it was gone. Instantly, like a lightning-flash, it was banished, and the stench of pollution with it. The air was as clean and fresh as if a summer storm had passed. The lights flickered and came back on, and the stone-flagged hall seemed just as usual, with the shaded lamp on the table, a Victorian landscape on the long wall, and a couple of Kilim rugs on the floor.

Nothing was disturbed, nothing was out of place: the evil presence was gone.

Forty Four

HAYDN WAS with them for another couple of hours. He concluded the exorcism of the house and barn, and assured them that the evil would not be back. Afterwards, he heard their separate confessions and gave formal absolution before administering Holy Communion at their table in the kitchen.

If that seemed extraordinary, like an echo from the days of religious persecution, it was nothing compared to what had gone before. Even so, it made a kind of sense to Natasha, and she was able to say that she understood. Not that she wanted to embrace religion in any of its organised forms, but she could at last accept its meaning. For her, the concept of God had been false, an invention, a blind attempt by man to explain his time on earth; and yet for some reason she had clung to her sense of morality, to values she described as humanitarian. But they were not enough, she saw that now. When she looked back, it seemed to her that she had been possessed by two forms of evil, both of which were impervious to reason and morality; and in order to escape, she'd had to make that leap of faith which recognised not just the individual soul, but its eternal life in the existence of God.

Because she had loved her father, she had clung to his principles and fought every attempt to fasten her into the straitjacket of conformist belief. But atheism was like a padded cell, and from that she had been freed. It was still an uneasy freedom, but worth exploring; and as Nick said so often, keeping an open mind was the best exercise of all.

She was unutterably grateful to Haydn, grateful for his wisdom and his patience, for the strength of faith he possessed. He looked so drained, she wished it were possible to comfort him; but when she tried to express something of what she felt, he simply said: 'Pray for me.'

Shortly after he left it started to snow, great mothlike flakes that settled immediately, covering the yard and lane and surrounding fields with a gentle blanket of white. To Natasha it seemed symbolic, as though even the snow had been holding back until that terrible thing had been banished for good.

As she put the thought into words, Nick agreed and claimed her hand. He did not remind her that it had snowed quite heavily back in November, nor did he take issue with the imprecision of her words. Such vague allusions seemed necessary, even to him: they were a way of reducing the magnitude of what had happened here. That open confrontation between good and evil was far too disturbing to contemplate with any degree of ease, and Haydn had been at pains to remind them not to dwell on such matters. His advice was to think instead of deliverance, and to praise God that one small, demonic spirit had been cast back into the outer darkness from whence it came.

But still, eight hundred years was a long time, in spite of Haydn's claim that it was nothing in the face of eternity. Eight hundred years of occasional, seemingly random appearances in the form of a spectral beast, its existence fed by fear and weakness and all the horrifying aspects of human sin. It was sentient, Haydn said, but not in any human way, despite the mimicry displayed that night. And it had probably been called into being by Reynald de Briec, with his occult practices and lustful, sadistic cruelty.

That was the point Nick had overlooked. David's original letter had stated quite clearly that de Briec was said to be in league with the devil, but Nick had not understood what that might mean. Well, thanks to Haydn, he understood something of it now, although it made him wince to think of innocents dabbling in the occult, with seances and ouija boards, and messages from the dead. And as for those who were serious, the seekers after power, those who imagined they could harness evil to their own ends . . .

'They can't,' Haydn had said, 'nobody can. But evil presents an attractive face to begin with – it lures you on. Like the first taste of a forbidden drug, it gives you pleasure – but it destroys you in the end. And other people too.'

It had certainly destroyed de Briec and, through his insanity, how many innocent victims? The claim, in David's first letter, that '*some good priest prevailed against him*,' was evidently untrue, and that violent death had apparently released the demon into the vicinity of Dagger Lane. It made Nick shudder to think of it.

The illustration of his own ignorance in such matters provoked an unaccustomed sense of humility. If there had been envy, lust and avarice aplenty in Sarah Stalwell's time, Nick felt that he himself had been guilty of the sin of pride, all the while imagining that he knew what he was dealing with. He had treated the matter of the beast and Reynald de Briec as an historical curiosity, and in the meantime it had been playing with him, leading him on until he was manoeuvred into the right position for the kill. Perhaps not a literal kill, as in the case of Sarah Stalwell and old Toby, but the death of love and goodness and all that he held dear. That he had unwittingly contributed by taking another woman to soothe his injured self-esteem was another factor; but what chilled him most of all was the knowledge that he had come so close to losing Natasha. The fact that she had stood in very real danger of being possessed in a true, demonic sense, sent a shiver through his soul.

If it was necessary to lose something before its value could be appreciated, then Nick felt he had come close enough, and the lesson was hard enough for him never to forget. He slipped an arm around Natasha's shoulders and drew her close, the warmth of her hair and skin a heightened pleasure against the soft cold kiss of the snow.

It was very late, and they were both drained by the overworked emotions of the last few hours. Having talked things over for a while after Haydn's departure, they were glad to go up to bed.

With Natasha curled inside the crook of his arm and her limbs fitting easily to his, Nick was very much aware that nothing else could intrude, that for the first time in months it was possible to abandon all worries and anxieties. He half expected Natasha to fall asleep at once, and was glad when she did not; she was relaxed and happy and so was he, comforted in the darkness by all the old certainties of warmth and scent and touch. That feeling of intimacy was precious, and he wanted to prolong it, not lose it in the oblivion of sleep. As he gently caressed her she murmured with wordless satisfaction, and the lips that touched his face soon turned their warmth to his mouth.

Aroused by her soft, languorous invitation, he responded with a tenderness which amounted almost to reverence, making love to her with a slow, emotional intensity that had little to do with sexual passion. He felt more truly aware of life and love than ever before; of Natasha and himself, of their unity and rightness together, which he had recognised so many years ago, and so mistakenly tried to hold. But the past was erased, the future was theirs to find; nothing else mattered. It was a releasing, liberating emotion which reached its climax with the physical one; and for the first time, in the aftermath, there was no sense of separation.

That elevated sense of awareness, the richness of love and relief and gratitude, sustained them throughout the next few days, past a barrage of phone calls from friends and acquaintances, most of whom had seen the articles in the local press and wanted an update on developments.

It was impossible to talk about the exorcism, and, except to Dr Wills, Nick confined these discussions to the matter of the bones. But by the end of the week he could not bear the situation. It seemed their lives were no longer their own, yet he wanted above all to be alone with Natasha, to restore and recapture that shared sense of happiness. He suggested a few days away, envisaging London or Paris, or even a country hotel somewhere in the depths of Devon or Cornwall. He was surprised and even a little amused when Natasha said she wanted to go no further than York, that she had a yearning to wander around the old city, absorbing the atmosphere like a tourist.

Touched by the simplicity of that request, he went at once to make some arrangements, and, as soon as they had packed and sorted out the problem of the cats, they set off for York. Nick, however, refused to tell her where they would be staying, and when they arrived it was Natasha's turn to be surprised.

She had stayed at the small hotel a couple of years previously, and although it had been refurbished since, the atmosphere of warmth and friendliness remained. As they registered, the girl at reception smiled quizzically at their home address, but made no comment. She showed them up to a pleasant room on the floor above, while Natasha struggled to contain her amusement.

When they were alone, she burst out laughing. 'That girl probably thinks we're having an affair!'

'So?' he demanded, kissing her. 'Anyway, it was your idea to come to York, so don't complain . . .'

'I'm not,' she whispered, thinking of the last time she'd stayed here, when Giles had invited her to speak to his students, just after *The English Lesson* was published. 'I was just thinking what a sentimental old thing you are . . .'

'God knows why,' he said with rueful amusement, 'you were incredibly rude to me that night I brought you back here from the pub. I seem to remember you telling me to go away and not come back – only you put it rather more strongly!'

She laughed. 'But you refused to take no for an answer!'

'Ah, well, you see,' he admitted softly, 'I was still suffering from the profound shock of seeing you again after all those years. It was so totally unexpected, and yet there you were, sitting in the same corner – '

'And it was as though nothing had changed,' she finished for him, recalling that moment so clearly. Giles taking her to the same old pub, that sense of time slipping backwards as he guided her to the corner table where she had been used to sitting with him and Nick so often in the past. 'I think I was forewarned,' she confessed, 'just by being there. Every time someone walked through the door, I expected it to be you – and then it was . . .'

He remembered that moment of suspended time, the sudden thud of recognition, a blur of weakness in which it seemed his bones were no longer capable of holding him upright; and he had somehow made it to the bar, crowded at that hour with businessmen taking a break between the office and the demands of home. Ordering a pint of bitter and a large scotch, he had downed the scotch at once, and when it seemed he was more in control, had made his way to where Giles and Natasha were sitting . . .

'. . . and I was so angry,' she said, 'I thought at first that you and Giles had cooked it up between you. But you were so *white*,' she added softly, glancing up at him, 'and so quiet, I realised you couldn't have known a thing about it.'

'Not a damn thing,' he agreed. 'I was so stunned, I could hardly speak.'

She half laughed and shook her head. 'But you made up for it later!'

'Had to – couldn't have you escaping me again.'

Smiling impishly at the memory of his persuasion, she eluded a fresh attempt to hold her, and turned to survey their room.

It was warm and attractively furnished, with a small bay window which looked out over the old boundary walls of St Mary's Abbey. Snow, whiter than the limestone, was still lodged in the crenellations; a short distance away, caught in the last rays of the sunset, the Minster's twin towers were gilded against a great dark mass of violet clouds. It would probably snow again tonight, and heavily, but that hardly mattered. There was something safe and reassuring about that view, like coming home after a long and distressing journey. It drew from Natasha a deep and very satisfied sigh.

They spent a couple of hours in town, walking the old, familiar streets, gazing in shop windows and browsing around the market. The stall-holders were packing up for the night, but Natasha bought a bag of tiny oranges, and, on a sudden impulse as they passed a flower stall, Nick stopped to choose a bunch of bronze and gold chrysanthemums. Presenting them with a flourish, he was rewarded by her expression as she held them to her face.

Breathing in their distinctive fragrance, she was almost

ecstatic. 'Oh, I do love these flowers! They're so rich and bold and showy – so inspiring on a dark day . . .'

They called at a pub neither of them had been in for years, and made their way back towards the hotel a little after half-past six. It was coming on to snow as they turned the corner into Bootham, but in spite of the cold Natasha was exhilarated, taken by the beauty of the city at night. By the round tower at the corner of Marygate she paused to look back, at the floodlit grandeur of the medieval gateway with the Minster behind it, graceful eighteenth-century buildings rising into the darkness, and the seductive swirl of snowflakes all around.

'Isn't it wonderful?' she breathed, and Nick agreed that it was; but for him the wonder lay in her smile, as happy as a child's at Christmas, and just as clearly tinged with tears.

Her loveliness, still so pared down, so fragile, brought a tightness to his throat; the recent past cut into him, and he knew how close they had ridden to disaster. But as he slipped a protective arm around her shoulders, Nick told himself that the danger was past, the pressure off; for these few days at least, they could relax and enjoy themselves.

The city, next morning, was covered with a fresh mantle of snow which enchanted them both. That dazzling background transformed everything, highlighting walls and windows, rooflines and ramparts, and lending new perspectives to the humblest prospect. Their explorations that day were filled with freshness and delight, reminding Nick of their early days together, when he had taken such pleasure in showing his view of the city to a young and promising student.

Well, he reflected with an inward smile, she had certainly fulfilled that promise, if not in the way he had envisaged at the time; but then she was never predictable, and that was part of her charm.

As they wandered in and out of bookshops, and deliberated over a late lunch, Natasha had a similar sense of the past revisited. But, like themselves, the city had undergone subtle changes in those years; the shops were different, new courtyards had opened out, buildings had been restored. If they had been discovering each other during their first explorations of the city, she felt they were finding out more now. And there would always be more; nothing stayed the same, after all. The trick was to look back and learn from the past, not to let it cripple the present and stultify the future.

Nevertheless, thinking of the printer's proofs waiting at home, she experienced a profound regret. Not so much that she had written the book, but that it had caused such a rift between herself and her sister Helen. Writers of fiction, she felt, were much misunderstood people, whose lives, thoughts and ambitions were often far removed from those of the characters they portrayed. But the more convincing the writing, the more they stood in danger of accusations like Helen's: of having thought, felt and experienced all that was in the book; or, conversely, having told a pack of lies. Reality and the imagination were two different worlds, and the best a writer could hope to be, Natasha thought, was an interpreter, someone who made a kind of sense out of all the apparently nonsensical trivia and tragedies of life.

Looking back on recent experience, Natasha hoped that in expanding her awareness of life itself, it would also expand her range as a writer. And hard on the heels of that thought came *Black Earth* again, and that sense of dissatisfaction which had come with the ending. It was a good novel, she was confident of that, but the ending was down, sad, as lacking in hope as that of *The English Lesson*. For the first time she began to think that she had been wrong, that there were other interpretations to be placed upon the nuts and bolts of the plot. She could change the ending –

'I could change it,' she said suddenly to Nick, startling him out of some abstract study of his own. 'I could do it – it would be expensive, I know, to do it at this stage, but it could be done. Quite easily, I think – anyway, it's worth a try!'

'What is?' he demanded, laughing.

Caught up by her enthusiasm, he ordered more coffee while Natasha outlined her ideas for a new ending to the book.

'. . . and the thing is, I don't think even Helen could object to that!'

It was late afternoon when they finally resumed their walk, and above the rooftops the high, clear blue of the sky was beginning to deepen into a cold, frosty cobalt. Lights were glowing in the shop windows along Petergate and glittering off the uncleared snow; what had been soft underfoot was starting to crunch, like a mass of granulated sugar.

On the thin, dry air the sound of the Minster bell, so close at hand, came like the knell of an almighty summons, so startling and compelling that they halted at the top of Stonegate to look and listen, gazing up at the height and breadth of the massive cathedral. Lights glimmered faintly through the great rose window and by the open doorway beneath it; a few minutes later, mounting the steps to go inside, they realised that Evensong had already begun.

With no more than a questioning glance, Nick would have continued into the nave, but Natasha stayed him with a touch; as a swell of music filled her ears, it seemed better to pause and listen from the shadows. The sonorous notes of the organ, overlaid by the rising sweetness of choirboys' voices, held her transfixed, while an unfamiliar longing kept her listening through the prayers. Although the responses were muffled, the acoustics were such that the priest's bidding seemed extraordinarily close.

There was no organ for the anthem, and no congregation to obscure it, just the richness of men's voices raised in the simplicity of medieval plainsong, the Latin so perfectly enunciated that she held her breath to listen, wondering for a moment whether time had shifted suddenly, to deposit them in some distant Catholic century before the Reformation.

Then the priest's voice, in English, came to break the spell. *'Lighten our darkness, we beseech thee O Lord; and by thy great mercy defend us from all perils and dangers of this night . . .'*

The prayer, finding its echo in her heart, made Natasha wish that she had been familiar with those words a long time ago; but by the grace of God the most vital danger was past –

By the grace of God, she repeated in silent astonishment. All at once the pieces of the puzzle slipped into place. As the sense of it dawned, she realised that it was Sarah's essential goodness which made everything clear, and that in this one respect Haydn had been mistaken . . .

'You see, she was good, after all,' Natasha explained later, when they were back at the hotel. 'I know she scared me sometimes, but that was because I thought I was going crazy. If I'd known then what I know now, I wouldn't have been scared at all.'

Nick poured himself a drink and came to join her at the little table in the bay window. Natasha glanced up and smiled, then turned to look at the floodlit Minster, visible through a tracery of trees. 'I know Haydn had his doubts,' she went on, 'but then his experience of Sarah wasn't direct, like mine – and I suppose he couldn't afford to make mistakes with that exorcism.'

'He couldn't afford *our* mistakes,' Nick said with feeling. 'Not then. The door had to be slammed shut – no half-measures.'

'I know, he explained that to me. But the point is, Nick, she's free now, no need to come back. *And we made that freedom possible . . .*'

She knew it, and the certainty was still exhilarating. It made sense of everything that had happened to them; it even cleared the way ahead. Nick might use different words to describe the strange coincidence of events, but he could see the pattern just as clearly, and she knew he was inclined to similar conclusions.

It had occurred to Natasha before, shortly after finishing Sarah's story, that the haunting might have something to do with themselves, with who and what they were, and she was now convinced of that. She thought the beginning of it probably went back a couple of years, and that events had been set in motion by the death of the last of the Whitehead family; and she saw Nick's burning desire to buy the house as an essential part of what was to happen later. To her it was a kind of predestination, but Nick described it as a moment of synchronicity, after which they were both locked in to future events.

'Oh, yes,' she agreed, 'but whatever you call it – destiny, fate, or plain coincidence – the fact remains that Sarah Stalwell needed your talents, Nick, to prove her existence. She needed your access to research material as much as she needed my abilities as a writer. We had to be there, on the spot – we had to buy that house . . .'

'And restore it?' he asked dryly. 'If so, she certainly got her money's worth with you and me!'

'Well, maybe that too,' Natasha conceded, amused by his streak of northern hard-headedness. 'After all, nothing happened while we were busy with the house.'

'Or while you were finishing your novel . . .'

'Ah yes, but my mind was occupied, wasn't it? I was working full-tilt then – didn't want to know about anything else.' But as soon as the book was finished, she thought with a sudden chill, when she had been mentally and emotionally vulnerable, they had gone to the Hallowe'en party, and, as Haydn described it, opened the door to evil.

And it was on the night of the Hallowe'en party that evil had crept in and thrust Sarah Stalwell aside.

Remembering that night, Natasha was reluctant to put her feelings into words, but Nick was braver. He took her hand and told her honestly what had taken place between himself and Jane Bardy. That he was ashamed of his intentions was obvious, but he could admit them now because he knew they were uncharacteristic; and so did Natasha. His behaviour that night, and her feelings of jealousy and insecurity, had driven in the wedge; after that, with their relationship beginning to fall apart, evil was able to take over.

Nick, remembering that malignity, spoke briefly of the changes he had observed in her then, and for Natasha that was still the most chilling part of all. Even with her own private memories of that time, she barely recognised the woman he described, and it was horrifying to realise how close she had come to losing her own personality. Her fears of schizophrenia had not been wildly inaccurate, it seemed, yet it was more frightening still to see herself as no more than a pawn in a deadly game of chess, where the protagonists were playing for souls, not pleasure.

But Sarah Stalwell had been benign. She had to have been. With Natasha in place, she had fought so hard to regain control; Natasha had been important, a perfect channel through which to pour the vibrant reality of her earthly existence. In that compelling tale she had been able to state her case and issue her warnings; and, as Natasha said, it was because of Sarah that Haydn Parker had been called in, not because of the beast.

'Well, she's at rest now,' Nick reminded her, laying his hand on her shoulder. 'She doesn't need us any more, does she? So it seems we're free to please ourselves at last . . .'

Natasha turned, answering his smile with a hint of concern. They had discussed the topic at some length over the past few days, but she was still in need of his reassurance. 'Are you sure you won't mind about the house?'

He shook his head. 'No, I don't think so. It's witnessed too much for my liking. I promise you, I won't be sorry to make a fresh start.'

Natasha's relief was enormous. The anxiety of wanting to leave, while knowing how important the house was to Nick, had been a considerable burden. In some respects, the fact of the exorcism had increased her anxiety, since she felt her desire to leave might well be interpreted as a sad lack of faith in its effectiveness. But while she had no doubt about Sarah Stalwell, there remained a trace of fear whenever she thought about the beast. It seemed to her that the brush with evil had been too close, that Nick had been much too intrigued by the mystery of Reynald de Briec. He would be better away from it, and away from Dagger Lane.

On a far more mundane level, she had definitely had enough of the isolation. She needed peace in which to work, that was true, but there were some lovely townhouses in York, with mature, secluded gardens which would suit them both admirably. And Nick, at last, had come round to her way of thinking. He too fancied a little less hard work with regard to maintenance, and a little more freedom to enjoy a social life which did not involve worrying about drinking and driving. He had even decided to give up smoking again, and wanted to look for a house close enough to the riverside for him to resume his regular morning run.

It was simply a matter of finding the right house in the right place, and praying they would find a buyer for Holly Tree Cottage. One who would not be dismayed by the recent publicity about human remains being found in the barn.

'Of course,' Nick remarked as they went down to dinner, 'there are those to whom such a story would be a bonus . . .'

Forty Five

IT WAS A brilliant morning, clear and sunny with the promise of spring. Thankful for the sun, uplifted by it, Natasha paused on the landing to look out across the fields. No sign of green in the hedgerows, it was far too soon for that, but the winter wheat was thriving, and somewhere a songthrush was calling to its mate.

There was something sweet and haunting in that repeated song, and for a moment, thinking of Sarah and Richard, she felt a pang of sadness for all that they had held dear and lost. 'I do hope they found each other,' she said softly to the silent house, and then, with a smile for Colette basking on the sunny windowledge, she went to finish dressing.

Reaching into the wardrobe, she pushed everything black aside and pulled out a heavy, knitted jacket in jewel shades of green and blue. It was bold, perhaps even outrageous for a normal funeral, but Natasha felt most strongly that this was not an occasion for sober clothes and long faces, it was a time for celebration. There might have been no one to mourn over Sarah's death, and no one to miss her presence other than a frail and failing Reverend Clive, but she had friends now to wish her spirit well, and they would all be there to see her to her final resting-place.

A little while later, as a car drove into the yard, she was delighted to see that Fay had turned up wearing a beautiful red and blue shawl over her navy-blue coat, and when Lesley arrived, that she too was brightly clad, with mustard-coloured jeans and an embroidered waistcoat under her jacket. Natasha was glad that they had agreed with her about clothes, and to see that even the men had done their best. Dave was wearing a red scarf with his usual anorak, and Giles was looking quite dashing as usual, his fair hair gleaming in the sun.

Nick was the last to arrive. He had been to collect the twins, who had been understandably furious at missing all the excitement of the dig. They had been away visiting relatives at the time, for which Nick was immensely thankful: he would not, he confessed to Natasha, have wanted them there with all the uncertainty attached to those few days. But he had promised they could attend the church service, for which their mother had insisted they be suitably dressed. They were wearing their best school uniforms, but their hair, Natasha thought with a satisfied grin, was a celebration in itself.

Just as Nick was checking the time and advising everyone that it would be far better to walk down to church, Giles turned from his study of the lane and said: 'By the way, did you ever see or hear anything more of that mysterious beast?'

For a fleeting moment Nick thought his expression must surely give everything away. He covered it with concern about the time, saying absently: 'What? Oh, no – no, we didn't.'

Giles studied him closely and then shrugged. 'Strange though,' he remarked. 'I wondered whether it had anything to do with your decision to sell up?'

'Only in a marginal way. After all this –' he gestured towards the barn as they set off, 'we'd simply had enough.'

He was glad when the boys interrupted with questions about who was going to buy the house and where they were going to live next; even more so when Lesley distracted Giles by admiring his rather flamboyant silk tie. There was something flirtatious in her manner which instantly made him wonder whether Giles wasn't up to his old tricks again; and on the heels of that thought, as the boys abandoned him to attach themselves to Natasha, Fay slipped her arm through his and proceeded to hang on to him as she negotiated the rough lane in her unsuitable shoes.

It seemed to him that Fay, who had not approved of his intentions and refused to be involved with the dig, had suddenly become very partisan about the matter of Sarah Stalwell. She pestered him relentlessly about the service, while he explained to her that Haydn had been invited to assist, but the local rector was keen to conduct things himself. 'Quite naturally,' he commented, 'since this is his parish.'

'Yes, I know,' she persisted, 'but I still think it would have been better if Haydn could have done it. I mean to say, Nick, he did help dig her up . . .'

He winced, wishing Fay were a little less forthright, and was inordinately glad that he'd said nothing to Giles about the exorcism, and had persuaded Natasha not to tell Fay. Haydn had advised them to keep the exorcism to themselves; people did not understand, he said, and there was an unfortunate tendency to sensationalise these things. Better to say nothing and let the folk memory of Reynard die a natural death.

'Plenty of cars outside the church,' Giles commented as they crossed the road, and with a groan Nick agreed. He had already spotted a gaggle of photographers attempting to look inconspicuous amongst the tombstones.

Trying to seem unconcerned, they ignored the ferociously clicking cameras as they crossed the churchyard to the lychgate, but were cornered for a moment by three journalists, each elbowing the others in an attempt to get the questions in first.

'*Later*,' Nick declared, as though addressing importunate students, and to Natasha's amazement they fell back before him, meek as lambs.

The twins were much amused and had difficulty controlling their grins as Haydn and the Rector joined them at the gate. A couple of minutes later a large white van drew up, unmarked, but with a police driver. A plain wooden coffin, surprisingly small and light, was carefully removed from the back and handed over to the two churchwardens, who carried it between them, while the group from Holly Tree Cottage, having been designated as chief mourners, followed the procession along the path and into the church.

'I am the resurrection and the life, saith the Lord: he that believeth in me, though he were dead, yet shall he live: and whosoever liveth and believeth in me shall never die . . .'

The church was full. It seemed the entire village had turned out for this extraordinary event; there were even people standing at the back. For a moment Nick wondered whether the clergy regarded it as unseemly, but as they turned to face the congregation, Haydn looked as unperturbable as ever, while the Rector waited only for the shuffling to die down before continuing the service.

It seemed fitting, however, that so many of Denton's inhabitants had turned out to pray for the soul of a woman murdered with such cold-blooded intent. Not that they were fully aware of the circumstances, since her true identity and the manner of her death could not be confirmed. All that was known had been published in a brief press release a few days ago, stating that the remains found in a barn at Denton-on-the-Forest belonged to a woman of child-bearing years, and that she had been dead between 250 and 300 years; the close proximity of a knife suggested that she had been murdered.

To that, Nick could add only the pointers suggested by his own research, that the bones *may* have been those of a former owner of Holly Tree Cottage, one Sarah Stalwell, widow, who had disappeared mysteriously in the autumn of 1723.

But nothing could be proved. Nothing. The contents of that small, plain coffin must remain officially anonymous. Except as a piece of fiction, he reflected wryly, the full story could never be written up, and he was not convinced that Natasha would ever want to do it.

In deference to the age of the bones, it had been decided to use the old form of service, with a psalm rather than hymns, which pleased Nick. The resonant phrases echoed the simple beauty of the church, its stone walls and lancet windows, the Early English tracery of an east window unspoiled by the garish colours of nineteenth-century glass. Apart from some relatively modern pews, the church was probably not much changed from Sarah Stalwell's time, and Nick felt that she would have been at ease here.

Haydn read the lesson, that lengthy extract from St Paul's first Epistle to the Corinthians which dealt with the certainty of the resurrection. Natasha was not keen on St Paul, that old misogynist, but she did admire Haydn's handling of the difficult seventeenth-century phrasing. Like an Olivier or a Gielgud, he managed to convey the exactitude of meaning, so that no one was left in doubt as to the importance of this burial, and a few were probably wishing that cremation had never been thought of.

With the ending of the lesson, Haydn closed the book in a gesture that seemed symbolic; a moment later they were following the procession of coffin and clergy out of the dim church and into the blustery brightness of late morning.

When all were gathered, the Rector raised his voice in familiar words: *'Forasmuch as it hath pleased Almighty God of his great mercy to take unto himself the soul of our dear sister here departed, we therefore commit her body to the ground: earth to earth, ashes to ashes, dust to dust: in sure and certain hope of the Resurrection to eternal life, through our Lord Jesus Christ . . .'*

Nick bent to cast a handful of earth upon the lowered coffin. As the fine soil splayed across the lid, he was aware of an obligation having been discharged, and a sense of lightness possessed him. He glanced at Natasha, and at the faces of their friends gathered around the grave, and knew that each of them had played a part; he did not care to contemplate what might have happened without their assistance. He met Haydn's glance and returned his faint smile; and, as his arms went protectively to the shoulders of his sons, he thanked God for them too, and for the future they represented.

But with the conclusion of the service and the departure of the clergy, that sense of peace and gratitude was at once tried by the onslaught of too many people. The ones he wanted to talk to were overwhelmed by the crush of village acquaintances and eager representatives of the press. His eyes, scanning possible avenues of escape, were suddenly caught by another familiar figure edging through the crowd towards the gate. As he stared in surprise, Sally Armitage turned and looked at him, and then, with a smile and a wave, made her way to the battered Citroën 2CV parked on the far side of the Green.

Touched by an unexpected moment of pleasure and regret, Nick watched her drive away, while answering questions with no more than half a mind on what was being asked. The journalists seemed inexhaustible, and one was replaced by another until Nick raised his hand and said, *enough*. He rescued Natasha from the group surrounding her and they moved away to talk to people they knew, trying to blend in with the crowd until the notebooks and tape-recorders and clicking cameras were gone.

As they rejoined the boys, Natasha noticed an imposing figure bearing down on them, a large elderly woman in a motley collection of shawls and cardigans. In her purple, floppy-brimmed hat, she looked like an eccentric dowager striding between the gravestones; her appearance prompted an aghast question, voiced in unison, from the twins.

'An old acquaintance,' Nick murmured in answer, and then proceeded to introduce them. But she seemed far more interested in Natasha, and was keen to speak to her on the subject of 'psychic experiences'.

Natasha was surprised, but not pleasantly so. Although Nick had described Dr Wills, nothing could have prepared her for that sense of being examined and assessed. She felt uneasy under that penetrating gaze, and Dr Wills had the kind of autocratic manner which was not at home with small-talk or in the presence of young people. It was obvious that she wanted to talk about recent events, and probably to Natasha, yet was not prepared to do so in front of the boys.

They shifted uncomfortably, uncertain what to do. Seizing the opportunity, Natasha made her excuses and eased them away, leaving Nick and Dr Wills to talk. She did not want to discuss those strange and deeply personal experiences with anyone else, least of all a clairvoyant, medium, or whatever, who would no doubt raise more questions to keep her awake at night. Especially when she had just about settled things to her own satisfaction.

As they moved away, the boys grinned with relief, and after a moment or two wandered off to examine the gravestones and monuments. She heard Adrian reading aloud from one of the lichen-covered memorials, and found herself thinking again about Richard Stalwell. She and Nick had found the record of his burial in one of the old parish registers, but they had searched in vain for his grave. The oldest surviving stone was from 1790s, and of another family entirely. Nevertheless, memorials or not, beneath these raised mounds of earth rested several centuries of Denton's former inhabitants, friends and foes all cheek by jowl in that rich earth. Somewhere within this crowded acre were the bones of Richard, his sisters Agnes and Hester, Hester's children, and her bullying husband, Tom Whitehead. Here too were the remains of those women who had been so goaded by fear and rage that they had been driven to murder.

Well, Natasha thought, there was no need for them to be afraid of Sarah Stalwell now. She hoped all would be reconciled here, where finding a vacant plot in which to bury Sarah's bones had presented something of a problem. Officially, the churchyard was closed for burials and had been so for a great many years, but in the circumstances, and for such a tiny coffin, space had been found on the south side, amongst the fat cushions of snowdrops and the upright stones of the last century.

On a fine day it would be sunny and sheltered there, a pleasant spot facing the ivy-clad cottages which abutted the foot of Dagger Lane. Above the chimney-pots and between the trees, she could just see the roofline of Holly Tree Cottage and part of the gable end, catching the midday sun.

It was a beautiful old house, and Natasha dearly wished she could feel a genuine regret at leaving. But as Nick said, too much had happened there, it had witnessed too much. Thinking of Sarah and Richard, she was beset by melancholy, remembering their lives here, the passion they had shared and lost, the centuries of separation. Since reading the manuscript again, she had come to the conclusion that theirs was an earthly and earthy passion, in many ways tied to the land which sustained them, to a powerful need for heirs and successors. That desire was so basic, their love so exclusive, that Sarah had nothing to hold on to when Richard died. His death took almost everything from her, and reduced what was left to ashes.

The insanity of her grief made her vulnerable, and her curses called that perpetually lurking evil into being; so the beast had watched and waited, nurturing despair into lust and fanning the embers of greed elsewhere. With fear and hatred to feed the flames, that fatal combination had erupted into murder, and after that the beast was satisfied . . . until the next time.

And how many times had there been, Natasha wondered as she looked around, in all these dead generations? Reynald de Briec had been gone for eight hundred years, but the shadow of his memory, Reynard, had lived on to wreak his sly revenge along the length of Dagger Lane.

But it was over now, the shadow had passed. Like any other country lane, the old track wound its way from Denton to the village of Brickhill, as it had done since before the Romans came. The ancient forest was gone, and only the oaks and World's End Wood remained, but the hedgerows would bloom in the spring, crops would grow in the fields, and with the autumn would come the harvest of fruits and berries and grain. Winter was the dead time, but winter was almost over, and maybe – just maybe – she and Nick would walk the lane again someday, and look at the house, and remember.

Lost in reverie, Natasha came to with a start, suddenly aware of the quiet presence at her shoulder. Dr Wills's gaze was unexpectedly gentle, her smile benign as she nodded towards the lane.

'There they are,' she said softly, 'do you see them?'

Natasha looked and shook her head. 'Who?'

'Why, Sarah and Richard, of course. . .'